DIGITAL COMMUNICATIONS

CW00796995

DIGITAL COMMUNICATIONS

For B.E. / B.Tech. Students of All Indian Technical Universities

---

V. K. KHANNA

M.Sc., Ph.D. (Physics), FIETE,

Scientist, MEMS & Microsensors
Solid-State Devices (SSD) Division
Central Electronics Engineering Research Institute
PILANI–333031 *(RAJASTHAN)*

S. CHAND
PUBLISHING
empowering minds

S. CHAND & COMPANY PVT. LTD.

(AN ISO 9001 : 2008 COMPANY)
RAM NAGAR, NEW DELHI - 110 055

S. CHAND & COMPANY PVT. LTD.

(An ISO 9001 : 2008 Company)

Head Office: 7361, RAM NAGAR, NEW DELHI - 110 055

Phone: 23672080-81-82, 9899107446, 9911310888 Fax: 91-11-23677446

Shop at: **schandgroup.com**; e-mail: **info@schandgroup.com**

Branches :

AHMEDABAD : 1st Floor, Heritage, Near Gujarat Vidhyapeeth, Ashram Road, **Ahmedabad** - 380 014, Ph: 27541965, 27542369, ahmedabad@schandgroup.com

BENGALURU : No. 6, Ahuja Chambers, 1st Cross, Kumara Krupa Road, **Bengaluru** - 560 001, Ph: 22268048, 22354008, bangalore@schandgroup.com

BHOPAL : Bajaj Tower, Plot No. 2&3, Lala Lajpat Rai Colony, Raisen Road, **Bhopal** - 462 011, Ph: 4274723, 4209587. bhopal@schandgroup.com

CHANDIGARH : S.C.O. 2419-20, First Floor, Sector - 22-C (Near Aroma Hotel), **Chandigarh** -160 022, Ph: 2725443, 2725446, chandigarh@schandgroup.com

CHENNAI : No.1, Whites Road, Opposite Express Avenue, Royapettah, **Chennai** - 600014 Ph. 28410027, 28410058, chennai@schandgroup.com

COIMBATORE : 1790, Trichy Road, LGB Colony, Ramanathapuram, **Coimbatore** -6410045, Ph: 2323620, 4217136 coimbatore@schandgroup.com **(Marketing Office)**

CUTTACK : 1st Floor, Bhartia Tower, Badambadi, **Cuttack** - 753 009, Ph: 2332580; 2332581, cuttack@schandgroup.com

DEHRADUN : 1st Floor, 20, New Road, Near Dwarka Store, **Dehradun** - 248 001, Ph: 2711101, 2710861, dehradun@schandgroup.com

GUWAHATI : Dilip Commercial (Ist floor), M.N. Road, Pan Bazar, **Guwahati** - 781 001, Ph: 2738811, 2735640 guwahati@schandgroup.com

HALDWANI : Bhatt Colony, Talli Bamori, Mukhani, **Haldwani** -263139 **(Marketing Office)** Mob. 09452294584

HYDERABAD : Padma Plaza, H.No. 3-4-630, Opp. Ratna College, Narayanaguda, **Hyderabad** - 500 029, Ph: 27550194, 27550195, hyderabad@schandgroup.com

JAIPUR : 1st Floor, Nand Plaza, Hawa Sadak, Ajmer Road, **Jaipur** - 302 006, Ph: 2219175, 2219176, jaipur@schandgroup.com

JALANDHAR : Mai Hiran Gate, **Jalandhar** - 144 008, Ph: 2401630, 5000630, jalandhar@schandgroup.com

KOCHI : Kachapilly Square, Mullassery Canal Road, Ernakulam, **Kochi** - 682 011, Ph: 2378740, 2378207-08, cochin@schandgroup.com

KOLKATA : 285/J, Bipin Bihari Ganguli Street, **Kolkata** - 700 012, Ph: 22367459, 22373914, kolkata@schandgroup.com

LUCKNOW : Mahabeer Market, 25 Gwynne Road, Aminabad, **Lucknow** - 226 018, Ph: 4076971, 4026791, 4065646, 4027188, lucknow@schandgroup.com

MUMBAI : Blackie House, IInd Floor, 103/5, Walchand Hirachand Marg, Opp. G.P.O., **Mumbai** - 400 001, Ph: 22690881, 22610885, mumbai@schandgroup.com

NAGPUR : Karnal Bagh, Near Model Mill Chowk, **Nagpur** - 440 032, Ph: 2720523, 2777666 nagpur@schandgroup.com

PATNA : 104, Citicentre Ashok, Mahima Palace , Govind Mitra Road, **Patna** - 800 004, Ph: 2300489, 2302100, patna@schandgroup.com

PUNE : Sadguru Enclave, Ground floor, Survey No. 114/3, Plot no. 8 Alandi Road , Vishrantwadi **Pune** - 411015 Ph: 64017298 pune@schandgroup.com

RAIPUR : Kailash Residency, Plot No. 4B, Bottle House Road, Shankar Nagar, **Raipur** - 492 007, Ph: 2443142, Mb. : 09981200834, raipur@schandgroup.com **(Marketing Office)**

RANCHI : Shanti Deep Tower, Opp.Hotel Maharaja, Radium Road, **Ranchi** -834001 Mob. 09430246440 ranchi@schandgroup.com

SILIGURI : 122, Raja Ram Mohan Roy Road, East Vivekanandapally, P.O., Siliguri, **Siliguri** -734001, Dist., Jalpaiguri, (W.B.) Ph. 0353-2520750 **(Marketing Office)** siliguri@schandgroup.com

VISAKHAPATNAM : No. 49-54-15/53/8, Plot No. 7, 1st Floor, Opp. Radhakrishna Towers, Seethammadhara North Extn., **Visakhapatnam** - 530 013, Ph-2782609 (M) 09440100555, visakhapatnam@schandgroup.com **(Marketing Office)**

© 1999, V.K. Khanna

All rights reserved. No part of this publication may be reproduced or copied in any material form (including photo copying or storing it in any medium in form of graphics, electronic or mechanical means and whether or not transient or incidental to some other use of this publication) without written permission of the copyright owner. Any breach of this will entail legal action and prosecution without further notice. Jurisdiction : All desputes with respect to this publication shall be subject to the jurisdiction of the Courts, tribunals and forums of New Delhi, India only.

First Edition 1999
Reprint 2003
Second Revised Edition 2009; Reprint 2011
Reprint 2012 Reprint 2014

ISBN : 81-219-3102-9   **Code : 10A374**

PRINTED IN INDIA

By Nirja Publishers & Printers Pvt. Ltd., 54/3/2, Jindal Paddy Compound, Kashipur Road, Rudrapur-263153, Uttarakhand and published by S. Chand & Company Pvt. Ltd., 7361, Ram Nagar, New Delhi -110 055.

Dedicated

To my father, the late Shri Amarnath Khanna
for shaping my life and career
&
To my mother, daughter and wife
for their care and affection

Preface to the Revised Edition

This book comprises a part of my previous book entitled DIGITAL SIGNAL PROCESSING, TELECOMMUNICATIONS AND MULTIMEDIA TECHNOLOGY. The original book was meant as a comprehensive treatise for communications engineering students. However, it was suggested by many readers and as per latest syllabi of different Technical Universities of India that the Digital Signal Processing portion of the book is also useful to the students of engineering branches like **Computer Science, Electronics and Instrumentation**, **Electrical and Electronics Engineering**, and therefore must be separated for this wide cross-section of readership. The second portion on Digital Communications is of interest for **Electronics and Communication Engineering** students and all those willing to specialize in digital communications.

Therefore at the demand of the readers, the previous book has divided into two separate independent parts, namely, "Digital Signal Processing" and **"Digital Communications"** to make the appropriate course contents available in handy focused form to the concerned students. Thus the two portions are aimed at specific audiences. It is earnestly hoped that in their present forms, the two books will fulfill the specific needs of the syllabi concerned.

This book on Digital Communications contains seven chapters, and its structure as follows: **The starting chapter** presents a glimpse of communication and information systems, and introduces the basic terminology of these systems. **The second chapter** deals with methods for digital coding of analog waveforms. **The third chapter** describes digital modulation techniques. **The fourth chapter** covers the principles of networking. **The fifth chapter** addresses digital satellite communications. **The sixth chapter** discusses the principles and practices of high-definition television. The concluding **seventh chapter** is devoted to multimedia communications.

Efforts have also been made to update the contents and correct any errors that have come to notice. However, constructive comments from the readers for improving the book are solicited.

Acknowledgements: The author wishes to thank the Director, senior scientists and colleagues at CEERI, for continued encouragement in his endeavours. He is also thankful to the readers for their valuable suggestions. Keen interest of the publishers in bringing out this book is acknowledged.

Dr. V.K. Khanna
Pilani

Preface to the First Edition "Digital Signal Processing, Telecommunications and Multimedia Technology" (Complete Book)

Everyone has experienced the new dimensions of lifestyles ushered in by the pantoscopic developments in the realm of telecommunications, particularly by the adoption of digital techniques. Many of the existing books concentrate on digital signal processing and its applications while many others focus entirely on digital communications and still others treat multimedia as a separte area, largely from the applications point of view. This book seeks to present a unified perspective of the field interweaving these disciplines into a common fabric. As you rummage through the pages of this book, you will not only feel incited to appreciate the mathematical elegance of signal processing but will also gasp over the enthralling applications.

This book, above all, offers an introductory survey of the conceptual development of the subject. It provides a simple and lucid presentation of the essential principles, formulae and definitions of digital signal processing, telecommunications and multimedia. Not only content with a preliminary overview, this book also provides a comprehensive and rigorous exposition of several advanced concepts, leading the reader confidently through the intricacies of current developments in audio and video signal processing, satellite communications, HDTV, multimedia, computers and so forth. There is a sprinkling of illustrative problems and revision exercises spicing the text throughout. These will rekindle the reader's interest and also help in fostering an intuitive grasp of theory. Indeed, one learns more easily by solving problems and trying to answer questions than by browsing through the text pages. The updated end-of-chapter bibliographies will afford the reader an opportunity to access the original literature in the field and also to keep abreast of the latest developments.

The book is aimed at a wide cross-section of readership. It will be useful as a textbook for undergraduate students of Electronics and Telecommunication Engineering and allied disciplines, as well as diploma and science courses. It is also intended to be used as a reference book for practising engineers and scientists. It is earnestly hoped that the book will serve as a unique resource for students and professionals alike.

Human mind works by straight-line logical thinking as well as lateral thinking. The subject matter can be approached from several angles of attack. The book is self-contained and provides adequate flexibility of organizing course material to suit individual requirements. The reader interested in singal processing would like to pursue chapters on signal processing fundamentals, coding techniques, speech and audio signals, and image and video signals. The telecom-oriented reader will be inclined towards digital communications, network technology and high-definition television. The computer-minded reader will have a bent for thinking towards multimedia, Internet, etc.

The study approach in the technology-intensive digital arena needs to be carefully planned. Currently, this pluridisciplinary field is humming with research activities worldwide. This is because the 'information explosion' has thrown up a formidable challenge for its application to create a better society. The breathtaking R&D pace is evidenced by the prolific deluge of research papers appearing in scientific journals. Also, new commercial products are being introduced regularly, setting different market trends. These products exhibit a continued improvement in performance characteristics.

However, as soon as a technology attains maturity, it is on the throes of obsolescence and oblivion.

Keeping in view this dynamic and fast-changing scenario, it is important for us to build a solid theoretical foundation by equipping ourselves with sufficient background in the underlying physics and mathematics. This should be strengthened by a pragmatic approach. In this way, we can not only digest and appreciate the 'high-tech breakthroughs' bus also attune ourselves with the launching of novel products and induction of new services, as they are announced.

With so much excitement in store, welcome to the *Digital world* where every question has only one definite answer, either 'Yes' or 'No'. Please come, let us blend together digital signal processing with telecommunication and multimedia engineering to acquire an integrated view of the field. The pages between the covers of this book will unfold interesting plays enacted by the binary 'zeroes' and 'ones', which, I am sure, you will greatly enjoy and relish.

Suggestions for improvement of the book are cordially welcome and will be incorporated in subsequent editions.

Dr. V.K. Khanna
Pilani

Acknowledgements

The creation of a book requires combined sincere efforts, hard work, talents and blessings of a great many people, who directly or indirectly contribute to the book. This book is no exception and I owe special gratitude to several persons.

First and foremost, it is a matter of great pleasure and proud privilege for me to thank the Director, senior scientists and colleagues at CEERI, Pilani for their kind co-operation and encouragement in my endeavours. The assistance of Dr. P.K. Khanna, Scientist, CEERI, is gratefully acknowledged.

I am thankful to the assiduous staff members of S. Chand & Co. Ltd. for extending their support and taking keen interest in this work. Without their dedicated efforts, this book would not have become a reality.

The comments of the reviewer helped in redressing errors and improving the readability and clarity of the text by way of constructive criticism.

The material presented in this book is based on a large number of previous books on the subject, research papers in journals, magazine articles, conference records and a host of related technical literature. I thank the authors of these excellent works, too numerous to mention individually. A list of the major sources of information is given in the bibliographies appended at the end of each chapter. The reader may refer to these impeccable sources for more details on a topic.

Finally, I am thankful to my daughter and wife for their unfailing and unstinted support which provided me with confidence to venture into this project. They tolerated my preoccupation with this work which absorbed a considerable proportion of my time at home spanning over the last two years and detracted me from paying them their well-deserved attention.

Once again, my sincere thanks to all of the above.

Contents

INTERNATIONAL SYSTEM OF UNITS AND UNIT PREFIXES

Base SI Units

Sl. No.	Physical Quantity	Name of the Unit	Symbol
1.	Length	metre	m
2.	Mass	kilogram	kg
3.	Time	second	s
4.	Electric current	ampere	A
5.	Thermodynamic temperature	kelvin	K
6.	Luminous intensity	candela	cd
7.	Amount of substance	mole	mol

Supplementary Units

8.	Plane angle	radian	rad
9.	Solid angle	steradian	sr

Unit Prefixes

Sl. No.	Submultiple	Prefix	Symbol	Multiple	Prefix	Symbol
1.	10^{-1}	deci	d	10	deca	da
2.	10^{-2}	centi	c	10^2	hecto	h
3.	10^{-3}	milli	m	10^3	kilo	k
4.	10^{-6}	micro	μ	10^6	mega	M
5.	10^{-9}	nano	n	10^9	giga	G
6.	10^{-12}	pico	p	10^{12}	tera	T
7.	10^{-15}	femto	f	10^{15}	peta	P
8.	10^{-18}	atto	a	10^{18}	exa	E

SELECTED PHYSICAL CONSTANTS

Sl. No.	Constant	Symbol	Value
1.	Acceleration of gravity	g	9.807 m/s^2
2.	Avogadro's Number	N_A	6.022×10^{23} molecules/mol
3.	Boltzmann constant	k	1.38×10^{-23} J/K $= 8.62 \times 10^{-5}$ eV/K
4.	Electronic charge	q	1.602×10^{-19} C
5.	Electronic rest mass	m_0	9.11×10^{-31} kg
6.	Electron Volt	eV	1 eV $= 1.602 \times 10^{-19}$ J $= 23.05$ kCal/mol
7.	Gas constant	R	8.31 J/K/mol $= 1.987$ Cal/mol/K
8.	Permeability of vacuum	μ_0	1.2566×10^{-8} H/cm
9.	Permittivity of vacuum	ε_0	8.854×10^{-14} F/cm
10.	Planck's constant	h	6.625×10^{-34} J-s $= 4.135 \times 10^{-15}$ eV-s
11.	Proton rest mass	M_p	1.67×10^{-27} kg
12.	Speed of light in vacuum	c	2.998×10^{10} cm/s
13.	Stefan-Boltzmann constant	σ	5.67×10^{-8} W/m^2 K^4
14.	Thermal voltage at 300 K	kT/q	0.0259 V

USEFUL CONVERSION FACTORS AND NUMERICAL CONSTANTS

$$
\begin{aligned}
\text{1 radian} &= 57.3^\circ = 0.159 \text{ rev, 1 sphere} = 12.57 \text{ steradians} \\
\text{1 atomic mass unit} &= 1.66 \times 10^{-27} \text{ kg} \\
\text{1 Å} &= 10^{-10} \text{ m} = 10^{-8} \text{ cm} = 10^{-4} \text{ } \mu\text{m} = 10^{-1} \text{ nm} \\
\text{1 mil} &= 10^{-3} \text{ inch} = 25.4 \text{ } \mu\text{m} \\
\text{1 eV} &= 1.602 \times 10^{-19} \text{ J} \\
\text{1 Calorie} &= 4.19 \text{ J, 1 J} = 0.239 \text{ Calorie} \\
\text{1 weber/m}^2 &= 1 \text{ tesla} \\
\pi &= 3.14, \pi^2 = 9.87 \\
e &= 2.72, e^{-1} = 0.368
\end{aligned}
$$

SELECTED PHYSICAL CONSTANTS

Sl. No.	Constant	Symbol	Value
1.	Acceleration of gravity	g	9.81 m/s
2.	Avogadro's Number	N	6.022×10^{23} molecules/mol
3.	Boltzmann constant	k	1.38×10^{-23} J/K, 8.62×10^{-5} eV/K
4.	Electronic charge	q	1.602×10^{-19} C
5.	Electronic rest mass	m	9.11×10^{-31} kg
6.	Electron volt	eV	1 eV $= 1.602 \times 10^{-19}$ J $= 23.05$ kcal/mol
7.	Gas constant	R	8.31 J/mole/K, 1.99 cal/mol/K
8.	Permeability of vacuum	μ_0	1.256×10^{-6} H/m
9.	Permittivity of vacuum	ε_0	8.85×10^{-12} F/m
10.	Planck constant	h	6.626×10^{-34} J-s, 4.135×10^{-15} eV-s
11.	Proton rest mass	M_p	1.67×10^{-27} kg
12.	Speed of light in vacuum	c	2.998×10^{10} cm/s
13.	Stefan Boltzmann constant	σ	5.67×10^{-8} W/m^2/K^4
14.	Thermal voltage at 300 K	V_T	0.0259 V

USEFUL CONVERSION FACTORS AND NUMERICAL CONSTANTS

1 radian $= 57.3° = 0.159$ rev, 1 sphere $= 12.57$ steradians

1 atomic mass unit $= 1.66 \times 10^{-27}$ kg

$1 \text{ Å} = 10^{-10}$ m $= 10^{-8}$ cm $= 10^{-4}$ μm $= 10$ nm

1 mil $= 10^{-3}$ inch $= 25.4$ μm

1 eV $= 1.602 \times 10^{-19}$ J

1 Joule $= 10^7$ erg $= 6.24 \times 10^{18}$ eV $= 0.239$ calorie

1 weber/m^2 $= 1$ tesla

$\pi = 3.1416$

$e = 2.718$

$e^{-1} = 0.368$

Communication and Information Systems Overview

The *Information* Age has incontestably arrived, the *Digital Era* is here to stay, *Networking* is the buzzword today and *Connectivity* is the key to leverage information. A social metamorphosis is taking place, heralding the emergence of an *Information Society* in which anyone can acquire and exchange information at any time, anywhere.

The *Microelectronics Revolution* which began in 1947 with the invention of transistor, has been dubbed "the first electronics revolution." The second breakthough came in 1959 with the innvention of integrated circuit. Since then, progress in microelectronics has continued unabated, upto the present day VLSI (Very Large Scale Integration) and ULSI (Ultra Large Scale Integration), the cornerstones for the development of computers and telecommunications.

1.1 THE SYNERGY OF COMPUTERS AND TELECOMMUNICATIONS

The synergistic march of computers as *information processing tool* and telecommunications as *information conveying vehicle,* has shrunk the barriers of distance and time, trasforming the world into a *Global Village.* As the domains of computer and telecommunication systems are converging, with the consequent blurring of their boundaries, new services are being established. These services are mainly computer based with the Digital computer as a general-purpose electronic device placed at the focal points of the network for processing and forwarding information. Figure 1.1 presents a conceptual view of the relationship among computers, telecommunications and multimedia technologies. Evidently, these diverse disciplines are interwoven to produce the fabric of *Information Technology,* and the basic element laying the foundation of this unification is the digital representation of data, leading to the technology of *Digital Signal Processing.* Along with the key to this technological synthesis, viz., digital signal

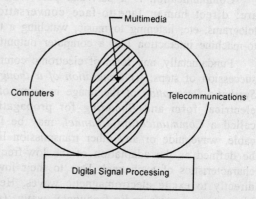

Fig. 1.1. Role of digital signal processing in amalgamating computers and telecommunications networks; multimedia is the simultaneous production, on a computer or a television screen, of varioius media such as text, pictures, graphics, voice, music, etc

1

processing, the application areas of telecommunications and multimedia, constitute the focal theme of this book.

1.2 DIGITAL ELECTRONICS AND THE TELECOMMUNICATION REVOLUTION

Digital Electronics is at the forefront of the advancement in the realm of telecommunications. It has come in a big way revolutionizing the telecom scenario. Recent years have witnessed a prolific growth in the field of *Digital Telecommunications,* and it continues to dominate the field of communication with enormous and indelible impact on futuristic telecommunication methodologies. The importance and applications of digtial telecommunications hardly need to be emphasized.

However, our world is still and will always be, to some degree analog. At present, the digital installations are speedily aggrandizing and crossing into regions which were once the sole province of analog signals. Digital installations look like *islands* of digital equipment in an *analog sea*, and these islands are rapidly growing larger.

Before formally launching on to the subject, let us equip ourselves with the language of information and communication systems. We begin by recapitulating the principal communication terms, and learning about signals and systems. This will be followed by a digest on the "mass telecommunications media", which are exerting a multi-pronged influence on the variegated facets of our lives. Then a presentation of analog and digital communications will be made, bringing out the relative merits, limitations and applications of these branches, restricting the discussion to a brief descriptive overview. We shall conclude this introductory chapter by laying out the organizational plan of this book.

1.3 INFORMATION AND COMMUNICATION

In everday usage, the word 'information' implies a collection of facts and figures, about a person, place or thing, discovered, heard or read. It is associated in our minds with a body of knowledge, news, etc. In the engineering sense, information is a *measurable quantity,* and a complete *information theory* exists, which enables the engineer to determine the rate of information transmission. Communication is concerned with the sending or conveying of information from one place to another; the transferred information is called a *message.*

Communication is a part and parcel of our lives. Some examples of communication are: direct human face-to-face conversation, postal correspondence through letters, telegrams, etc; listening to music, watching a theatre or a television programme, or machine-to-machine interaction like a computer outputting instruction to the printer to start printing.

Fundametally, any form of electronic communication entails some or all of the following succession of steps: (*i*) *Generation of a thought pattern or image* in the person's mind. (*ii*) *Symbolic Description* of the image in terms of visual or aural symbols. (*iii*) *Conversion* into electrical form and *Encoding* for propagation over a physical medium. This medium, called a *Communication Channel,* may be free space or an engineering structure like a cable, waveguide or any other transmission line. (*iv*) *Modulation* of the carrier which may be defined as the adaptation of the low-frequency or baseband electric oscillations to the characteristics of a channel. Due to their low frequency, these oscillations cannot be used directly to excite electromagnetic waves. Hence, they are utilized to vary the parameters of a stong carrier radio-frequency wave. (*v*) *Radiation* of the modulated wave by the antenna of the transmitter. (*vi*) *Excitation* of feeble electric oscillations in the antenna at the receiver. (*vii*) *Demodulation or Detection* which is the inverse of modulation. (*viii*) *Decoding* and reproduction of original symbols. (*ix*) Recreation of the incipient mentally conceived thought pattern or image, producing a faithful replica of the message sent at the user destination, i.e., the receiving end.

Figure 1.2 depicts the electrical generation of information or its transformation from other forms into the electrical form with the help of sensors and transducers, for the purpose of dissemination. In Fig. 1.3 we show the elements of a communication system illustrating the information transmission and reception process.

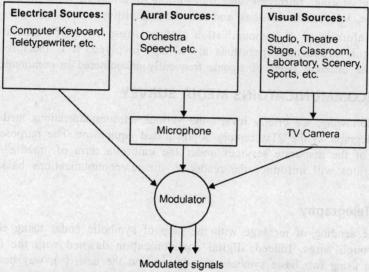

Fig 1.2. Electrical generation or conversion of information

The transmission path for information may be very short such as in the dialogue between the persons sitting in the same room, or it may be too long, for example, between two geographically distant points on the globe. Communication between two points situated far apart, is known as *Telecommuncation* which may be defined as long-distance communication through metallic cables, optical fibres, or air and space with the help of microwave and satellite links.

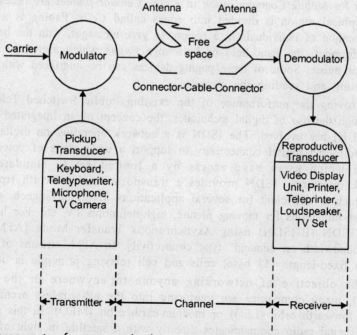

Fig. 1.3. Three parts of a communication system : Transmitter, Channel and Receiver

Communication has three major subdivisions : (*i*) Audio communication, (*ii*) Video communication and (*ii*) Data communcation.

The allied discipline of *Information Technology* deals with the study of various processes for acquiring, storing, retrieving and transmitting information through the combined use of computers, telecommunications and ancillary facilities.

In any information or communication system, irrespective of its nature, some basic forms of signal processing operations are always involved. It is therfore of interest to understand the different types of signals frequently encountered in communication practice.

1.4 TELECOMMUNICATOINS MEDIA SURVEY

In the following, we briefly review the various telecommunications media commencing from the telegraph to the 21st century sophisticated equipment. The purpose is to provide a snapshot of the disparate services under the umbrella term of "media". This and the ensuing sections will introduce the reader to the telecommunications background of the subject.

1.4.1. Telegraphy

It is the sending of message with the help of symbolic codes using electric currents flowing through wires. Indeed, digital communication dawned with the introduction of *Morse Code* using two basic symbols: the dot (.) and the dash (–), way back in 1865, for long-distance communication.

1.4.2. Telephony

It is concerned with the transmission of human voice to a distant place by wire or through space (radio). A *Video telephone* or *Picturephone* allows interpersonal video communicatoin between two individuals seated at geographically distant locations.

Mobility upto 100 m is provided by the *Cordless Telephone*. While this may be adequate in a premises for *Mobile Communication* in a city, *Cellular phones* are necessary in which a given geographical region is divided into zones called *Cells*. Paging is a communication facility for location of individuals in a region, to give messages, with the help of a battery-operated instrument, the hand-held or belt-worn *Pager* which alerts the user through a beep signal or music. Some of these paging devices can be interfaced with a computer for storing, printing and reading the message.

For improving the performance of the existing Public Switched Telephone Nework (PSTN) through the use of digital techniques, the concept of an Integrated Services Digital Network (ISDN) has evolved. The ISDN is a network operating on digital principles and providing end-to-end digital connectivity to support a wide range of voice and non-voice services, to which users have access by a limited set to standard multipurpose user-network interfaces. ISDN provides a transportation bandwidth from 64 kbit/s to 2 Mbit/s which is sufficient for several applications involving speech, data, image and video but has limitations for moving picture, high-definition TV, etc. For higher bandwidth, Broadband ISDN (B-ISDN) using Asynchronous Transfer Mode (ATM) is proposed, providing "bandwidth on demand" type connectivity. In ATM, streams of information are divided into fixed-length (53 byte) cells and cell relaying principle is utilized.

With the objective of networking anyone to anywhere in the world (Global Networking), many companies are venturing into the all-wireless arena by catapulting satellites in low-earth orbit (LEO) or medium-earth orbit (MEO). In this network strategy, the caller's digital radio communicates directly with a satellite in sight of the caller. This satellite transmits the information to another satellite which is in sight of the intended reciever from where it is sent to the receiver. The returning information from the responding receiver flows in the reverse direction. A constellation of LEO satellites is necessary to achieve radio line-of-sight links from every point on the earth.

1.4.3. Telex

An abridged form of "Teleprinter Exchange", this service is similar to the public telephone service except that it carries teleprinter signals instead of speech signals for typing messages at far-off places. Teleprinters employing keyboard-printer combination generate paper records of messages sent as well as received. The signalling rate is 50 bit/s.

1.4.4. Facsimile (FAX) system

This refers to the transmission of faithful copy of a letter, document, illustration, etc., through the telephone or telex network. FAX as a remote photocopying machine allows rapid document transfer, making business deals more efficient. The transmission signal is produced by scanning the page to be sent at typically 3.85 scan lines/minute. Higher scanning rates are required to increase the resolution and speed.

1.4.5. Radio Broadcasting

This is a system using a centrally located transmitter to radiate signals concerning news, sports, entertainment, etc., to a wide audience receiving at a large number of remote points. It includes *AM Broadcasting* using amplitude modulation and *FM Broadcasting* by frequency modulation. *Television Broadcasting* employs amplitude modulation for picture carrier and frequency modulation for sound carrier.

The common AM radio receiver is based on the *superheterodyne principle* in which the incoming signal is frequency converted to an intermediate frequency (IF) lower than the signal frequency. The IF signal is applied to an envelope detector to recover the baseband signal. After power amplification, the signal is fed to a loudspeaker.

1.4.6. Television

It is the transmission of motion pictures and sound of events, plays, etc., using coaxial cables, optical fibres, satellites, video tapes or discs. It comprises two types: *Monochrome* (black-and-white) and *Colour* Television.

Each picutre is *sequentially scanned* in a TV camera whereby the charge pattern produced on its photocathode is transformed into an output current varying *temporally* in accordance with the *spatial* changes in brightness, constituting a *video signal*. The scanning performed from left-to-right on a line-by-line basis is called *Raster Scanning*. Each picture is divided into 625 lines which form a *Frame*. In turn, each frame is split up into two *interlaced fields* consisting of 312.5 lines. At the end of scanning of a particular line, the spot flies back to the start of the next line; this is known as *Horizontal Retrace*. The flyback at end of a field is called *Vertical Retrace*. During the retrace intervals, *blanking pulses* are applied. The *field frequency* is 50 Hz and the *line scanning frequency* is 15, 625 Hz. Due to *persistence of vision*, flashing 25 pictures per second, results in the perception of moving pictures.

Obviously, TV picture quality is determined by: (*i*) Number of lines in a raster scan limiting vertical picture resolution, and (*ii*) Available video channel bandwidth limiting horizontal picture resolution.

The video bandwidth is given by

$$B = \frac{k}{2}\left(\frac{b}{a}\right)\left(\frac{N-2N_{vr}}{T-T_{hr}}\right) \qquad \ldots (1.1)$$

where k is the Kell Factor ~0.6 – 0.7, b is the raster width, a the raster height, the ratio b/a is called the *Aspect Ratio*, N is the total number of lines per frame, N_{vr} is the number of lines per field lost during vertical retrace, T is the total scanning line time and T_{hr} is the horizontal retrace duration. Substituting the values, the vision bandwidth $B = 5$ MHz. Due to the large bandwidth requirement and significant low-frequency content, vestigial sideband (VSB) modulation is used. Figure 1.4 illustrates the amplitude spectrum of the TV signal.

In *Colour Television*, the colour information is approximated by the summation of three primary colours : red, green and blue represented by the video signals $R(t)$ $G(t)$ and $B(t)$ so that the transmitted signals have the form

$$S_L(t) = 0.30\ R(t) + 0.59\ G(t) + 0.11\ B(t) \qquad \ldots(1.2)$$
$$S_I(t) = 0.60\ R(t) + 0.28\ G(t) + 0.32\ B(t) \qquad \ldots(1.3)$$
$$S_Q(t) = 0.21\ R(t) + 0.52\ G(t) + 0.31\ B(t) \qquad \ldots(1.4)$$

Signal $S_L(t)$ is called the *Luminance Signal* while the signals $S_I(t)$ and $S_Q(t)$ are known as *Chrominance Signals*. The former regenerates a black-and-white picture on a monochrome receiver while the latter indicates the departure of the picture colour from grey shades.

There are three major colour TV systems: NTSC (National Television System Committee), SECAM (Sequence de Couleurs Avec Memoire) and PAL (Phase Alternation Line)

Presently, recording and transmission of TV signals is accomplished mainly by analog methods Over-the-air and coaxial cable transmission is carried out by amplitude modulation (AM) of RF carriers in the VHF of UHF band, satellite and terrestrial microwave transmission as well as magnetic tape or disc recording is performed by frequency modulation (FM) while optical video disc recording and optical fibre transmission is done using pulse frequency modulation.

However, digital signals are employed in various TV studio signal processing equipment, e.g., time *base correctors* to reduce the scan line time variation due to tape stretching in video recorders, frame *synchronizers to synchronize* two video signals so that switching from one point to another is achieved without disrupting raster scanning in receivers, and *special effect generators* for combining, reshaping, accelerating or decelerating different picture and graphics material. Notwithstanding the above remarks, digital TV broadcasting is still in its infancy.

1.4.7. High-Definition (HDTV)

It is high-fidelity colour television with life-like 35 mm cinematographic images using an aspect ratio of 16 : 9 as compared to 4 : 3 used in standard TV practice, and raster scanned with at least double the vertical resolution and double the horizontal resolution of present TV. Also, large area and interline flicker are avoided. A prime consideration is compatibility between HDTV and standard TV although such compatibility may not be economically viable or subjectvely approved.

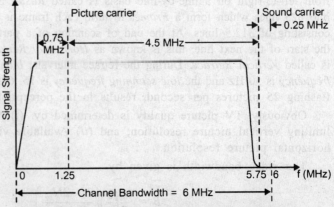

Fig 1.4. Amplitude spectrum of the transmitted television signal : Picture and Sound

In *Extended Definition Television* (EDTV), picture resolution is improved over HDTV by increasing the bandwidth of both luminance and chrominance signals while maintaining the standard number of scanning lines per frame.

1.4.8. Videoconferencing

This is an arrangement allowing two or more groups of persons at widely separated places wishing to communicate both visually and orally, in *real time* thus saving the valuable time and monetary expenditure incurred in physically bringing all the conferees together at the conference site. Since the participants are generally seated with cameras fixed, the motional flexibility in a videoconference scene is much less than in broadcast TV. In order to accommodate more participants, several cameras are used, each pointed at a different sub-group. Switching among the cameras is performed depending on the individual talking at a particular instant. Alternatively, a split-frame video signal is used employing two cameras at each location with one camera aimed at one group of participants in the bottom half of the frame and another camera focussed at a different group in the top half frame.

Videoconferencing along with videotelephony is gaining popularity particularly in the business class as an adjunct to voice telephony and as a low-cost replacement for time-consuming and expensive journey.

1.4.9. Teletext

It is the generic name for a one-way non-interactive computerized service transmitting still frames of news, alphanumeric textual and simple graphical information on the television screen of subscribers retrieved from a computer data base, as part of broadcast transmission. Certain frames in the data base serve as indexes and the required frame can be accessed by calling specialized indexes. Once the terminal is purchased or rented, these frames are accessible charge-free using a numeric keypad.

1.4.10. Videotex

Also called Viewdata, Videotex is the generic name referring to the interactive two-way systems for transference of video, text and graphics material stored in computer databases through the telephone network, for displaying on the TV screen of subscribers who have their TV sets suitably modified. Videotex services can also be provided by an interactive cable TV system. As in teletext, the customer uses a keypad to dial a database located in a central telephone office to request an information frame to be transmitted. A fee is charged for each frame besides rent.

Both teletext and videotex use a narrow band transmission medium in which communication from the user is of much lower bandwidth than communication to the user. Both services are intended as simple economic general public interest information systems.

They however differ in the respect that user terminals link to database computers via braodcast channels for teletext and through the telephone network for videotex. Secondly, only videotex has reverse linkage permitting communication with computer. Thirdly, in teletext a customer captures one of the several transmitted frames in a round robin fashion so that the response time increases with the size of the database. In videotex, due to the two-way connection of the customer to the database, the number of accessible frames can be much higher while maintaining a reasonably low response time. Thus teletext and videotex differ in the way data are transmitted in these services and also in the manner the user controls the data to be displayed (See Fig. 1.5)

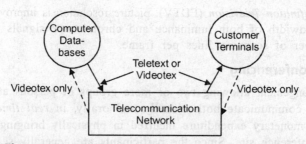

Fig. 1.5. Distinguishing between teletext and videotex

1.4.11. Electronic Mail (E-Mail)

It entails the sending of a message entered through a computer keyboard at one location on the earth to the video screen of a computer far away on the globe. Each person having an E-mail connection is assigned an E-mail address or number consisting of four parts: (*i*) *The User Name* This part identifies the unique user on a server. (*ii*) *The symbol @* It is used for demarcation between the user and host names which may contain multiple parts known as *subdomains* in a large organization. (*iii*) *The three Letter Suffix in the Host Name* such as 'org' for non-commercial, 'edu' for educational, 'mil' for military 'net' for network, 'gov' for government, etc., specify the kind of organization (*iv*) *The Final Two Letter Attachment* This represents the name of the country in which the server is situated, e.g., 'in' for India, 'jp' for Japan, 'uk' for United Kingdom and so on.

For every E-mail number, there is an E-mail box. The arriving message is stored in the box and can be retrieved by the individual on convenience. Furthermore, E-mail messages can be sent in real time or in store and forward mode. E-mail thus allows a range of features exploiting the storing and processing capabilities of computers.

Advantages of E-mail over conventional postal services include: speed, reliability and convenience, the ability to transfer huge amounts of information without moving any physical medium (paper). Its superiority over the telephone service lies in the fact that it is independent of the simultaneous availability of the calling party and the person called upon because the message can be stored and later forwarded to the recipient.

1.4.12. Multimedia

Multimedia is the integration of diverse information and communication technologies such as *textual and data* alphanumeric information, *still pictures* of real and imaginary scenes, two-or three-dimensional *graphical drawings* and geometrical shapes, dynamic graphical sequences called *animation, audio* (speech, musical sounds, noise, etc.) and moving pictures or *video* into an interactive combination of media, bringing together several existing facilities like the personal computer, television, telephony, etc. It falls under the province of both computer and telecommunication technologies. Since television itself is able to provide the viewer with text, graphics, animation, audio, video, etc., it must be noted that the primary difference between TV and multimedia lies in the 'interactivity' provided by multimedia.

The human body receives inputs simultaneously from the five senses, viz., sight, hearing, taste, smell and touch with the mind as the sixth integrating sense enabling us to react intelligently to a situation. Similarly, the power of multimedia arises from the capability to combine the useful features of the different media, opening up an unlimited vista for making the world easily understandable. Multimedia applications are already making inroads in business, academia and sciences for advertisement, shopping, entertainment, education, library/reference/archival, medical, news, etc.

1.4.13. Internet and Other Computer Networks

It is a global net of computer networks interlinking millions of computers across the world and allowing our computer to exchange data, message and files with any other computer connected to the internet.

An important component of the internet is the *World Wide Web* (WWW) which is a collection of pages and related resources. *Browser* is a program to navigate WWW. *Telnet* is the program allowing one computer to connect to another to avail of its information. *Gopher* is a program organizing the information according to menus. *File Transfer Protocol* (FTP) is a software tool for transferring files from one computer to another.

Apart from the above, the mushroom growth of computer networks has found a plethora of applications including: (*i*) *Train or Air Ticket Reservation Facility* for flexibility and convenience to travellers to plan their journey. (*ii*) *Railway Traffic Management and Signalling* for safety system, efficiency and fault tolerance. (*iii*) *Computer-Integrated Manufacturing* (CIM) commencing from product market survey, designing, technology development, material procurement, production and distribution to selling. (*iv*) *Electronic Funds Transfer* for financial transactions among banks, institutions, business houses, etc.

1.5 TELECOMMUNICATION MODALITIES

The wide-ranging media of telecommunication as outlined above, can be placed under two distinct heads, viz., cable communication and radio communication.

1.5.1. Cable or Line Communication

Here electric current is passed through copper wires laid beween the transmitting and receiving ends. Amplifiers called *Repeaters* in analog systems or *Pulse Regenerators* in digital systems, placed at a distance several kilometres apart on the way, help in strengthening the signal.

In *Optical Fibre Communication,* also referred to as *Optical, Photonic* or *Light Wave Communication*, the electric signal is used to modulate the intensity of a laser beam at the transmitter. The varying laser output is coupled to an optical fibre and propagates along the fibre, as in a waveguide. At the receiver, it is reconverted into an electrical signal which is processed by the usual methods.

Since the transmission lines or transmission media form the physical links for interchange of data, it would be worth while to briefly mention the types of transmission lines commonly employed in communication practice. Broadly speaking, these lines fall under two major classes: (*i*) *Baseband Links* In this category, are placed the common telephone *Twisted-Pair Wire* and the *Baseband Coaxial Cable* In a twisted-pair wire, the pairs of wires are spiralled about each other throughout their lengths making the electrical properties uniform and debilitating the electromagnetic interference effects between adjacent cables. The baseband coaxial cable consists of a central carrier wire surrounded by a woven mesh of Cu wire and an outer protective insulation sheath. The space intervening the inner wire and the mesh serves as an insulating medium for uniformity of electrical properties while the insulation sheath reduces both the electrical losses and the noise factor. (*ii*) *Broadband Links* Included in this class are the broadband coaxial cable and the fibre-optic cable. The broadband coaxial cable, the cable delivering the satellite cable TV programs to homes, has the capacity to carry hundreds of TV channel signals. This type of cable consists of a central core carrying current surrounded by an aluminium jacket with the intervening space filled with insulation and the complete unit enveloped by a protective cover. The fibre-optic cable will be dealt with in the section on Fibre Optic Communication.

1.5.2. Radio or Wireless Communication

This method utilizes electromagnetic waves as carriers of information without any connecting wires beween the transmitter and the receiver. Two important radio communication techniques are : (*i*) *Microwave Communication* in which microwaves are transmitted from one tower to another forming a chain of repeater stations, and (*ii*) *Satellite Communication* using a satellite or a group of orbiting satellites as repeaters in the sky. Both these modes will be discussed in separate sections ahead.

1.6 FIBRE OPTIC COMMUNICATION

1.6.1. Construction of Optical Fibre

An optical fibre, shown in Fig. 1.6, consists of a central cylindrical core, made of fused silica, quartz or plastic (through which the light wave travels by multiple *total internal reflections*), surrounded by a Si or teflon layer having lower refractive inde than the core (to confine the light beam within the core), known as cladding, and finally a polyurethane *jacket* (to protect from environmental effects and abrasion).

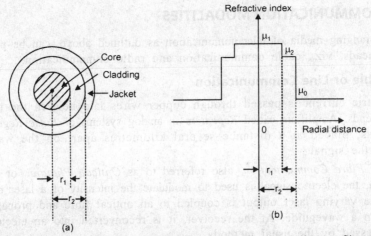

Fig. 1.6. (a) Cross-sectional view of an optical fibre (b) Refractive index profile of a step-index fibre

1.6.2. Types of Optical Fibres

Optical fibres are classified as: *Single Mode Fibre* (one path of light propagation) and *Multimode Fibre* (several paths). Single mode fibres are used for carrying signals over long distances for inter-building connections whereas multimode fibres having distance limitation < 2 km, are employed for intra-building connectivity.

Multimode fibres are subclassified according to their refractive index profile, as: (*i*) *Step-Index Fibre* in which the refractive index is constant throughout the core and changes abruptly at the boundary between the core and the cladding. (*ii*) *Graded-Index Fibre* in which the refractive index decreases gradually from the core centre radially outwards moderating the dispersion of signals. This type of fibre has the highest transmission rate but the attenuation losses are also large.

1.6.3. Layout of an Optical Fibre Communication Link

A Fibre Optic Link (Fig. 1.7) consists of a *Transmitter* for conversion of electrical signal into an optical signal using a Light Emitting Diode (LED), a *p-n* junction laser or a gas laser, the *Optical Fibre Cable* passing through an underground conduit or laid on telephone pole or on a river or ocean bed, and a *Receiver* for reconverting the light into electrical signal with the help of photodetectors like *p-i-n* diode or avalanche photodiode.

1.6.4. Advantages of Fibre Optic Communication

(*i*) *High Bandwidth Capability* A significant advantage of fibre optic telecommunication over Cu-wire transmission is the extremely large, almost unlimited bandwidth over which huge amounts of information in various forms like voice, data, video or combinations of these can be transferred. Present bandwidth limit is around 3.3×10^3 MHz while the ultimate bandwidth may be as high as 10^4 MHz.

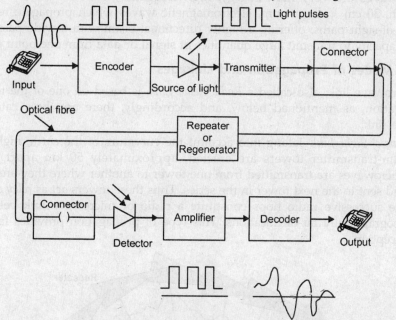

Fig. 1.7. Schematic layout of a fibre optic link

(*ii*) *Electromagnetic Interference Immunity* The light-carrying optical fibres due to their glass/plastic composition are unperturbed by radio-frequency interference (RFI) or electromagnetic interference (EMI) such as caused by lightning, electric motors and other appliances leading to noise-free transmission. The fibres are also not susceptible to any cross-talks. These inherent properties are exploited in defence, railways, etc. In addition, the bulky shielding required in metallic cables is dispensed with.

(*iii*) *Low Signal Attenuation* The optical fibres give lower signal attenuation ~0.5 dB/km requiring a smaller number of repeaters than Cu-wire systems.

(*iv*) *Security from Tapping* Tapping of information from optical fibres is easily detected, a vital factor in military, banking and computer networks.

(*v*) *Size and Weight Reduction Benefits* The smaller diameter and hence reduced size and weight of the optical fibres, as compared to copper cables, make them suitable for aviation, ships and tall buildings.

(*vi*) *Human Safety Factor* Absence of fire hazards due to a short circuit is an important feature of fibre optical cables making them useful in coal mines and chemical plants. Moreover, there is no risk of electric shock.

(*vii*) *Superior Corrosion Resistance* The fibres are highly resistant to the chemical attack of corrosive liquids as well as to the extremes of temperature. They are endowed with more capability to sustain the vagaries of environmental hazards ensuring longevity of fibre optic systems. Their longer life span of 20-30 years as against the 12-15 years of Cu cables has made them very attractive.

(*viii*) *Economic Viability* Above all, the lower costs of optical fibres due to the cheaper raw materials and other ingredients is a boon to us.

1.7 MICROWAVE LINKS

1.7.1. What are Microwaves?

Microwaves are very high energy, high frequency, 1 GHz $<f<$100 GHz, short wavelength, 30 cm $< \lambda <$ 3 mm, electromagnetic waves which propagate rectilinearly along line-of-sight paths, offering a highly directional beam with a wide passband and having a capacity to transmit large quantities of signal or data from one point to another.

1.7.2. Modes of Propagation and Linkages

A microwave link, also called a *Radio Relay Link,* is based on one of the three types of propagation, as mentioned below, and accordingly, there are three categories of microwave link:

(*i*) *Line-of-Sight Link* Taking into account the curvature of the earth, high receiver-cum-transmitter towers are erected, approximately 50 km apart (Fig. 1.8). Microwaves are transmitted from one tower to another where they are amplified and sent to the next tower in the series. Thus these towers act as *relay centres* and the successive radio hops constitute a radio or microwave link between two geographically far-off locations. This type of propagation provides fairly stable reception.

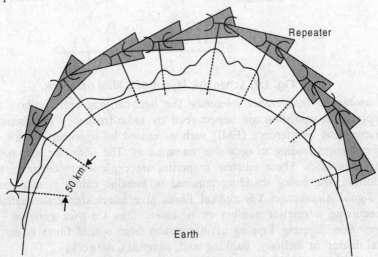

Fig. 1.8. A line-of-sight microwave link

(*ii*) *Troposcatter Link* These links (Fig. 1.9), used as complementary links to line-of-sight transmission, are based on the forward scattering of radio waves from the atmospheric layer called *Troposphere,* the lowest layer of the atmophere with thickness varying from 7 km at the poles to about 28 km at the equator, and responsible for weather changes. The advantage gained is that towers can be placed beyond the optical horizon, at large distance ~200-500 km apart because the range of this radio hop is much longer. The shortcoming is the narrower bandwidth accounting for the reduced data rates. Further, only a small fraction of the transmitted power is reflected so that powerful transmitters and big antennae are necessary.

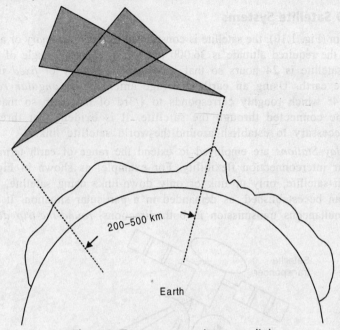

200–500 km

Earth

Fig. 1.9. Troposcatter microwave link

(iii) *Artificial Satellite-based Line-of-Sight Link* This link (Fig. 1.10) exploits a satellite placed in a geostationary orbit (Sec. 1.8) and containing a repeater along with receiving and transmitting antennae oriented towards the earth.

1.8 SATELLITE COMMUNICATIONS

1.8.1. The Satellite Channel

A *Communication Satellite* consists of a spacecraft orbiting the earth in a circular or elliptical orbit and carrying on board microwave transmitting or receiving equipment; microwave frequencies are employed to penetrate the ionosphere and to handle the wide signal bandwidth.

The *Satellite Channel* (Fig. 1.11) comprises: (i) an Uplink connecting the terrestrial transmitting station to the on-board satellite transponder, (ii) the *Transponder* amplifying the signal to overcome noise effects and thus working as a *sky-based repeater*, and (iii) a *Downlink* connecting the transponder to the receiving station on the earth; the earth station is connected to the subscriber terminals. The uplink frequencies generally used are 4 and

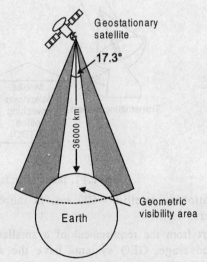

Geostationary satellite

17.3°

36000 km

Earth

Geometric visibility area

Fig. 1.10. Line-of-sight microwave link with a geostationary artificial satellite showing the earth coverage limit

12 GHz while the corresponding downlink frequencies are 6 and 14 GHz respectively.

The satellites are placed in geostationary or non-geostationary orbits leading to GEO and non-GEO satellite systems.

1.8.2. GEO Satellite Systems

In this system (Fig. 1.10), the satellite is constrained to a *geostationary* or a *geosynchronous orbit* for which the required altitude is 36,000 km for an elevation angle of 90°. The orbital period of this satellite is 24 hours so that it appears *stationary* or *fixed* in the sky to an observer on the earth. Using an earth coverage antenna, the *angular range* of such a satellite is 17.34° which roughly corresponds to 1/3rd of the earth so that regions within this area can be connected through the satellite. It is evident that three geostationary satellites are necessary to establish around-the-world satellite link.

Satellite Relay Stations are employed to extend the range of earth terminals as well as to enhance their interconnection flexibility. For example, as shown in Fig. 1.12, up and down links with satellite, only up-link or only down-links using satellite, and satellite-to-satellite links can be established, as demanded in a particular situation. It may be pointed out that for simultaneous transmission in both directions, *round-the-trip delay* incurred in

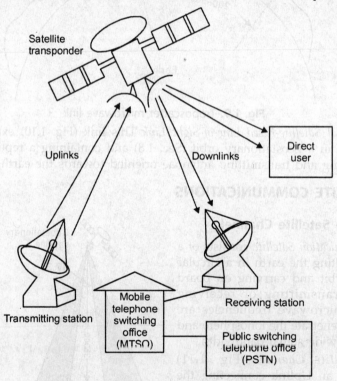

Fig. 1.11. Basic structure of a satellite channel

a geostationary satellite ~600 ms, is inordinately long, much to the dissatisfaction of customers.

Apart from the requirement of a smaller number of only three satellites for complete global coverage, GEO systems have the advantage of a smaller installation cost and higher reliability over other systems. However, the excessive propagation delay suffered renders interactive voice services difficult. This disadvantage is offset by system simplicity and the easy fixation of antennae on the ground.

1.8.3. Non-Geo Satellite Systems

In these system, the satellites are placed in proximity to the earth either in *Low-Earth Orbits* (LEO) or *Medium-Earth Orbits* (MEO), (See Fig. 1.13). Non-GEO systems are superior to GEO systems for *interactive voice services*. However, for real-time applications, at least one satellite must always be in view between any two links. This increases the number of satellites, system complexity and cost. Non-GEO systems are therefore targeted for global markets with local regulatory approvals in different countries.

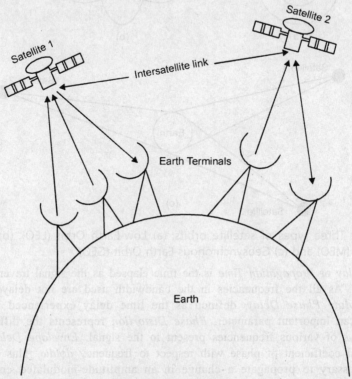

Fig. 1.12. Satellite relay

1.9   TRANSMISSION PARAMETERS

After the discourse on telecommunications media and modalities, we would like to take a quick look at the figures of merit for the performance evaluation of any telecommunication medium. These parameters fall into three main groups: (*i*) *Bandwidth Parameters* Attenuation distortion and phase and envelope delay distortion fall in this class. (*ii*) *Interface Parameters* This category includes terminal impedance in-band and out-of-band signal power, test signal power and ground isolation. (*iii*) *Facility parameters* In this group fall the noise; frequency, phase and amplitude distortion; and non-linear distortion.

1.9.1. Bandwidth Parameters

Attenuation Distortion, also called *Frequency Response* or *Differential Gain* is defined as the difference between the current gain at a particular frequency and the current gain at a reference frequency. For the telephone circuit, the 1004 Hz frequency is used as a standard test tone frequency. In a 3002 channel, the circuit gain between the frequencies 500 Hz < f < 2500 Hz should not be > 2 dB than the circuit gain at 1004 Hz while not < 8 dB below the 1004 Hz gain.

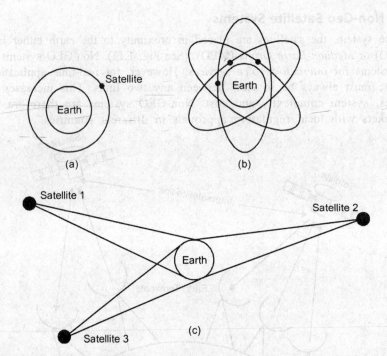

Fig. 1.13. The Three types of satellite orbits: (a) Low-Earth Orbit (LEO), (b) Medium-Earth Orbit (MEO) and (c) Geosynchronous-Earth Orbit (GEO)

Phase Delay or *Propagation Time* is the time elapsed as the signal traverses from source to destination. As all the frequencies in the bandwidth used are not delayed by the same amount, *Absolute Phase Delay,* defined as the time delay experienced by a particular frequency, is an important parameter. *Phase Distortion* represents the difference between absolute delays of various frequencies present in the signal. *Envelope Delay Distortion* is the differential coefficient of phase with respect to frequency $d\phi/d\omega$. This parameter gives the time necessary to propagate a change in an amplitude-modulated envelope through a medium. It is determined by transmitting a narrow-band carrier and measuring the phase variations of the low-frequency envelopes at the receiver. Then the phase difference for different carrier frequencies is obtained.

1.9.2. Interface Parameters

Considering the telephone network, the two primary requirements of these parameters are the electrical protection of the network and the personnel using it, and the design standardization. Station equipment impedance (resistive) should be > 600 ohm and the ground isolation impedance of equipment should be > 20 Mohms DC and 50 kohms AC value. Similarly, specifications are laid down for the circuit gain with respect to in-band signal power as well as for the transmitted signal power.

1.9.3. Facility Parameters

Noise is the name given to the undesired energy vitiating the useful passband of a comunications channel. *Correlated Noise* such as non-linear distortion is the noise associated with a signal whereas *Uncorrelated Noise, e.g., Thermal Noise,* is present even in absence of the signal.

Background Noise, referred to by different names as *White, Thermal, Gaussian* or *C-Message Noise* is the noise inherently present in a circuit by virtue of its electrical make-up or constitution. It is an additive parameter and its magnitude increases with the electrical length of the circuit.

Impulse Noise refers to the short-duration high amplitude peaks in the noise spectrum of a signal (Fig. 1.14).

A *Gain Hit* (Fig. 1.15 (a)) is a sudden random variation in circuit gain and is called temporary if the change is > ±3 dB for > 4 ms and reverts to the orginal value within 200 ms. A dropout is a fall in circuit gain > 12 dB and lasting for > 4 ms.

A *Phase Hit* (Fig. 1.15 (b)) is a sudden

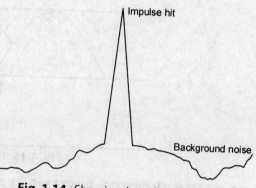

Fig. 1.14. Showing impulse noise

irregular phase change in a signal while a *Phase Jitter* in a signal (Fig. 1.16) implies continuous uncontrolled changes in its zero crossings.

Non-linear Distortion is exhibited in the form of additional tones present in the signal due to its non-linear amplification. It manifests itself, for example, as *distorted sine waves*. The two basic types of this distortion are: (*i*) *Harmonic Distortion* in which undesired multiples of transmitted frequencies are seen, (*ii*) *Intermediate Distortion* which produces cross products—sums and differences of the input signal frequencies.

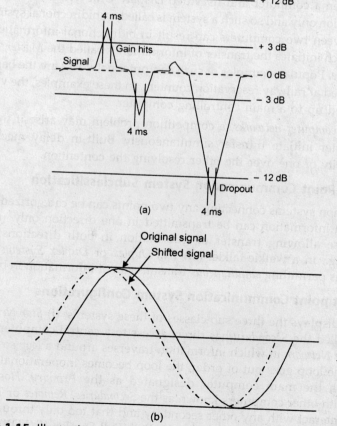

Fig 1.15. Illustrating : (*a*) Gain hits and dropouts, (*b*) A phase hit

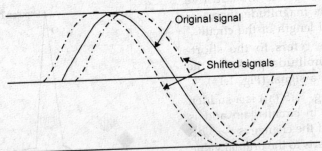

Fig. 1.16. Phase jitter

1.10 COMMUNICATION SYSTEMS CLASSIFICATION

Our discussions so far have centered around the general aspects of signals, systems, telecommunications media and modalities. We now divert the focus of our attention to communication systems and then make a progression towards analog and digital communication systems.

1.10.1. Two-Point and Multipoint Systems

Based on the number of points linked, these systems fall into two major divisions, namely, Two-Point and Multi-Point Systems. An example of a *two-point system* is the connection between a computer and its Video Display Unit terminal. Here information flows in one direction only and so such a system is called a unidirectional system. However, a connection between two computers can result in bidirectional information flow. Here the computer which initiates the transfer of information is called the *Master*, and the other computer the *Slave*. Popular examples of such computer networks are the bank computers and those employed at railway reservation counters. In these examples, the various branch computers are tied up to a main controlling computer.

In *multipoint computer networks*, a competition problem may arise if the branch and the main computer initiate transfer simultaneously. Built-in delay mechanisms then introduce a priority of one over the other resolving the contention.

1.10.2. Two-Point Communication System Subclassification

Communication systems connecting any two points can be categorized as follows: (*i*) *Simplex* in which information can be transmitted in one direction only. (*ii*) *Half-Duplex Systems* are those allowing transfer of information in both directions although *not simultaneously*, e.g., in a walkie-talkie. (*iii*) *Full-Duplex* or *Duplex Systems* are generally four-wire systems permitting *simultaneous* transmission of information in both directions.

1.10.3. Multipoint Communication System Configurations

Figure 1.17 displays the three sub-classes of these systems: (*i*) *Star Network* in which each element called the *Secondary* has direct access to a central computer known as the *Primary*. (*ii*) *Ring Network* in which information traverses around a *loop* so that if any one component of the loop goes out of order, the loop becomes inoperational, (*iii*) *Multidrop System* in which the main computer designated as the *Primary*, *Host* or *CPU* can communicate with other computers known as the *Secondaries*, *Remotes* or *Tributaries* but a secondary can interact with any other secondary and that too only through the primary. In particular, a multidrop system is said to be Full/Full Duplex (F/FDX) if the primary

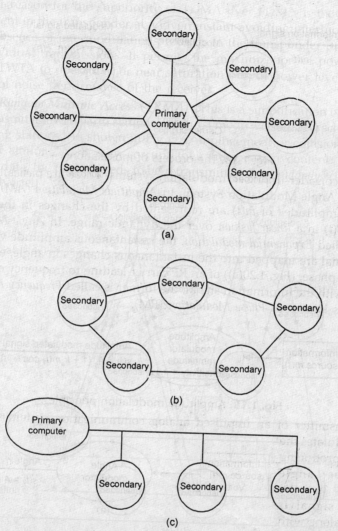

Fig. 1.17. Multipoint system configurations: (a) Star network, (b) Ring network and (c) Multidrop system

can transmit information to a secondary while simultaneously receiving information from another secondary.

1.11 ANALOG AND DIGITAL COMMUNICATION SYSTEMS

1.11.1. Analog System

Based on the technique adopted for modulation, the analog communication systems fall under two main headings: Unpulsed and Pulsed Modulation System. A *Modulator*, (Fig. 1.18) is a device which constructs some function $s(t) = f\{m(t), c(t)\}$ of the information signal $m(t)$ and the continuous RF carrier wave producing a modulated signal containing the information signal: this modulated signal is in a form more suitable than the information signal for transmission over the distance required at the frequency specified and for the service or function desired.

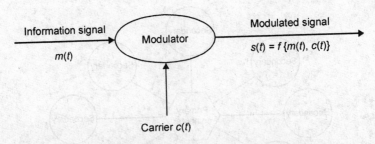

Fig. 1.18. The process of modulation

First, let us consider unpulsed modulation systems. These are basically of two types: Amplitude and Angle Modulation System. In *Amplitude Modulation (AM)* (Fig. 1.19), the instantaneous amplitudes of $m(t)$ are represented by the changes in the instantaneous amplitudes of $s(t)$ in a *linear fashion* over the dynamic range. In *Angle Modulation*, (Fig. 1.20(a)), also called *Exponential modulation*, the instantaneous amplitude variations of the information signal are mapped into the instantaneous changes in angle, either frequency (Fig. 1.20(b)) or phase, (Fig. 1.20(c)) of an RF carrier leading to frequency or phase change in accordance with the information signal; the former is called *Frequency Modulation* (FM) and the latter is known as *Phase Modulation* (PM).

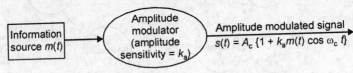

Fig. 1.19. Amplitude modulation principle

In the transmitter of an unpulsed analog communication system, the information waveform modulates the carrier wave producing amplitude or angle modulation. In the receiver, the signal is demodulated along with its noise content and the required information is measured in terms of the signal-to-noise ratio.

We now consider the other analog modulation variant referred to as the *Pulse Modulation System.* In this system (Fig. 1.21), the pulsed information waveform is used to modulate the carrier wave producing an intermittently perturbed signal of a discrete nature instead of a continuous

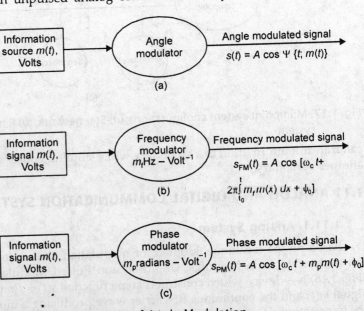

Fig. 1.20. (a) Principle of Angle Modulation
(b) Frequency Modulation (FM) and
(c) Phase Modulation (PM)

wave. Three types of pulse modulation include: Pulse Amplitude Modulation (PAM), Pulse

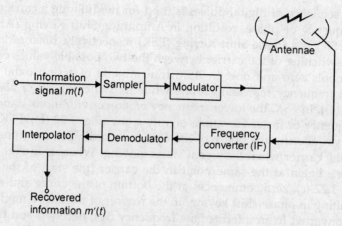

Fig. 1.21. Flow diagram of a pulse modulation system

Position Modulation (PPM) and Pulse Frequency Modulation (PFM). The different implications of the term 'modulation' in unpulsed and pulsed analog systems deserve special mention. In unpulsed systems, modulation is a *single-level process*. It maps the angular deviations of the information signal into the continuous amplitude, frequency, phase or other variations of a radio-frequency carrier wave. On the contrary, pulse modulation is a *two-level structure*. In PAM technique, for example, the first modulation level refers to the conversion of an analog waveform into a pulse sequence resembling the sampling operation. This first level of modulation is aptly called *Signal Conditioning*. For radio propagation, the unquantised signal thus produced is used in a second level of modulation or *Secondary Modulation* by using it as an information signal to modulate a high-frequency carrier. These modulations are in amplitude, frequency or phase as follows: (*i*) *Amplitude*: PAM/AM, PPM/AM, PDM/AM; (*ii*) *Frequency*: PAM/FM, PPM/FM PIM/FM; and (*iii*) *Phase*: PAM/PM, PPM/PM and PDM/PM.

Upon reception, a single-channel receiver converts the signal to an intermediate frequency, demodulates it and interpolates the baseband pulsed signals to analog form.

Looking at the complete pulse modulation method, the pertinent question which immediately comes to mind is regarding the justification for the additional complexities introduced. The question is answered if we look at the accompanying advantages of higher modulation efficiency and the possibility of multiple channel multiplexing which means the simultaneous transmission of two or more information channels on the same physical or radio link.

1.11.2. Digital System

The analog signal is first *sampled* producing a pulsed waveform; this sampling is accomplished in accordance with the *Sampling Theorem* enunciated as follows: If the highest frequency contained in a band-limited analog signal possessing a finite energy is W Hz, then the signal is completely described by specifying its sample values at instants of time separated by $1/(2W)$ seconds and is exactly recovered from a knowledge of the sample taken at a rate of 2W Hz; the interval = $1/(2W)$, measured in seconds, is the *Nyquist Interval* while the sampling rate of 2W samples per second or Hz, is the *Nyquist rate*.

The sampled pulses are quantised to a finite number of quantum amplitude levels. Then each quantum level is encoded into a digital equivalent and transmitted. The sampler-quantiser-encoder combination constitutes an *A/D Converter* and the sum-total method of obtaining the coded pulsed waveform is known as *Pulse-Code Modulation* (PCM).

The above sequence of digital pulses is used for modulating a carrier wave either in amplitude, frequency or phase, resulting in Amplitude-Shift Keying (ASK), Frequency-Shift Keying (FSK) and Phase-Shift Keying (PSK) respectively. *Binary Modulation* simply comprises the switching of the carrier between the two possible values corresponding to the binary symbols zero and one. In *ASK*, transmission of a sinusoidal carrier of fixed amplitude and frequency represents a one while its switching off or absence denotes a zero (Fig. 1.22 (*a*)). In *FSK*, the lower frequency or slower vibrations stand for a zero and the higher frequency or faster vibrations signify a one (Fig. 1.22 (*b*)). PSK technique (Fig. 1.22 (*c*)), involves altering the phase of the carrier according to the signal, i.e., changing the timing of the carrier when the signal starts moving. Whereas in Fig. 1.22 (*b*), the one and zero signals begin at the same point in the carrier (the start of the upswing of the curve), in Fig. 1.22 (*c*), zero commences at the bottom of the curve and one at the top of the curve resulting in phase-shift keying. In the *receiver* of the above modulation systems, the signal is converted to an intermediate frequency (IF), decoded and then interpolated back to the analog signal.

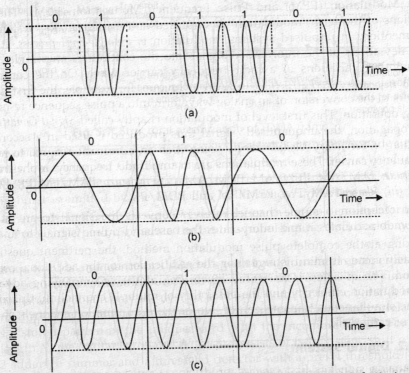

Fig. 1.22. Three basic binary modulation techniques: (a) Amplitude-Shift Keying (ASK), (b) Frequency-Shift Keying (FSK), and (c) Phase-Shift Keying (PSK)

A communication system based on PCM in conjunction with the keying techniques described above such as ASK, FSK, PSK, etc., is referred to as *Digital Communication*. Digital communication systems of this type form the subject matter of this book.

The perplexing query is obviously about the Need of Quantisation. Why is it necessary to introduce an additional step of quantisation, thereby further complicating the transmission and reception processes? The reasons are explained below:

The pulse amplitude, position and duration in PAM, PPM and PDM are proportional to the corresponding parameters and vary continuously as in the original information signal. However, bearing in mind, the limited resolving power of the human eyes, ears or even electronic instrumentation, the finer details of a signal need not bother us for effective and efficient information transference. Moreover, the pulse amplitudes and edges are prone to noise. By quantisation and encoding, only the bare essential portion of information is transmitted, thereby increasing the modulation efficiency. Improvement in the noise immunity leads to a superior signal-to-noise ratio. These factors work, hand in hand, contributing to quality and reliability enhancement. Additional facilities of error detection, correction encryption and other advantages associated with coded transmission then naturally follow. These advantages will be elaborated in the sequel.

1.11.3. Overall Advantages and Limitations of Digital Communications

The factor of far-reaching consequence in favour of digital communications is the *Noise Immunity* of this technique (Fig. 1.23). When analog signals traverse long distances, they are corrupted by noise due to undesirable amplitude, frequency and pahse variations introduced by the hardware itself or by the external noise sources. Amplification of the signal further complicates the problem because the noise is also amplified proportionately.

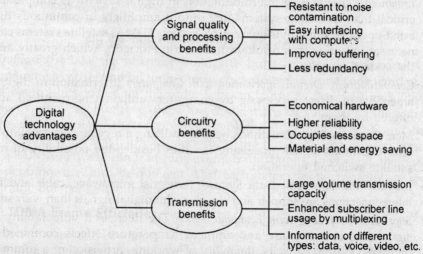

Fig. 1.23. Advantages associated with the use of digital techniques

To circumvent the noise problem, it was thought desirable to approximate the signal by a stream of digital pulses. Provided these pulses are periodically *regenerated* (not amplified) on the way, typically at distances of 1-3 km before impairment beyond recognition, theoretically the signal can be transmitted upto infinite distance without any deterioration. The major source of error vitiating the technique is the approximation involved in representation of the analog signal by the digital pulse train, which is termed the *Quantisation Noise*.

The other strong points in support of digital communications are operational flexibility, integration of diverse information sources, e.g., computer data, audio and video signals into a common format and security of information from its source to destination through the use of *encryption*.

The above-mentioned attractive features of digital communications should not foreshadow its limitations. The main shortcoming of digital communications is the *large bandwidth requirement* of the digital signal. This was the chief deterrent to the adoption of digital techniques in the early phases of telecommunication progress. It also explains why analog communications dominated the scene during this period. However, the rapid strides made by the digital integrated circuits technology have tilted the balance in the favour of digital communications. Although digital methods are now commonplace in several TV studies, digital televison broadcasting has still to carve its niche. The pictures contain huge amounts of data, occupying excessively large bandwidth, evading economical magnetic tape recording and rendering disc storage or electromagnetic wave transmission impractical. However, the pictures contain large quantities of repetitive data in the form of blue sky, common successive frames and other minute details which can be safely discarded without being perceived by the eye. This technique called *Video Compression* is being increasingly followed in digital practice.

1.11.4. Advantages of Digital Satellite Communications Over Analog Satellite Communications

Some of the advantages are summarized below:

(*i*) *More Robust and Noise Proof* Carrier-to-interference ratios in the range of 20-30 dB yield satisfactory performance with digital systems while analog systems need much higher ratios. Because the digital signal is impervious to noise, the quality of digital transmission is virtually independent of distance and network topology.

(*ii*) *Enhanced Capacity* Sine intermodulation in digital systems is comparatively less critical than in analog systems, the output amplifiers in continuous digital and burst-operated time-division multiple access (TDMA) satellite systems can operate near saturation with a resultant increase in efficiency which greatly ameliorates the system capacity.

(*iii*) *Compatibility of Digital Information with Computers* Information in digital form is amenable to direct processsig by computers utilizing the manifold advantages offered by them.

(*iv*) *More Flexibility* Digital methods help in realizing a regenerative satellite endowed with enormous signal processing facilities besides the possibility of multibeam satellite switched operation.

(*v*) *Low-Cost Interlinks with Earth Systems* Terrestrial microwave, cable and fibre optic interconnections are simpler and cheaper with digital signals than with analog ones.

(*vi*) *Short-term and Long-term Economic Gains* The decreased vulnerability of digital signals to channel noise and ambient temperature effects combined with the increased system capacity, flexibility of working, provision of a common format for different types of signals and cost-effective production have contributed to the economic benefits of digital satellite systems, both immediate and in the long run. This has also received impetus from the advancements in ultra-high speed logic circuitry, digital processors and microprocessors.

1.11.5. Digital TV versus Analog TV

Below we enlist some of the advantages of digital television over its analog counterpart:

(*i*) *Easy Adaptation to the Three Basic Colour TV Systems* Because the sampling check for the A/D Converter is phase-locked to the broadcast colour-burst frequency, by changing the clock frequency, the system can accommodate NTSC or PAL colour burst systems and the SECAM system in black-and-white (the SECAM and PAL colour transmission techniques differ).

(*ii*) *Flicker Reduction* The observed flicker caused by interlaced scanning is decreased, accompanied by an apparent increase in resolution, by storing all the 625 or 525 lines of the digital image and displaying the complete picture on the screen all together at once instead of having only half the scanning lines on the screen for each field.

(*iii*) *Signal Quality Improvement* Phase-locked loop (PLL) circuits are employed for checking the synchronization on each horizontal line. The smaller number of resistive-capacitive circuits, along with the capacitive and inductive elements used considerably aid in reducing signal distortion.

(*iv*) *Tricks for Creating Special Effects* Some digital TV receivers have provision for producing special effects among which may be mentioned:

— *Mosaic Effect* in which the screen is composed of small blocks.

— *Paint Effect* or *Posterization* like oil painting.

— *Freeze Mode* bringing the picture being viewed to a halt.

— *Preview Mode* displaying the stationary pattern of several channels in sequence arranged in columns and rows on the screen.

— *Picture-in-Picture Mode* in which a small-size real-time picture from another channel or external input is inserted at a screen corner.

— *Strobe Mode* displaying several time-sequenced pictures at once while simultaneously the real-time picture appears at screen corner.

— *Editing Mode* permitting the viewer to alter the still pictures in the strobe mode.

1.11.6. Comparison of Analog and Digital Tape Recorders

It will be interesting to examine the performance of analog and digital tape recorders :

(*i*) In an analog tape recorder, the tape driving mechanism should ensure precise tape speed control so that the speeds, while recording and playing back a high-fidelity analog signal, are exactly same. Such close speed control for the entire tape length is nearly impossible in a cost-effective system.

(*ii*) The air gap between the tape and the magnetic head should remain constant during both tape recording and playback, a condition very difficult to realize in practice.

(*iii*) Tape homogeneity is necessary over its entire length of accurate recording which is again difficult to achieve.

As digital tape recorders use discrete symbols 'zero' and 'one' for both recording and playback, the above problems are automatically solved. The circuit complexity of the digital methods is overcome by using digital signal processing chips manufactured by advanced VLSI fabrication technology.

1.12 AIMS, SCOPE AND ORGANIZATIONAL PLAN OF THE BOOK

Before embraking upon a journey, a tourist carefully plans for the places to be visited, the routes to be followed, the hotels, resorts, etc., by looking at the tourist guides, road maps, etc. Similarly, we define the aim, coverage and organization of the book and present a summary of the book by chapters which would help the reader to plan the course according to individual requirements.

The stupendous expansion and progress of telecommunication is inextricably linked to and synonymous with the developments in digital signal processing techniques. Candidly, the students and professionals interested in telecommunications (as also instrumentation, automatic control and allied engineering disciplines) must keep abreast of the 'state-of-the-art' parctice and current technological advancements in the field.

Concomittantly with the retrospective studies and up-to-date surveys, one must also enquire about the futuristic projections and technological forecasts by the experts. This will help the students in building a platform from where to launch their career.

Chapter 1 is an introductory chapter offering the reader a broad overall perspective of telecommunication and information systems. The material selection is oriented towards facilitating entry into the subject to the newcomer.

Chapter 2 enlightens the reader on the aspects of digital coding which serves as the gateway from the analog to the digital domain. *Pulse-code Modulation* is the heart of techniques for applying digital methods to analog waveforms. Differential Pulse-Code Modulation, Delta Modulation and Delta PCM are discussed.

Chapter 3 reviews binary modulation techniques including amplitude, frequency and pahse-shift keying, and quadrature amplitude modulation, as well as *M*-ary modulation methods like quadrature and offset-keyed phase-shift keying. The exciting world of Modems is investigated.

The approach and strategy for building a unified network which can be interfaced to various digital services, popularly called the Integrated Services Digital Network (ISDN), is outlined in *Chapter* 4. The methodology of Asynchronous Transfer Mode (ATM) network is described and the principal types of networks are examined. In this chapter, the reader can also make a perusal of the structure of the internet, its protocols and and the facilities available. The links of the digital telecommunication channel are thus set up.

Chapter 5 on digital satellite communications is geared towards understanding the radical and revolutionary changes these methods have ushered in for around-the-world long-distance communication. These methods are studied under the power-efficient and spectrally-efficient categories. Other interesting topics include Very Small Aperture Terminal (VSAT), Time-Division Multiple Access (TDMA) and Single Channel per Carrier (SCPC) systems, and so forth.

High-Definition Television (HDTV) has been a burning topic since long. Methods proposed, likely problems and suggested solutions for HDTV realization are surveyed in *Chapter* 6. Digital TV standards are discussed, building block technologies are introduced ar d system architecture is explained followed by a brief account of the studio practice in F DTV system.

The concluding *Chapter* 7 familiarizes the reader with various multimedia tools, the so. ware and hardware facets of multimedia, the handling and management of audio and vid o on a computer, etc. Although digital technology has made dents in many areas and br ught forth in its wake a deluge of applications and boons to mankind, the future holds a even greater promise. At the end, we peep into the future world of telecommunications ar 1 multimedia, providing the reader with a glimpse of the amazing developments which ar likely to add a new dimension to the capabilities of *homo sapiens*.

1.13 CONCLUSIONS

This capter has launched our study of the subject. The main terms about communication systems and their modalities were reviewed. After perusal of this chapter, the reader will have an intuitive grasp of the language of communication and information systems.

REVIEW QUESTIONS

1.1. What are the main constituents of a communication system? Among the transmitter, channel and receiver of a communication system, which one contributes most to noise?

1.2. Is it necessary that the source of information in a digital communication system be digital only or it can be analog also?

1.3. (*a*) What are the main features of High-Definition Television (HDTV)? (*b*) What is video-conferencing? (*c*) How does videotex differ from teletext?

1.4. Highlight the advantages of optical fibre communication over the conventional copper wire system?

1.5. (*a*) What is the advantage of microwave links over coaxial cable for TV transmission? (*b*) Why are microwave repeaters necessary (at typically 50 km distances) for establishing a micro-wave communication link? (*c*) Explain the idea of a troposcatter microwave link.

1.6. Explain giving reason why cannot a frequency of 10 GHz be used for beyond-the-horizon terrestrial communication?

1.7. (*a*) What is the angular range of a geostationary satellite?

(*b*) How many such satellites are required to establish around-the-world communication link?

(*c*) In what respects are digital methods for satellite communications superior to analog methods?

1.8. Distinguish between: (*a*) Simplex, Half-Duplex and Full-Duplex Systems, and (*b*) Star and Ring Networks.

1.9. Are the following systems digital: (*a*) Pulse Width Modulation (PWM), (*b*) Pulse Position Modulation (PPM)? Why?

1.10. Which of the following is susceptible to quantisation noise:

(*a*) Amplitude Modulation (AM), (*b*) Frequency Modulation (FM), and (*c*) Pulse-Code Modulation (PCM)? Which of the above is most noise resistant and why?

REFERENCES AND FURTHER READING

1.1. G.A. Silver and M.L. Silver, *Computers in Information Processing*, Harper and Row Publishers, New York, 1986.

1.2. P.E. Green, Jr., *Fibre Optic Networks*, Prentice Hall, Englewood Cliffs, 1993.

1.3. B.L. Smith and M.H. Carpentier, *The Microwave Engineering Handbook, Vol. 3, Microwave Systems and Applications*, Chapman and Hall, London, 1993.

1.4. J.D. Lenk, *Lenk's Digital Handbook: Design and Troubleshooting*, Mc Graw-Hill, Inc., New York, 1993.

1.5. C.R. Pollock, *Fundamentals of Optoelectronics*, Irwin, Chicago, 1995.

1.6. J.G. Nellist, *Understanding Telecommunications and Lightwave Systems, An Entry-Level Guide*, Wiley-IEEE press, NJ, 2001.

1.7. A.A. Huurdeman, *The Worldwide History of Telecomunications*, Wiley-IEEE Press, NJ, 2003.

1.8. T.K. Sarkar, R. Mailloux, A.A. Oliner, M. Salazar— Palma and D.L. Sengupta, *History of Wireless*, Wiley - IEEE Press, NJ, 2005.

1.9. R.L. Freeman, *Fundamenatals of Telecommunications*, Wiley-IEEE Press, NJ, 2005.

1.10. W.H. Tranter, D.P. Taylor, R.E. Zeimer, N.F. Maxemchuk and J.W. Mark. *The Best of the Best Fifty Years of Communications and Networking Research*, Wiley-IEEE Press, NJ, Dec. 2006.

2 Digital Coding of Analog Waveforms

A vast majority of signals resulting from physical phenomena are analog in nature. An elegant technique for signal transmission entails conversion of these signals into a number sequence which is expressed in a predecided *code language*, usually in binary form.

For coding, the continuous-time signal is first sampled and quantised. The *sampling operation* generates flat-top pulses whose height is modulated by instantaneous amplitudes of the signal. *Quantisation* converts the sampled values into the nearest of the M selected standard or quantum amplitude levels. *Encoding* translates the discrete set of sample values into a more appropriate signal in the form of *digital codewords* or *characters* constituted by particular arrangements of signals for transmission, termed *symbols*. A *Code* is a plan laying down the guidelines for representing each discrete value of the signal as a specific arrangement of symbols in a form which is more suitable for transmission.

In *Binary Code*, the agreeable symbols may be the presence of a pulse, denoted by 1 or its absence indicated by 0. A binary code consisting of N binary digits or bits, can represent a maximum of $2N'$ distinct values, *e.g.*, a three-bit code can be used to quantify the levels 000, 001, 010, 011, 100, 101, 110 and 111 which add up to a total of $2^3 = 8$ different representions.

The reader may enquire whether the quantised pulses can be transmitted directly, as produced ? If not, in what way is coding helpful ? The answer is that pulses directly sent are degraded by noise *en route* and valuable information may be lost as the pulses deteriorate beyond recognition. By coding the sample voltage into a binary number, the corruption of sample height by noise is avoided. Digital coding yields a *rugged signal* highly immune to distortion and interference, permitting long-distance communication through regenerative repeaters. For this reason, a sound knowledge of encoding techniques for signal transmission is mandatory. This chapter will review the "methods for signal transmission involving the use of sampling, quantising and encoding operations in different ways."

The first step in these conversion methods is the representation of the signal as a sequence of pulses uniformly spaced apart with amplitude modulated by the signal. It will be interesting to begin by discussing analog pulse modulation vis-à-vis digital pulse modulation.

2.1 ANALOG PULSE MODULATION AND DIGITAL PULSE MODULATION

Analog pulse modulation is a process in which a peiodic pulse train is used as a carrier wave and some characteristic feature such as amplitude, duration or position of each pulse in the train is modified in accordance with the baseband signal, leading to pulse amplitude modulation (PAM), pulse duration modulation (PDM) and pulse position modulation (PPM) respectively. In the three versions of analog pulse modulation, viz., PAM, PDM and PPM, only the time variable is expressed in discrete form while the respective modulation parameters are varied continuously. Essentially, information is sent in analog fashion at discrete times.

On the other hand, in digital pulse modulation, the transmitted samples are discrete in time by virtue of sampling and discrete in amplitude by virtue of quantisation. Thus both the independent and dependent variables are quantised, resulting in a truly digital approach. On the contrary, in analog pulse modulation, only the independent variable is quantised giving a quasi-digital or discrete-time method.

This demarcation is reminiscent of the familiar distinction between-time Fourier transform (DTFT) and discrete Fourier transform (DFT). While in the former, only the time variable is quantised, in the latter both the signal amplitude and time are quantised.

Now let us consider digial pulse modulation. This technique has three basic forms : Pulse-Code Modulation (PCM), Differential Pulse-Code Modulation (DPCM) and Delta Modulation (DM). Table 2.1 provides a quick look at the working principle and main features of these three forms.

Now considering PCM as a reference, the performance of other modulation methods can be assessed in terms of their complexity of hardware implementation and the rate of transmission of bits constituting the digital version of the continuous-time information signal, over the communication channel, referred to as the transmitted bit rate. A comparison of both the parameters of DPCM and DM, relative to PCM, is made in Fig. 2.1.

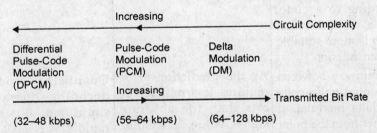

Fig. 2.1. Relative assessment of differential pulse-code modulation and delta modulation with respect to pulse-code modulation

Table 2.1. Digital Pulse Modulation Forms : At a Glance

Sl. No.	Pulse-Code Modulation (PCM)	Differential Pulse-Code Modulation (DPCM)	Delta Modulation (DM)
1.	2.	3.	4.
1.	A modulation method comprising three basic operations : sampling, quantising and encoding, in tandem. In *sampling*, the analog	Also involves the same operations : sampling-quantising-encoding, with the difference that the absolute value of the sample is not quantised	Primarily a sub-class of DPCM and utilizing the trio of sampling, quantising and coding operations, this method differs from DPCM in respect that a single-bit

signal is broken down into a sequence of numbers representing the instantaneous magnitudes of the signal at discrete time instants.   For *quantisation*, the total amplitude range occupied by the signal is subdivided into a finite set of amplitude levels called *standard or quantum levels* ; practical systems typically employ 128 levels. A particular sampled value of message signal is rounded off by selecting the quantum level nearest to its value. *Coding* involves conversion of each quantised sample, according to a code, into a digital word which is more suitable for transmission.

and encoded but its relative value expressed by the difference between the unquantised input sample and predicted sample value called the *prediction error.* The predicted value is obtained from local signal characteristis using a prediction filter. At the receiver, an identical filter is employed to decode and reconstruct the signal. The rationale behind this system is that many signals like speech contain redundant information to the extent that large variations from one sample to another are unlikely.

quantiser is used. This one bit per sample represents the difference between the input message signal and an oversampled staircase approximation to it. If at any sampling instant, the approximation is < signal value, it is incremented by δ; otherwise, it is decremented by δ.

2.   Lies midway between differential pulse-code and delta modulation schemes from the point of view of both circuit complexity and transmitted bit rate.

As the prediction error requires less number of bits than the absolute signal value, a smaller bandwidth is necessary for signal transmission as compared to PCM. However, additional circuitry designed for *linear prediction*, to utilize the correlation between adjacent samples and hence reduce the bit rate, complicates the coding and decoding processes relative to PCM, obviating the bandwith advantage.

Quantising, coding and decoding operations are simplified. But signals of rapidly varying amplitudes produce a high quantisation noise unless samples are sufficiently closely spaced. To enhance the correlation between adjacent samples, the sampling rate must be chosen > the Nyquist rate resulting in a much higher bit rate than PCM.

2.2 PULSE-CODE MODULATION

2.2.1. Preliminary Ideas

Pulse-Code Modulation is a special type of analog-to-digital conversion in which the information contained in the instantaneous samples of an analog signal is represented by digital words in a serial bit stream. A PCM communication system can be visualized as a digital system with an analog-to-digital converter (ADC) at the transmitter and a digital-to-analog converter (DAC) at the receiver. Regenerative repeaters on the way, help in restoring the impaired pulses so that the signal can be propagated over long distances, theoretically upto infinite distances.

Indeed, PCM was conceived as a solution to the problem of noise contamination which becomes severe in long distance communication. The greater the distance, the more is the noise introduced. Amplification is not much helpful because the noise is amplified along with the signal. So it was thought that the analog signal could be converted into a stream of pulses. As long as the pulses are not damaged to the limit that their identity is lost, it is possible, in principle, to transmit the signal to infinitely long distances without any degradation in quality except for the approximation inherent in transformation of the analog signal to digital domain and back again.

Advantages of PCM over analog methods are essentially the same as those of analog pulse modulation over digital pulse modulation. Noteworthy encouraging features of PCM include its sturdy signal resistant to noise and interference, on the path from transmitter to receiver; efficient regeneration of coded signal on the way; and acceptability of various services working with different kinds of baseband signals and their integration into a uniform digital format. Demerits of PCM are the large bandwidth consumed by the digital signal as compared to the analog one so that less number of signals can be sent in the available frequency space. Added to this is the intricate circuit requirement which has, however, become easier by the advent of new devices and technologies.

2.2.2. Basic Components of a PCM System

Figure 2.2 depicts the layout of a pulse-code modulation system. The main components of a PCM system are briefly described below :

   (*i*) *Low-Pass Antialias Filter* The is placed at the front end of the sample to remove frequencies > Highest frequency component of the message.

   (*ii*) *Sampler* In this element, the message wave is sampled with a train of rectangular pulses at a rate > 2 × Highest frequency in the message signal, in accordance with the Sampling Theorem. The continuous-time information signal $x\,(t)$ after quantisation yields the signal $x\,(nT)$ where T is the sampling interval and n, the discrete-time index.

   (*iii*) *Quantiser* Here the sampled values are approximated by a set of discrete amplitude levels. This step is justified because human senses (eye or ear) are capable of detecting only finite intensity differences. Hence choice of a limited number of levels is sufficient to replicate the signal satisfactorily.

   If the rounding-off operation is done in a set of L quantum levels, the output of the quantiser will be equal to $x_q\,(nT_s)$.

   (*iv*) *Encoder* The quantised samples are translated into codewords according to a Code defined as a system of rules and symbols for expressing information. Working with M-ary digits, the encoder gives a codeword comprising v digits in parallel for each sample.

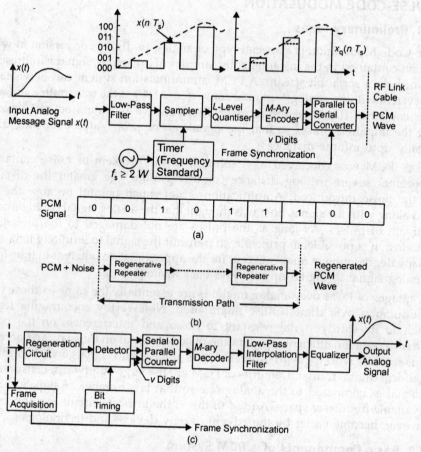

Fig. 2.2. Essential elements of a PCM communication system : (*a*) Transmitter, (*b*) Path of transmission, and (*c*) Receiver

(*v*) *Parallel-to-Serial Converter* Successive codewords are read out serially to build the PCM waveform. This is an *M*-ary digital signal.

(*vi*) *Regenerative Repeaters* The PCM wave is reconstructed on the transmission route by a chain of regenerative repeaters stationed at desired spacings on the way. Regeneration involves reshaping and cleaning up the pulses to overcome the effects of distortion and noise.

(*vii*) *Serial-to-Parallel Converter* Functionally, this element performs the inverse operation to component (*v*) above. The pulses are reground into codewords for decoding.

(*viii*) *Decoding* It is the production of a pulse whose amplitude is the linear sum of the pulses in the codeword. Each pulse is assigned a weight according to its place value in the code, *e.g.*, 2^0, 2^1, 2^2, 2^3, ...The output waveform from the decoder is a "staircase approximation" of the input information-bearing signal $x(t)$, similar to the flat-top quantised signal $x_q(nT_s)$.

(*ix*) *Low-Pass Reconstruction Filter* The signal from the decoder is fed to a low-pass filter having a cut-off frequency equal to message bandwidth. This filter called the *Interpolation Filter* gives a smoothened output $y(t)$ which differs from the message $x(t)$ by the amount the quantised samples $x_q(nT_s)$ deviate from the exact samples $x(nT_s)$.

(x) *Equaliser* This component corrects for the so-called "Aperture Effect" due to flat-top sampling. It decreases the in-band loss of the filter with increasing frequency bringing about a compensation for the aperture effect.

After summarizing the main operations undergone by a continuous-time signal in traversing through a PCM communication system, let us now exmine closely the crucial issues pertaining thereto.

2.2.3. Pre-Alias Filter and the Sample-and-Hold Circuit

The reader might recall the underlying assumption in the derivation of the Sampling Theorem, studied in Digital Signal Processing that the analog signal must be strictly bandlimited to ensure complete recovery of the signal from its samples. This assumption is generally not valid in practice because the amplitude spectrum of the signal $\to 0$ asymptotically as the frequency $\to \infty$ (Fig. 2.3 (a)). Consequently, an effect called *Aliasing* or *Fold-Over* takes place in which a high-frequency component in the spectrum of the analog signal apparently acquires the identity of a lower frequency in the spectrum of its sampled version (Fig. 2.3 (b)) leading to distortion. Figure 2.3 (b) displays the original spectrum and two frequency-shifted replicas of it which result when the signal is sampled at the rate $f_s = 2 \times$ Highest frequency component in the signal. One replica is shifted to the left by the sampling rate f_s and the other replica is shifted to the right by an equal amount (f_s). These replicas originate from the periodic spectrum formed by sampling the message signal at the rate f_s. Spectrum of the sampled signal $=$ Message spectrum + Frequency-shifted replicas. Hence, the recovery of the original message spectrum is not possible without distortion.

A two-pronged remedy for aliasing is adopted, as shown in Fig. 2.4. First, a low-pass pre-alias filter is inserted before the sampling operation to weaken those high-frequency components which fall outside the frequency band of interest. Secondly, the signal obtained after filtration is sampled at a rate > Nyquist rate = $2W$ where W is the bandwidth of the pre-alias filter. This is accomplished by adjusting the pulse repetition frequency f_s of the timing pulse generator at a value > $2W$.

Sampling is performed by the *Sample and Hold Circuit* (Fig. 2.5 (b)) consisting of two FET switches and a capacitor. A short pulse (Fig. 2.5 (a)), applied to the gate G_1 of the transistor Q_1 renders it conducting. This charges the capacitor to a voltage equal to the instantaneous sample value of the signal. It retains this voltage until discharged by another pulse applied to the gate G_2 of transistor Q_2. Thus Q_1 acts as a *Sampling switch* and Q_2 as a *discharge switch*.

The output sampled waveform of this circuit (Fig. 2.5 (c)), is a sequence of pulses with flattened top regions representing pulse-amplitude modulation (PAM) in which the amplitudes of uniformly spaced rectangular pulses vary according to the instantaneous sample values of the analog signal. Also, this circuit produces flat-top pulses instead of the perfect instantaneous pulses, as envisaged in the Sampling Theorem.

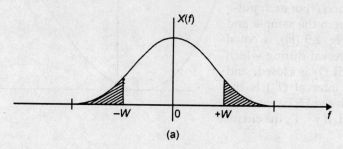

(a)

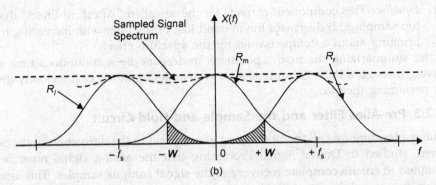

Fig. 2.3. The effect of aliasing : (a) Spectrum of the message signal, (b) Spectrum of the sampled signal showing the replicas of message spectrum (R_m), message spectrum shifted leftward by the sampling rate f_s (symbol R_l) and message spectrum shifted rightward by the same amount (denoted by R_r).

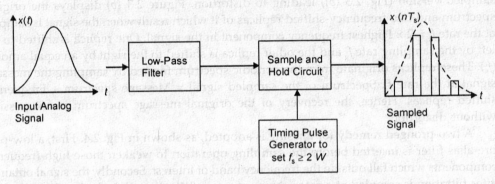

Fig. 2.4. Two-way strategy to combat aliasing

It would be worthwhile to mention here about the transfer characterisitc required of the low-pass filter to enable error-free reconstitution of the signal $x(t)$. The requisite characteristic is shown in Fig. 2.5 (d). It is apparent that the transfer function $H(f)$ of the filter given by

$$H(f) = \frac{V_0(f)}{V_i(f)} \qquad \qquad \dots (2.1)$$

must be flat at least upto the frequency f_m, the maximum frequency component of $x(t)$. Therefore, $H(f)$ should fall to zero before the frequency $f_s - f_m$. In order to allow any signal, whose spectral characteristics lie in the passband of the filter from 0 to f_m, to pass through the filter without experiencing distortion, its phase characteristic must be linear in the passband.

Another significant observation needs to be pointed out. The duration (τ) of each pulse (Fig. 2.5 (c)), from the sample and hold circuit (Fig. 2.5 (b)), is equal to the time interval during which the FET switch Q_1 is closed, and the sampling interval (T_s) is the time for which the FET switch Q_2 remains closed. If $\tau = T_s$, the circuit

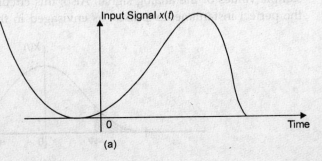

(a)

will transmit all the time and the amplitude of the reconstructed signal $y(t)$ is equal to all the signal $x(t)$. Practically, the extent to which the signal $x(t)$ is available in the sampled signal $x(nT_s)$ is proportional to the pulse width τ. The circuit will transmit for only

a fraction $\eta = \dfrac{\tau}{T_s}$ of the total time.

For a gain H_0 of the low-pass filter, the recovered output signal $y(t)$ is expressed as

$$y(t) = \frac{\tau}{T_s} \, H_0 \, x(t) \qquad ...(2.2)$$

In reality, the distance of separation between the signal source and its destination may be quite large. Then such a connection is referred to as a *Telecommunication Channel* ('tele' meaning far). The channel comprising gigantic cable distribution or radio networks or both, requires enormous capital, efforts and time to be established. Maximum utilization of the channel is therefore warranted. However, it appears from the above discussion that the channel is engaged only for a certian percentage of the available time. For the remaining time, it lies idle. The question obviously arises

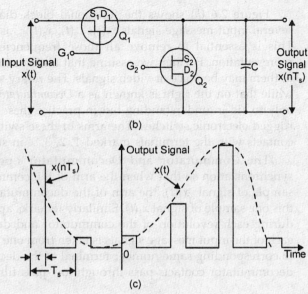

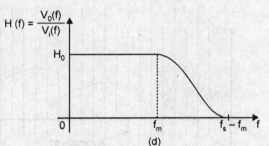

Fig. 2.5. The Sampling process : (a) Input waveform, (b) Sample and Hold circuit, (c) Flat-top samples of the pulse amplitude modulated (PAM) output waveform showing also the input signal for comparison. (d) Required transfer characteristic of the low-pass filter—

whether the channel can be used for the time during which it is not busy. Indeed, it is possible to do so by simultaneous propagation of different signals on the same channel. The intervening time interval between adjacent samples is exploited by other independent signal sources on a time-shared basis, without causing any mutual interference. This kind of sharing of a common communication channel by several independent message signals on a temporal scale is known as *Time-Division Multiple* (TDM) *Access System*; it is primarily a consequence of the sampling process.

2.2.4. Time-Division Multiplexing

Figure 2.6 illustrates the concept of a TDM system. Figure 2.6 (a) shows the interlacing of two signals $x_1(t)$ and $x_2(t)$ for multiplexing. For the sake of simplicity, only two signals have been considered but more signals $x_3(t)$, $x_4(t)$, ...may be included depending on the available space. Both the signals $x_1(t)$, $x_2(t)$ have been sampled regularly with the same sampling interval T_s but their samples are taken at different times. The trains of samples of signals $x_1(t)$ and $x_2(t)$ are designated as Channel 1 and Channel 2 respectively.

Figure 2.6 (b) shows the functional block diagram of a TDM system. Each of the several input message signals $x_1(t)$, $x_2(t)$, $x_3(t)$, ...is first passed through a low-pass filter. This is essential to remove all those frequencies which are not required for signal representation. Further, we assume that all the signals are similarly bandlimited, e.g., all of them may be voice or video signals. The rotary switch at the left is called a *Commutator* while that on the right is known as a *Decommutator*. The mechanical switches are shown only to aid in understanding but in practice these switches are replaced by the fast and rugged electronic switches. The arms of these switches swing around and rotate making contacts with the terminals marked 1, 2, 3, ...in succession.

The Commutator and Decommutator operate in perfect co-ordination and synchronization so that when the arm of the commutator contacts terminal 1 taking one sample of signal $x_1(t)$, the arm of the decommutator also touches terminal 1 delivering this one sample of signal $x_1(t)$. Similarly remarks apply to other signal $x_2(t)$, $x_3(t)$, ..so that during each revolution of the commutator and decommutator switches, one sample of each of the input message signals is taken from one terminal of commutator and presented to corresponding same number terminal of the decommutator. The signal emerging from decommutator contacts pass through low-pass filters ensuring a smooth reconstruction.

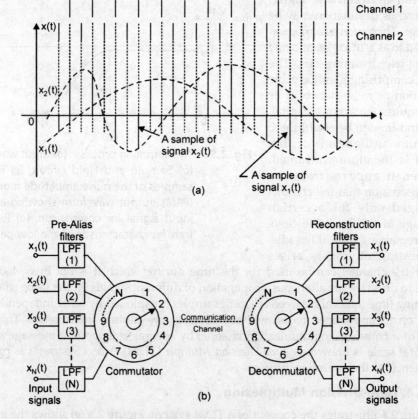

Fig. 2.6. The concept of time-division multiplexing : (a) Interlacing of two baseband signals $x_1(t)$ and $x_2(t)$. (b) Block diagram of a TDM system to transmit N bandlimited signals over a single communication channel

It is evident that if f_m is the highest frequency spectral component in any of the signals $x_1(t)$, $x_2(t)$, $x_3(t)$, .., then both the switches must complete a minimum of $2f_m$ revolutions per second for satisfying the Nyquist criterion. Moveoer, it may be noted that the commutator combines the samples of the various signals and interleaves them sequentially constituting the composite TDM signal. The decommutator splits the signal into individual component samples enabling their reconstruction.

Time-Division Multiplexing causes *Bandwidth Expansion* by a factor N because N samples derived from N independent message sources are packed into a time slot of one sampling interval. Also, the system is highly sensitive to *dispersion effects* in the transmission channel, arising due to variations of amplitude with frequency or owing to non-linearity of phase responses. For satisfactory operation of the system, this problem is solved by accurate *equalization* of both amplitude and phase responses of the channel.

2.2.5. The Quantising Principle

Within finite amplitude range of a continuous-time signal lie an infinite number of amplitude levels but it would not be worthwhile to forbear either the cost of the efforts spent for transmitting all the levels because the ultimate receiver, the *human senses*, cannot differentiate between closely spaced levels beyond a certain limit. Over and above, for digital representation, the sample values do not vary in a continuous manner, rather they must differ, at a minimum, by the last significant of the digits agreed upon. Hence, from the points of view of human limitation and adopting a digital system, the process of digitising samples involves an approximation which is given the name "Quantisation".

The next question that may be posed is that how many quantisation levels will be necessary to represent the signal amplitude with adequate precision ? The answer is straightforward. If the levels are located in close proximity, giving *fine quantisation*, the approximate signal will be indistinguishable from the original continuous-time signal. Conversely, a *coarse quantisation* using a smaller number of levels will result in an unacceptably impaired signal. At the same time, it must be remembered that the number of binary digits required to represent the quantisation level is governed by the number of levels in the quantisation process. Thus if we indefinitely go on increasing the number of levels to achieve a close replication of the signal, we will face the problem of an excessive requirement of the number of binary digits for representing each amplitude sample. Therefore we seek an optimum or compromising balance between the number of levels and the number of digits.

Let us cite a concrete example. As telephonic speech is generally bandlimited between 300 Hz and 3.4 kHz, the sampling frequency selected for PCM transmission is 8 k samples/ sec. Now, it has been found that a choice of 256 amplitude levels results in sufficiently good speech quality. But since $\log_2 256 = 8$, these 256 amplitude levels correspond to 8 binary digits per sample. Taking a sampling rate of 8 k samples/sec along with a data of 8 bits per sample, the net binary data rate needed to transmit a PCM speech signal is 8 × 8 = 64 k bits/sec, which is the accepted international standard forming the basis of all PCM transmissions.

For a deeper insight into the quantisation operation, we look at its graphical representation given in Fig. 2.7 (a). Graphically, a linear relationship between the input and the output of a continuous system yields a staircase characteristic. The behaviour of a continuous-time signal $x(t)$ is shown. This signal is the input waveform V_i applied to the quantiser giving the output V_0. A smooth variation of the input signal $V_i = x(t)$ over its range, produces leaps of the quantised signal $V_0 = x_q(t) = x_q(nT_s)$ at one or another of the fixed level $...x_{-2}, x_{-1}, x_0, x_1, x_2, ...$so that the signal $x_q(t)$ either does not alter at all or changes abruptly by a quantum jump. The difference between any two adjacent discrete values of the signal is termed as *Quantum* or *Step Size,* denoted by Δ. Quantisation is carried out by sorting the input signal into *amplitude slices,* which are the "treads of the staircase", and replacing the signal value within $\pm\dfrac{\Delta}{2}$ of the midvalue of a slice by the concerned midvalue, in the output.

Because of the location of the origin in the middle of a tread of the staircase, a quantiser having the aforesaid input-output amplitude characteristic is called a *Midtread Type Quantiser.* Its output can be expressed as $V_0 = i\,\Delta$ where i can acquire positive and negative integral values, $i = 0, \pm 1, \pm 2, \pm 3, ...\pm k$, assuming $+k$ levels on the positive side and an equal number of $-k$ levels on the negative side (Fig. 2.7 (*a*)), whereby the total number of representation levels is given by

$$L = 2k + 1 \tag{2.3}$$

including the level at the origin. This obviously produces an *odd* number of levels for a midtread type quantiser. The *Peak-to-Peak Excursion* or *Dynamic Range R* of the quantiser input is expressed as

$$R = L\Delta = (2k + 1)\,\Delta \tag{2.4}$$

The *Overload Level* of the quantiser equals $R/2$. When the quantiser input is in this level, overload distortion is produced. For the quantiser example of Fig. 2.7. (*a*), $\Delta = 1$, $K = 7$, $L = 15$, $R = 1 \times 15 = 15$ and absolute value of overload level $= 15/2$.

2.2.6. Quantisation Noise

As the continuous signal is replaced by a signal constructed from discrete amplitudes by rounding off the sampled values, the quantisation process is inherently prone to an error measured by the difference between the input and the output signals of the quantiser. This error is called the *Quantisation Error* or *Quantisation Noise*. From Fig. 2.7 (*a*), it is easy to see that the maximum instantaneous value of this error $(q_e) = \dfrac{\Delta}{2}$, varying from $-\dfrac{\Delta}{2}$ to $\dfrac{\Delta}{2}$. The error voltage $E(t)$ is plotted as a function of the instantaneous value of the message signal $x(t)$ in Fig. 2.7 (*b*).

Let us study a quantising process in which the uniform quantum step size $= \Delta$ Volts. For this process, the representation levels are located at

$$0, \pm \Delta, \pm 2\Delta, \pm 3\Delta, ... \tag{2.5}$$

We focus our attention on a particular sample at the quantiser input having an amplitude in the range from.

$$i\Delta - \frac{\Delta}{2} \text{ to } i\Delta + \frac{\Delta}{2} \tag{2.6}$$

where $i = 0, \pm 1, \pm 2, \pm 3, ...$The quantiser output is $= i\Delta$. This suggests the existence of a *region of uncertainty* having a width Δ and centred about $i\Delta$ (Fig. 2.7c). Then the amplitude of the sample at the quantiser output may be written as $i\Delta + q_e$ where $q_e = \pm\dfrac{\Delta}{2}$ stands for the quantising error. For a random input signal, q_e lies within the limits.

$$-\frac{\Delta}{2} \le q_e \le \frac{\Delta}{2} \tag{2.7}$$

In the event of sufficiently fine quantisation, the distortion due to q_e influences the behaviour of a PCM system in such a way as though it were an additional independent noise source. This noise source has a mean value of zero and its mean-square value is

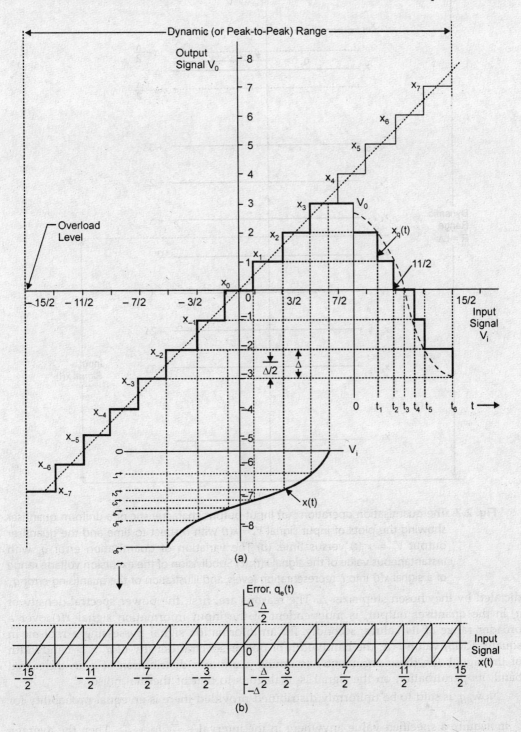

Fig. 2.7. (Contd)

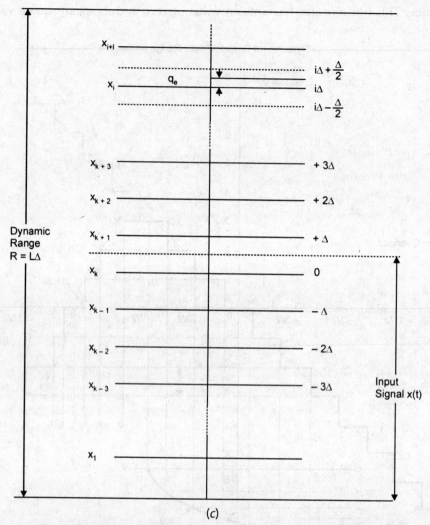

Fig. 2.7. The quantisation operation : (a) Input-output characteristic of a uniform quantiser showing the plots of input signal $V_i = x(t)$ with respect to time and the quantiser output $V_0 = x_q(t)$ versus time; (b) The variation of quantisation error q_e with instantaneous value of the signal $x(t)$. (c) Subdivision of the excursion voltage range of a signal $x(t)$ into L representation levels, and illustration of the quantising error q_e

dictated by the chosen step size Δ. The reasons are, first, the power spectral density of q_e in the quantiser output, is independent of the input information signal $x(t)$ over a broader range of its values; secondly, for an information signal possessing a root-mean square (RMS) value $> \Delta$, the bandwidth of power spectral density of q_e is $>$ bandwidth of the signal. On these arguments, assuming a uniform distribution of q_e in the signal band, its perturbation on the signal is analogous to that of thermal noise.

Now, q_e is said to be uniformly distributed provided there is an equal probability for q_e to acquire a specified value anywhere in the interval $-\dfrac{\Delta}{2}$ to $+\dfrac{\Delta}{2}$. Then the average power of quantising noise is found out by averaging q_e^2 over the permissible values of q_e.

viz., those values contained in the above-mentioned interval. The *Average Power P_q of Quantising Noise* is simply.

$$P_q = \frac{1}{\Delta} \int_{-\frac{\Delta}{2}}^{\frac{\Delta}{2}} q_e^2 \ dq_e = \frac{\Delta^2}{12} \qquad \qquad ...(2.8)$$

According to this equation, P_q is proportional to the square of the step size Δ. Since the selection of Δ is at the designer's discretion, the quantising noise diminishes when Δ is taken very small. But there are other constraints also in the choice of Δ, as already discussed.

2.2.7. Companding : μ-Law and A-Law

Uniform quantisation, although generally favoured from the viewpoint of linear signal processing, is not necessarily the best solution to any problem. This is because the ratio of voltage levels for voice signals is ~ 10 : 1 from the peaks of loud talks to the lower values of relatively feeble or whispering sounds. Also, there are relatively infrequent excursions of sound intensity from a normal medium level to the peak level. Keeping these observations in mind, it is easily surmised that the use of a variable separation between representation levels is preferable to that of a uniform separation. The quantisation should be planned in such a way that the step size decreases as the distance from the origin of the input-output characteristic increases. So, near the origin, the levels are closely spaced and the quantisation is fine. As we recede away from it, the quantisation becomes gross. The significant advantage gained by non-uniform quantisation is that a smaller number of steps is required than will be needed for a uniform quantiser. This also ensures the constancy of the signal-to-noise ratio throughout the range of audio signals, making these ratios virtually independent of the signal level. In effect, more attention is paid to weaker signals at the expense of stronger signals and a uniform precision is obtained throughout the range of input signal amplitudes.

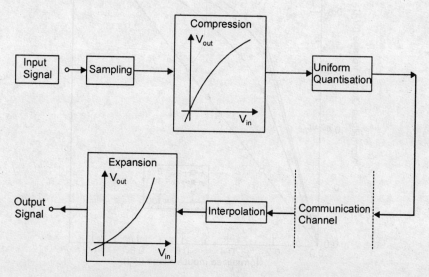

Fig. 2.8. Stages in the companding of a signal

Non-uniform quantisation tantamounts, at the transmitting end, to passage of the signal through a compressor, and then feeding it to a uniform quantiser. At the receiver, by proportionately expanding the signal, we recover the original quantised samples. The name of this operation is constructed by the first four letters of *Compressing* with the last six letters of *Expanding*. It is called *Companding* (Fig. 2.8)

Two widely used companding laws, accepted as international standards for telephony, are the North-American μ-law and the European A-law. The compression μ-law (Fig. 2.9) is written as

$$|v_0| = \frac{\log(1+\mu|v_i|)}{\log(1+\mu)} \qquad ...(2.9)$$

where v_1 and v_0 are the normalized input and output voltages respectively and μ is a constant > 0. Uniform quantisation is described by the value μ = 0. Assigning a value to μ, the quantum jumps are defined by the reciprocal gradient of the compression characteristic given by

$$\frac{d|v_i|}{d|v_0|} = \frac{\log(1+\mu)}{\mu} \cdot (1+\mu|v_i|) \qquad ...(2.10)$$

This expression clearly shows that the μ-law is a combination of linear and logarithmic patterns of behaviour. The linear relationship holds at low input voltages, $\mu|v_i| \ll 1$, and logarithmic variation is preponderant at high input voltages for $\mu|v_i| \gg 1$. This is desirable since a purely logarithmic law such as $y = \log x$ does not give a curve passing through the origin. So the linear law is required in the region of lower values.

The expansion law for the expander in the receiver is the inverse of the above law, possessing a characteristic complementary to that of the compressor.

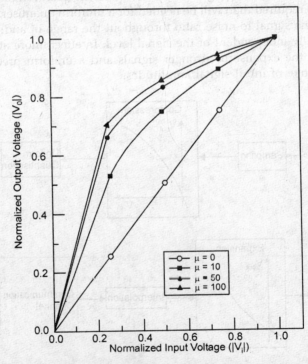

Fig. 2.9. The μ-law for compression of signal showing the plots of normalized value of output voltage as a function of normalized input voltage for varying μ

The defining equation for the A-law of compression (Fig. 2.10) is

$$v_0 = \begin{cases} \dfrac{A|v_i|}{1+\log A}, & 0 \le |v_i| \le \dfrac{1}{A} \\[4mm] \dfrac{1+\log(A|v_i|)}{1+\log A}, & \dfrac{1}{A} \le |v_i| \le 1 \end{cases} \qquad \text{...(2.11)}$$

having the reciprocal slopes

$$\frac{d|v_i|}{d|v_0|} = \begin{cases} \dfrac{1+\log A}{A}, & 0 \le |v_i| \le \dfrac{1}{A} \\[4mm] (1+\log A)|v_i|, & \dfrac{1}{A} \le |v_i| \le 1 \end{cases} \qquad \text{...(2.12)}$$

Practically $A = 1$. The case $A = 1$ represents uniform quantisation. The quantisation levels over the central linear portion predominantly control the smaller signals. These

steps decrease by the factor $\dfrac{A}{1+\log A}$.

Implementation of μ- and A-laws employs non-linear signal processing followed by linear quantisation. Together with the complementary non-linearity at the receiver, this presents a complicated situation.

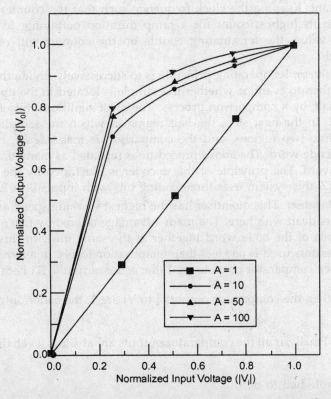

Fig. 2.10. The A-law for signal compression showing the variation of normalized output voltage with normalized input voltage for different values of the parameter A

Piecewise linear segmental approximations to these laws are therefore made. A-law companding comprises eight linear segments for each polarity. The slope is halved for each segment with the exception of the lowest two segments. In μ-law companding, the gradient is halved over all the eight segments, following exactly the same procedure. A-law companding is also called *13-segment companding* while μ-law companding is known as *15-segment companding*. The difference between these two laws is particularly noticeable at low levels.

For implementation of the piecewise linear companding laws in analog-to-digital conversion process, the passage of the sample from one segment to another is accompanied by doubling the step size of the analog-to-digital converter by discarding the least significant bit of the converter output on a segment threshold.

2.2.8. Different Forms of Quantisers

We shall now introduce the generic forms of circuits used for performing the quantisation operation called *Quantisers*. These circuits produce a codeword for the output and thus carry out the coding function also. Quantisers are broadly divided into three classes :

(*i*) *Counting Quantiser.* This kind of quantiser serially counts through each quantising level. In Fig. 2.11 (*a*) at each sampling point, the ramp generator is switched on and a binary counter is also started at the same time. The sample and hold circuit gives a staircase approximation to the signal $x(t)$, Fig. 2.11 (*b*). The time span of the ramp and hence that of the count T_s varies with the sample value because the ramp slope is maintained constant. Keeping the clock frequency such that the counter gets sufficient time to reckon to its highest count for a ramp duration pertaining to the maximum possible sample value, the terminating counts on the counter will refer to various quantisation levels.

(*ii*) *Serial Quantiser.* Its operating principle is to successively divide the ordinate into two regions and then to examine whether the sample is located in the upper half region or in the lower half, by a comparison process. The most significant bit of the codeword is thus produced. In the next step, the half region in which the sample is situated, is further divided into two regions, and the comparison is made again, resulting in the second bit of the code word. The above procedure is repeated as many times as there are bits in the code word. The principle of this encoder is illustrated by the block diagram shown in Fig. 2.12; this system uses three coding bits with inputs 0 to 1.

(*iii*) *Parallel Quantiser.* This quantiser has the highest working speed among the three types of quantisers dealt with here. The main advantage offered by this quantiser is that it forms all the bits of the code word together at the same time. In this quantiser, the number of comparators used is one less than quantisation levels. In a *three-bit encoder*, Fig 2.13, if all the seven comparator outputs are 1, the coder output = 111 because the sample had to be $> \dfrac{7}{8}$. When the comparator outputs I to VI are 1, the coder output = 110, since $\dfrac{6}{8} <$ sample $< \dfrac{7}{8}$. Finally, if all the comparator outputs are at a low level, the coder output = 000, as the sample had to be $< \dfrac{1}{8}$.

2.2.9. Coding Schemes

A code is a methodical way of representing information symbolically. Coding plays a central role in efficient information transmission and control of error performance in digital systems.

Suppose that an information source is capable of generating M distinct messages, and let p_i be the probability of occurrence of an individual message event. Then the amount of information carried by one message is written as

$$I = \log \left(\frac{1}{p_i} \right) \qquad \qquad ...(2.13)$$

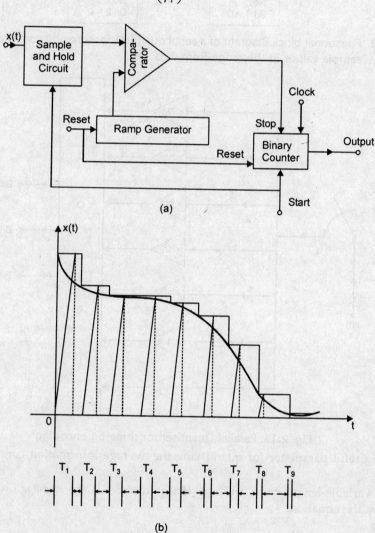

Fig. 2.11. The Counting Quantiser : (a) Structural layout, (b) The signal waveform with the ramp pattern

where

$$\sum_{i=1}^{m} p_i = 1 \qquad \qquad ...(2.14)$$

The entropy E of an information source is defined as

$$E = \sum_{i=1}^{m} p_i \log_2 \left(\frac{1}{p_i} \right) \qquad \qquad ...(2.15)$$

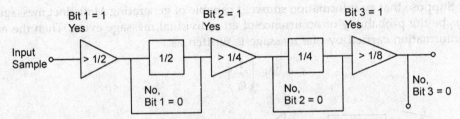

Fig. 2.12. Functional block diagram of a serial quantiser for three-bit code words and input sample values in the range from 0 to 1 V

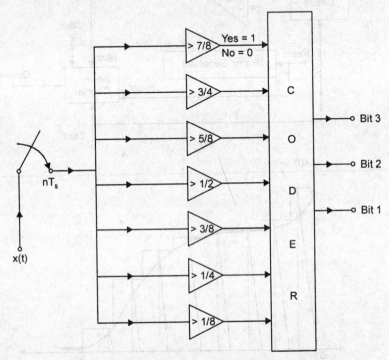

Fig. 2.13. Parallel Quantiser for three-bit encoding

It is a useful parameter for quantifying the average information content per source symbol.

For a variable-length code, an important parameter is the *Average Code Word Length* defined by the equation.

$$L = p_i \, l_i \qquad \qquad \qquad ...(2.16)$$

where l_i is the number of binary symbols assigned to the i th message event.

Although codes can be grouped in several ways, it will be logical to study the commonly used codes in accordance with the classification scheme presented in Fig. 2.14 under the following heads :

(*i*) *Numeric Codes* Different combinations of binary symbols 0 and 1 can be used to represent the decimal numbers 0 through 9. This has given birth to a large number of codes like the Binary Code, Binary-Coded Decimal (BCD), Gray Code, Excess-3 Code, Bar Code and so forth.

In the Numeric code category are two subdivisions : *Weighted* and *Non-Weighted*. If a code is defined such that the bit positions are arranged weights with the sum of the

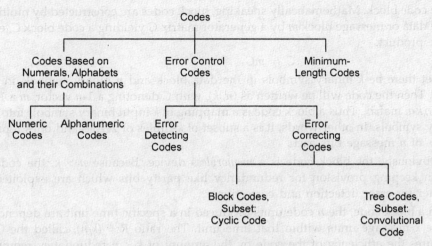

Fig. 2.14. Classes of codes

weighted digits corresponding to the coded number, the code is called a *Weighted Code*. If this condition is not met, it is a *Now-Weighted Code*. Example of weighted codes are binary and BCD codes. Excess-3 and Gray codes belong to the non-weighted subdivision.

(*ii*) *Alphanumeric Codes* These codes use letters of the English alphabet along with numbers, common punctuation marks like brackets, full stop, etc. Familiar examples are the Baudot code, ASCII and EBCDIC codes.

(*iii*) *Error Control Codes* These codes are based on the tremendous capability of coding to represent information by binay symbols in such a manner that any changes caused by faulty transmission of the signal including those during its storage, are detected and the necessary corrections are implemented. Error control codes can be classified in various ways, among which we first discuss the branches : Error detecting codes and Error correcting codes.

Error Detecting Codes—The necessity of these codes stems from the need to alleviate the influence of noise, interference and artifacts in communication systems. These factors creep in to cause errors in bit streams, changing 0's to 1's and conversely. Error detection strngth is built into the design of the code by special artifices. A common trick makes use of the addition of a *parity bit* to a code word of arbitrary length. Incorporation of the parity bit is meant to render the number of zeroes/ones in the code word even/odd. Simplicity and efficiency are the main merits of the parity-checking method making it immensely popular. Nevertheless, it has limitations also. It detects only those errored words having an odd number of errors and also does not indicate the number or positions of the errors in the code word.

Error Correcting Codes—These codes, used for remedying transmission bugs in the forward direction, are sometimes referred to as Forward Error Correcting (FEC) codes. In these codes, the code word contains information bits as well as redundancy bits. The latter bits for error correction, result from parity checking on a subset of information and parity bits. If calculated parity bits are the same as the received ones, no errors have occurred in transmission. If not, errors have crept in and the code also allows us to calculate the position of the error.

Error correcting codes can be further grouped into two heads : *Block Codes* and *Tree Codes*. The simplest form of *Block Codes* is the use of a parity bit. Other block codes are primarily extensions of the basic parity concept, formed by taking parity over different combinations of bits in a long data block and using the check bits produced to build part of the code block. Mathematically speaking, block codes are constructed by multiplication of the data or message block m by a generator matrix G yielding a code block C, expressed as the product.

$$C = mG \qquad \qquad ...(2.17)$$

Let there be k binary symbols in the data block and n binary symbols in the code block. Then the code will be written as (n, k), with C denoting a 1*n vector, m a 1*k vector and G, k*n matrix. Thus a block code is a mapping of k input binary symbols into n output binary symbols. In other words, it is a subset of k-tuples of zeroes and ones representing blocks of n message bits each.

Obviously, the block code is a *memoryless* device. Because n > k, the code can be chosen keeping provision for redundancy like parity bits which are exploited by the decoder for error detection and correction.

In a block code, the n code units produced in a specific time unit are dependent only on the k message units within that time unit. The ratio R = (k/n), called the *Code Rate* measures the efficiency of the code by the amount of k < n redundancy required for a particular error detection and correction capability. Practically, R values lie in the range from 1/4 to 7/8 while k varies from 3 to several hundred.

A *Linear Code* is defined as one which includes the k-tuple of all zeroes (0, 0, 0, .., 0) as a code word. Also, the set of code words is closed under modulo-2 addition. The weight of a code equals the number of non-zero elements of the k-tuple representing it. A major subset of the linear block code is the *Cyclic Code*, which finds widespread usage for data storage and computer communications. The name "cyclic" arises from the fact that in this code, each code word is a cyclically shifted version of a previous code word. This implies that starting from a given code word, another code word can be obtained by shifting the bits to the right and placing the bits that have been dropped off on the left-hand side.

The cyclic code is an error correcting code but it does not give any knowledge about which bits are erroneous. The code works as follows : The data in question are considered as a continuous string of binary symbols and divided by a predecided bit pattern. The remainder obtained by this division process is attached to the data which is being transmitted or stored in memory. The quotient is discarded. On receipt of the data or reading from memory, the division is carried out again using the same divisor. A comparison is made between the remainder thus calculated and the one received with the string of data. If any discrepancy is found between the two remainders, it can be inferred that some change has taken place during transit or in storage. In mathematical language, the coding procedure for the cyclic code can be described by the equation

$$D/G = n + R \qquad \qquad ...(2.18)$$

where D stands for the data stream, G is the divisor called the generator polynomial, n is the quotient obtained after division and R is the remainder which is annexed to data.

Now, focussing on the *Tree Codes*, this is class of error correcting codes differing from the block code in that the encoding process exhibits *memory*. So, such a code is produced by a device having memory. A significant subset of the tree code is the *Convolution Code*. The conspicuous feature of this code is that the block of n code digits produced by the encoder in a certain unit of time is dependent not only on the block of k message digits within that time unit but also on the block of data digits within a preceding duration of N-1 time units (N > 1). Accepting k binary symbols at its input, the convolution code generates n binary symbols at its output. Here, n output symbols are affected by v + k input symbols, and since v > 0, memory is built in the code. Describing the code as

(n, k), the ratio $R = k/n$ termed the *Code Rate*, signifies the amount of information carried per coded bit. Typically, k and n values lie in the range 1 to 8, and v ranges between 2 and 60. The range of variation of R is from 1/4 to 7/8. Apart from n and k, a third digit K known as *Constraint Length*, determined from the length of the memory element in the encodig circuit, is necessary to completely describe the convolution code.

(*iv*) *Minimum-Length Codes* (*Entropy Coding*) These codes aspire to achieve a high efficiency of transmission by transferring a maximum amount of information using a minimum number of bits. The *Hauffman Code* employing variable-length code words is an example of such a code. In this code, the code words are assigned in accordance with the frequency of occurrence of each source alphabet taking care that the more frequent source letters are assigned shorter-length codes and vice versa. Hauffman code is used for data, video and text compression.

2.2.10. Digital Formats

The encoded digital data is sent over a communication channel using a digital format or waveform, sometimes referred to as *Line* or *Transmission Code*. A digital format should possess the following properties :

(*i*) Ability to resist noise and interference; (*ii*) Should have *sufficient timing content* to allow the extraction of clock information for synchronization of the receiver to the transmitter; (*ii*) Competence to detect errors; (*iv*) Matching of the power spectral density of the digital format with the channel frequency response for decreasing the signal distortion to the lowest level; and (*v*) Transparency of the correct transference of data over a channel to the ones and zeroes in the data.

Some examples of digital formats are displayed in Fig. 2.15. These include : (*i*) *On-Off* or *Unipolar Signalling* Here 1 is denoted by transmitting a constant duration pulse for the duration of the symbol and zero by switching off the pulse (Fig. 2.15 (*a*)) ; (*ii*) *Return-to-Zero* (RZ) *Signalling* Transmission of half-symbol wide rectangular pulse indicates 1 while the absence of the pulse means 0, Fig. 2.15 (*b*). (*iii*) *Polar Signalling* The symbol 1 is represented by a positive pulse of a given amplitude and 0 by an equal amplitude negative pulse (Fig. 2.15 (*c*)). It is a form of *Nonreturn-to-Zero* (NRZ) *Signalling*. (*iv*) *Split-Phase* or *Manchester Code* A positive pulse followed by a negative pulse, with both the pulses equal in amplitude and half-symbol in width, is taken as 1 while reversal of the

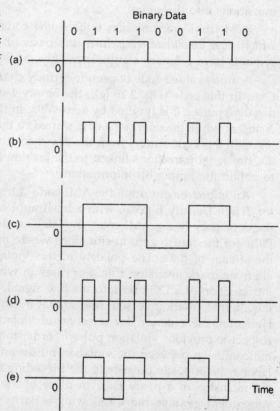

Fig. 2.15. Different formats for representation of binary data by electrical pulses: (*a*) On-off Signalling, (*b*) Return-to-Zero (RZ) Signalling (*c*) Polar Signalling, (*d*) Manchester Code, and (*e*) Bipolar Signalling

polarities gives 0 (Fig. 2.15 (*d*)). The useful quality of this code is that the direct current and low-frequency components in the power spectrum of the transmitted signal are suppressed. (*v*) *Bipolar Signalling* In this format, equal amplitude positive and negative pulses are alternately employed for 1 whereas absence of a pulse represents 0 (Fig. 2.15 (*e*)). As in the case of (*iv*) above, the outstanding feature of this format is the debility of its DC and lower frequency content.

From these discussions, it is clear that bipolar signalling is endowed with the desirable properties of a digital format, which make it useful for the transmission of binary encoded PCM data over telephone channels. Nonetheless, a careful consideration of the distribution of spectral energy density makes us realize that its spectrum is far from ideal for transmission over wire pairs which constitute a major proportion of the trunk network. It is found that a large fraction of energy of the signal is concentrated at the DC level and low frequencies. Added to this is the shortcoming that when long strings of binary zeroes and ones occur, absence of signal transition inhibits the extraction of bit timing information for synchronizing the receiver. A two-course strategy is followed to solve these problems, first, by modifying the shape of the spectrum and secondly, by the introduction of additional transitions into the signal.

PCM trunk transmission utilizes line code evolved from a *pseudo-ternary format* in which *three amplitude levels* form the basis of the line signal although the transmitted symbols have a binary significance only.

A much valued code of pseudo-ternary character is the *Alternate Mark Inversion (AMI) Code*. In this code (Fig. 2.16 (*a*)), the binary 1 is represented alternately by positive and negative pulses; 0 is typified by zero volts. In the spectrum of AMI code, DC component is absent while the energy peak is shifted to the middle of the frequency band (Fig. 2.16 (*b*)). Still this code suffers from the drawback that during transmission of long streams of 0's, no signal transitions linked to the bit rate take place, rather there is no signal at all, to obtain the timing bit information.

An improvement upon the AMI code is the HDB3 Code. The acronym HDB3 stands for "High Density Bipolar, with a maximum of three consecutive zeroes." To overcome the deficiency of the AMI code, the HDB3 code allows for the substitution of a *Violation Pulse* for the fourth zero in situations where more than three successive zeroes occur in the stream of data. The polarity of this violation pulse is selected so as to break the alternate mark inversion rule. For cases in which the violations are associated with the introduction of a DC bias into the line signal, the first violation pulse is chosen against the alternate mark inversion rule so that it can be readily recognized as denoting a zero. Hereafter, the criterion for selection of violation pulses is alternation in polarity with respect to previous violation pulse in order to maintain the DC balance at zero. To avoid the confusion between the violation pulses and the genuine marks, any violation pulse having the opposite polarity to the preceding mark pulse, is compelled into violation by the inclusion of a *parity pulse* in place of the first zero after the preceding mark. The subsequent genuine mark following a parity pulse, bears the opposite polarity to the parity pulse.

As shown in Fig. 2.16 (*b*), the spectral energy for the HDB3 is evenly distributed throughout the frequency band, as opposed to the mid-band concentration for the AMI code.

Another interesting ternary line code which has found widespread application in PCM transmission is the *4B3T Code*. In the 4B3T code, the original binary data stream is broken into code groups comprising four bits. Then each of these groups is encoded into a group of three ternary digits, in compliance with prescribed rules. The power spectrum of the 4B3T resembles that of the AMI code.

2.2.11. Signal Regeneration

On its journey from the transmiter to the receiver, the waveform is periodically reconstructed by regenerative repeaters. A repeater performs three main functions (Fig. 2.17); (*i*) *Equalization* In this step, the received pulses are shaped to counter the effects of amplitude and phase distortion experienced *en route*. (*ii*) *Timing* This is carried out by a circuit supplying a periodic pulse train, derived from the received pulses, for the purpose of sampling the equalized pulses at the instants of time corresponding to maximum signal-to-noise ratios. (*iii*) *Decision* The decision step is executed by a device which is activated at the sampling times to determine whether or not the amplitude of a quantised pulse together with the noise is greater than a predetermined voltage magnitude. For instance, in a PCM system with on-off signalling, the repeater has to take a decision in each bit interval, to discriminate between the presence or absence of a pulse. If the decision is that a pulse is present, a clean new pulse is passed on to the next repeater. If otherwise, a clean base line pulse is sent.

Despite the best efforts, the regenerated signal deviates from the original and this departure is ascribed to : (*i*) *Transmission noise and interference* which causes sporadic erroneous decisions by the repeater vitiating the signal through *bit errors*. (*ii*) Deviation of the spacing between received pulses introducing a jitter in the position of regenerated pulse.

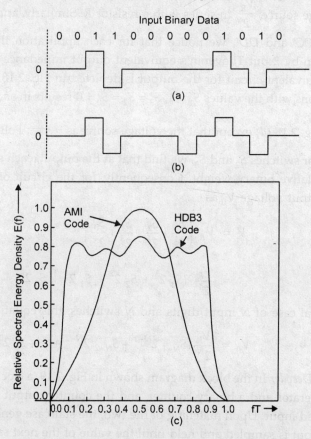

Fig. 2.16. Transmitted waveforms and line power spectra of pseudo-ternary codes : (*a*) AMI code, (*b*) HDB3 code, and (*c*) spectra of AMI and HDB3 codes

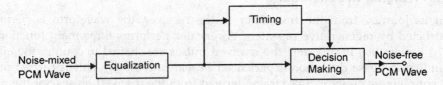

Fig. 2.17. The three basic functions of a Regenerative Repeater

2.2.12. Decoding

We now divert our attention to the conversion of a digital signal to analog signal performed by a Digital-to-Analog Converter by associating a value with each binary code word. Some of the circuits for carrying out this function are :

(*i*) *R/2R Ladder D/A Converter* This circuit comprises a resistor array using resistors of two values only, R and $2R$, as shown in Fig. 2.18 (*a*). In Fig. 2.18 (*b*), the electronic switches S_0, S_1, ...are set as $S_0 = 1$, $S_1 = S_2 = S_3 = 0$. The reference voltage V_R is in series with a resistor $2R$. Application of Thévenin's Theorem at AA' (Fig. 2.18 (*c*)) shows that we now have a voltage source $\dfrac{V_R}{2}$ in series with a resistor R. Similarly, applying Thévenin's Theorem at BB', CC' and DD', we notice that for each application the voltage source undergoes division by 2 but Thévenin's equivalent output impedance remains constant at R. The final equivalent circuit for the output is depicted in Fig. 2.18 (*d*). Repetition of the above operations with the values $S_1 = 1$, $S_3 = S_2 = S_0 = 0$ results in an equivalent circuit like that shown Fig. 2.18 (*d*) except that the voltage source is $= \dfrac{V_R}{2^3}$. Following exactly the same procedure for switches S_2 and S_3, we find that at the output, each switch contributes its appropriate relative binary weight. Consequently, for the circuit of Fig. 2.18 (*a*), we may write the output voltage V_0 as

$$V = V_R \left(\frac{S_3}{2^1} + \frac{S_2}{2^2} + \frac{S_1}{2^3} + \frac{S_0}{2^4} \right) \qquad \qquad ...(2.19)$$

$$= \frac{V_R}{2^4} (S_3\, 2^3 + S_2\, 2^2 + S_1\, 2^1 + S_0\, 2^0) \qquad \qquad ...(2.20)$$

For the general case of N input digits and N switches, this equation becomes

$$V_0 = \frac{V_R}{2^N} (S_{N-1}\, 2^{N-1} + S_{N-2}\, 2^{N-2} + ... + S_0\, 2^0) \qquad \qquad ...(2.21)$$

(*i*) *Counting Decoder* In the block diagram shown in Fig. 2.19, a clock signal is applied to a staircase generator and a binary counter, and the counter output is compared with the binary digitised input. Upon matching of the two, the staircase generator stops. Then the generator output is sampled and held until the value of the next sample is obtained. By smoothing the staircase approximated result with a low-pass filter, the original signal is recovered.

2.3 DIFFERENTIAL PULSE-CODE MODULATION

Pulse-Code Modulation (PCM) is an excellent method for sending data or analog signals when noise is critical. It finds far-flung applications from computer-type arithmetic circuits to transmission of data for voice, video and computer signals. However PCM needs complex coders and decoders. Moreover, on increasing the resolution, the number of bits per sample rises, limiting the number of channels which can be time-division multiplexed. As bandwidth is usually at a premium, we have to look for alternative modulation techniques having noise immunity but not requiring to send as many bits per second as in PCM. Differential Pulse-Code Modulation (DPCM) is one such technique. The basic idea and motivation for DPCM are traced below.

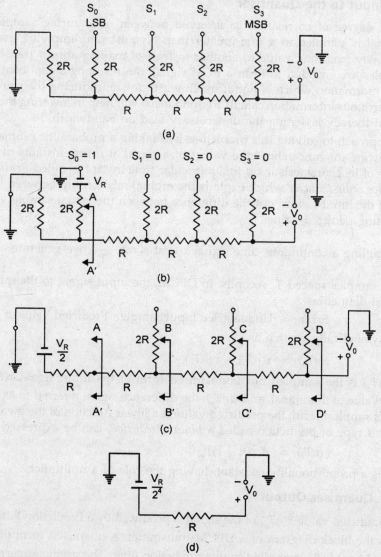

Fig. 2.18. (a) Circuit arrangement of the $R/2R$ Ladder D/A Converter for decoding, (b, c) Application of Thévenin's Theorem for determining the output voltage V_0, and (d) The final Thévenin's equivalent circuit, as seen at the output

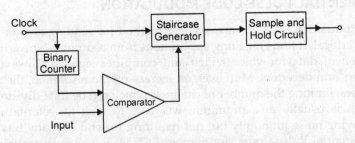

Fig. 2.19. The counting decoder for digital-to-analog conversion

2.3.1. Input to the Quantiser

A high degree of correlation is observed between neigbouring samples when an analog signal is sampled at a rate greater than Nyquist rate, implying that the signal changes slowly from one value to another instead of making abrupt transitions. When these samples are encoded to form a PCM signal, the resulting signal contains a lot of irrelevant information which is not of much worth for reproducing the signal. Removal of this superfluous information called "Redundancy" will help in lowering the transmitted bit rate and thereby lessening the unnecessary load on bandwidth.

One approach to solving this problem is by making a probabilitic estimate about the signal. Drawing inference about the values of a signal at future instants of time from a knowledge of its characteristic up to a particular time instant is called *Prediction*. DPCM is a *predictive coding scheme* which exploits the mutual relationship between the adjoining samples of the input to find out the difference between the actual sample value and the corresponding pedicted value.

By sampling a continuous-time signal $x(t)$ at a rate $\dfrac{1}{T_s}$, we generate a sequence of correlated samples spaced T_s seconds. In DPCM, the input signal to the quantiser is the error signal defined as

$$\text{Error} = \text{Unquantised Input Sample} - \text{Predicted Value of Input Sample}$$

which is symbolically written as

$$e(nT_s) = x(nT_s) - \hat{x}(nT_s) \qquad\qquad ...(2.22)$$

where $x(nT_s)$ is the sampled but unquantised form of the input signal $x(t)$, $\hat{x}(nT_s)$ the predicted value of this signal, and $e(nT_s)$, the difference signal referred to as the *Prediction Error*. In its simplest form, the predicted value is a linear function of the measured sample values. This type of prediction called a *Linear Prediction*, can be expressed as

$$\hat{x}(nT_s) = A\,x(n-1)T_s \qquad\qquad ...(2.23)$$

where A is a proportionality constant, having the role of a multiplier.

2.3.2. Quantiser Output

The predicted value $x(nT_s)$ of the signal is produced by a Prediction Filter. Figure 2.20 (a) shows the block diagram of a DPCM transmitter. A quantised form of input signal, represented by $x_q(nT_s)$ is applied to this prediction filter. The prediction error, measuring the extent to which the filter fails to make an accurate prediction of the input, is encoded, and this methodology is called DPCM.

The quantiser output is given by

$$e_q(nT_s) = e(nT_s) + q_e(nT_s) \qquad \qquad ...(2.24)$$

where $e_q(nT_s)$ denotes the quantised form of $e(nT_s)$ and $q_e(nT_s)$ is the quantisation error.

2.3.3. Relation Between the Quantised Version $x_q(nT_s)$ and the Sampled Version $x(nT_s)$ of the Input Analog Signal $x(t)$

Referrring to the block diagram of Fig. 2.20 (a), we can write : Prediction Filter Input = Predicted Value + Quantiser Output,

i.e., $$x_q(nT_s) = \hat{x}(nT_s) + e_q(nT_s) = \hat{x}(nT_s) + e(nT_s) + q_e(nT_s) \qquad ...(2.25)$$

on substituting for the quantiser output $e_q(nT_s)$. But using the equation for the error signal fed as input to the quantiser, we find, after arranging terms, that

$$x(nT_s) = \hat{x}(nT_s) + e(nT_s) \qquad \qquad ...(2.26)$$

applying which the prediction filter input becomes

$$x_q(nT_s) = x(nT_s) + q_e(nT_s) \qquad \qquad ...(2.27)$$

Stated in words,

Quantised sample $x_q(nT_s)$ at the prediction filter input = Sample $x(nT_s)$ of the input signal $x(t)$ + Quantisation Error $q_e(nT_s)$.

Since , in the derivation of this equation, no consideration was taken of the properties of the prediction filter, the equation has a deeper connotation : No matter what is the nature of the prediction filter, the difference between the quantised sample applied at the input of the prediction filter and the sample of the original signal is only the quantising error.

Hence, assuming that the prediction is fairly close to the actual values, we may conclude that :

Average Power P_e of the prediction error sequence $e(nT_s)$ < Average Power P_m of the message signal sequence $x(nT_s)$.

Thus using a quantiser with a certin number of levels, it is possible to make adjustments to produce a quantising error sequence having a smaller average power than that obtained by the direct quantisation of the message sequence as is done in the usual PCM practice.

2.3.4. Output Signal-to-Quantising Noise Ratio

The average power of the message sequence of length N, is

$$P_m = \frac{1}{N} \sum_{n=0}^{N-1} x^2(nT_s) \qquad \qquad ...(2.28)$$

In the same manner, the average power of the quantising error sequence, also of an equal length N, is

$$P_q = \frac{1}{N} \sum_{n=0}^{N-1} q_e^2(nT_s) \qquad \qquad ...(2.29)$$

The output signal-to-quantising noise ratio of a DPCM system may be defined as the ratio of the average power of the message sequence to that of the quantising error sequence; thus, we have

$$(\text{SNR})_0 = \frac{P_m}{P_q} \qquad \qquad ...(2.30)$$

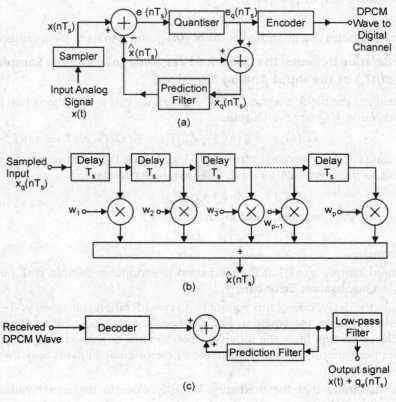

Fig. 2.20. Differential pulse-code modulation : (*a*) Transmitter, (*b*) Use of the Tapped-Delay
Line Filter as a Prediction Filter, and (*c*) Receiver

which can be expressed in terms of the average power (P_e) of the prediction error sequence
as

$$(SNR)_0 = \frac{P_m}{P_e} \cdot \frac{P_e}{P_q} = G_p\,(SNR)_Q \qquad \qquad ...(2.31)$$

where
$$G_p = \frac{P_m}{P_e} = \text{Prediction Gain} \qquad \qquad ...(2.32)$$

and
$$\frac{P_m}{P_e} = (SNR)_Q = \text{Signal-to-Quantising Noise Ratio} \qquad ...(2.33)$$

A G_p value > 1 signifies a gain in the signal-to-noise ratio due to differential
quantisation. To increase the signal-to-noise ratio, it is desirable to obtain a high value of
G_p. To achieve this, P_e has to be minimized because P_m cannot be changed for a given
message signal. This means that the prediction filter should be designed in such a way
to get the minimum P_e value keeping $(SNR)_Q$ constant.

2.3.5. Design Consideration for Prediction Filter

A *Tapped Delay Line Filter*, shown in Fig. 2.20 (*b*), can be used as the basis of prediction
filter design. Modelling the predicted value as a linear combination of past values of the
quantised input, it can be expressed as a superposition summation

$$x(nT_s) = \sum_{k=1}^{p} w_k x_q (nT_s - kT_s) \qquad \qquad ...(2.34)$$

where the w's are the tap weights of the filter written as $w_1, w_2, w_3, ..., w_p$; these define the filter coefficients. p is the order of the filter.

Substituting this predicted value in the equation for the input to the quantiser, the prediction error is

$$e(nT_s) = x(nT_s) - \sum_{k=1}^{p} w_k x_q (nT_s - kT_s) \qquad \qquad ...(2.35)$$

The mathematical approach to the design of the tapped-delay-line filter is that the average power of the prediction error with respect to the filter tap weights, should be lowered as far as possible. Assuming that $(SNR)_0 \gg 1$, this minimization yields a set of simultaneous equations which can be expressed in matrix form as

$$\begin{bmatrix} 1 & r(T_s) & \cdots & r(pT_s - T_s) \\ r(T_s) & 1 & & r(pT_s - 2T_s) \\ \vdots & \vdots & & \vdots \\ r(pT_s - T_s) & r(pT_s - 2T_s) & \cdots & 1 \end{bmatrix} \begin{bmatrix} w_1 \\ w_2 \\ \vdots \\ w_p \end{bmatrix} = \begin{bmatrix} r(T_s) \\ r(2T_s) \\ \vdots \\ r(pT_s) \end{bmatrix} \qquad ...(2.36)$$

where $r(kT_s)$ is the normalized autocorrelation function of the input signal to the prediction filter for a lag kT_s,

$$r(kT_s) = \frac{R_M(kT_s)}{R_M(0)}, \ k = 0, 1, ..., p \qquad \qquad ...(2.37)$$

In this equation $R_M(kT_s)$, $k = 0, 1, 2, 3, ..., p$ is the set of autocorrelation functions of the input. Thus for a given set of autocorrelation functions, the tap weights of the filter can be calculated. This lays down the design criterion for the prediction filter.

2.3.6. The DPCM Receiver

The block diagram of the receiver for DPCM system is illustrated in Fig. 2.20 (c). The receiver consists of a decoder to reconstruct the quantised error sequence $e_q(nT_s)$ employing a prediction filter analogous to the one at the transmitter. As long as the transmission noise is restricted to a negligible value, the received signal is the same as the signal emanating from the transmitter output. The received signal differs from the message signal only by the amount of quantising error vitiating the quantisation of the prediction error signal at the transmitting station.

Another pertinent remark we wish to make is about the fact that in the absence of transmission noise, the two prediction filters, one in the transmitter and its counterpart in the receiver, operate on an identical number of samples $\{x_q(nT_s)\}$. It is for this reason that a feedback path is added to the quantiser in the transmitter (Fig. 2.20 (a)).

2.4 DELTA MODULATION

2.4.1. Delta Modulation as One-Bit Version of DPCM

In DPCM, the correlations between the adjacent samples of the continuous-time information signal were beneficially applied to make predictions of the future values of the samples. In delta modulation (DM), we advance still further by oversampling the signal at a rate much larger than Nyquist rate ($2W$, W is the signal bandwidth) for enhancing the sample-to-sample relationship and formulate a simplified scheme for modulation based on an easier quantisation procedure.

The principle of DM can be understood with reference to Fig. 2.21. After oversampling the signal, it is quantised into discrete levels keeping the size of the step constant. The purpose is to represent the analog signal in the form of a staircase by augmenting or decreasing the sample value by a single step of the stairs only. So, for quantisation, the sampled value is constrained to move, whether up or down, by only one step at each transition. It can either increase by this standard step size or diminish by the same amount but cannot remain constant. This upward or downward step movement is decided by finding the difference between the input signal $x(t)$ and its quantised version $x_q(nT_s)$, henceforth termed the *approximation*. This approximation is quantised into two levels of representation, $\pm\ \delta$. A positive difference is called $+\ \delta$, a negative difference is known as $-\ \delta$; hence the name δ–modulation. If at any sampling instant, the approximation is less than the sample of the signal, the sample value is raised by an amount δ. If it is greater than the sample, the value of this sample is lowered down by δ. Barring sudden and abnormally wide signal variations, the staircase approximation does not lie beyond $\pm\ \delta$ of the original information signal so that it gives a fairly reasonable estimate of the signal. Thus delta modulation can be considered as a one-bit or two-level version of DPCM providing a *staircase approximtion* to the incoming analog information signal $x(t)$.

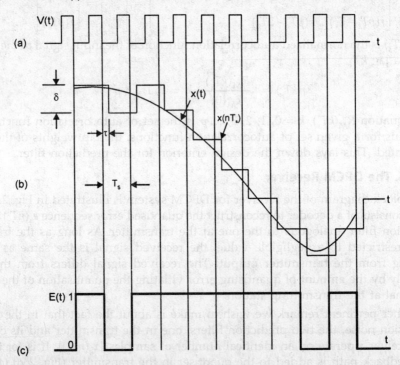

Fig. 2.21. Principle of Delta Modulation : (*a*) Clock, (*B*) Analog signal and its approximation, and (*c*) Transmitted stream of bits. t is the delay time introduced by the circuit in following the signal variations

2.4.2. Mathematical Formulation of Delta Modulation

We shall write the algorithm describing the operations involved in delta modulation, in the form of discrete-time equations. In this connection, we note that the two quantum levels in DM, namely, $\pm\ \delta$, can be conveniently incorporated in the signum function defined as

$$\text{sgn}(r) = \begin{cases} 1, & t > 0 \\ 0, & t = 0 \\ -1, & t < 0 \end{cases} \qquad \qquad ...(2.38)$$

It is an odd function of time. The shape of its wave is shown in Fig. 2.22 (a).

It is conceived in delta modulation that during quantisation the sampled signal is changed at each sampling instant, by $+\delta$ or $-\delta$. Its constancy would suggest three possible actions, negating the use of binary techniques, and is therefore inadmissible. Thus the signum function would serve as a suitable embodiment of this plan.

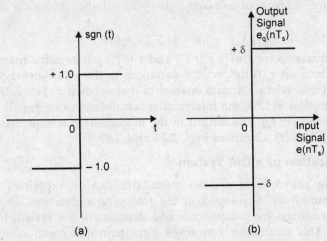

(a)   (b)

Fig. 2.22. (a) Wavefrom of the signum function, (b) The *hard limiter* input-output characteristic of the quantiser in the DM systems

In this formalism, we shall use the following notation :

$x(t)$ = Input analog signal containing the message

T_s = Sampling period

$x(nT_s)$ = Present value of input signal

$x_q(nT_s)$ = Quantised form of $x(nT_s)$

$\hat{x}(nT_s)$ = Recent approximation to input signal

$x_q(t)$ = Final quantised signal in the form of staircase approximation

$e(nT_s)$ = Error signal

$e_q(nT_s)$ = Quantised error signal, the desired DM wave for varying values of n.

The DM system under consideration is a linear one which has the property that the approximation or estimate $x(nT_s)$ changes by a constant amount $\pm\delta$ after each sample pulse. This means that if the signal $e_q(nT_s)$ consists of a long stream of logic 1 bits, $\hat{x}(nT_s)$ will look like a voltage ramp or a stepwise resemblance to it. In view of this linear change in $x(nT_s)$, whereby an input time function is represented by a series of constant gradient linear segments, this type of modulation system is called by the name "*Linear Delta Modulation.*"

Now it is easy to see that

Error signal = Present sample value of input − Latest approximation to it,

i.e., $\qquad\qquad e(nT_s) = x(nT_s) - \hat{x}(nT_s)$

But $\qquad\qquad \hat{x}(nT_s) = x_q[(n-1)T_s]$

Therefore, $\qquad\qquad e(nT_s) = x(nT_s) - x_q[(n-1)T_s]$ $\qquad ...(2.39)$

Also, in tems of the signum function and the step size, δ, the quantiser output is

$$e_q(nT_s) = \delta \, \text{sgn} \, [e(nT_s)] \qquad \qquad \ldots(2.40)$$

because depending upon $e(nT_s)$ value, we have :

(i) When $e(nT_s)$ is positive, $e_q(nT_s) = + \delta,$ ...(2.41)

(ii) When $e(nT_s)$ is negative, $e_q(nT_s) = - \delta,$ ...(2.42)

(iii) When $e(nT_s) = 0$, $e_q(nT_s) = 0$; there is no change of state.   ...(2.43)

Fingure 2.22 (b) presents the transfer or input-output characteristic of a delta modulator.

Further, Quantised form of message signal = Latest approximation value + Quantised error signal

i.e., $x_q(nT_s) = x_q[(n-1) \, T_s] + e_q(nT_s)$ ...(2.44)

The set of equations for $e(nT_s)$, $e_q(nT_s)$ and $x_q(nT_s)$ portrays the manner in which the staircase approximation $x_q(t)$ follows the variations in the input message signal $x(t)$. The signal curve and the staircase approximation to it are shown in Fig. 2.23 (a). It is evident from the diagram that in DM, the information transmission rate equals the reciprocal of the sampling period $(1/T_s)$. The output of the modulator is a sequence of binary digits, as shown in Fig. 2.23 (b). Compare Figs. 2.21 and 2.23.

2.4.3. Realization of a DM System

The working principle of a delta modulator can be explained in terms of the mathematical framework developed in the foregoing subsection. In the light of this algorithm, let us discuss the components and structure of the system for producing the DM waveform. This modulator comprises three principal components, viz., Summer, Quantiser and Accumulator, as shown in Fig. 2.24 (a).

The reader may compare the delta modulator of Fig. 2.24 (a) with the modulator for DPCM system shown in Fig. 2.20. Two vital differences strike our attention. First, a one-bit quantiser is used in delta modulation while the quantiser in DPCM has to handle more bits covering the full error signal. Secondly, we notice the replacement of several delay elements constituting the prediction filter of DPCM by a single delay element in DM.

Now, continuing our discussions on DM, the operation of the modulator, Fig. 2.24 (a), can be easily verified to be in conformance with the algorithm. When the output of the quantiser is applied to the accumulator, we obtain from the equations for the quantised message and quantised error signals, the result

$$x(nT_s) = \delta \sum_{i=1}^{n} \text{sgn} \, e(iT_s) = \sum_{i=1}^{n} e_q(iT_s) \qquad \qquad \ldots(2.45)$$

At each sampling instant (nT_s), the algebraic sign preceding the error signal $e(nT_s)$ determines whether the accumulator increases or decreases the approximation by a magnitude $- \delta$. If the input signal exceeds the latest approximation $\hat{x}(nT_s)$, the approximation is raised by applying a positive increment δ in the direction of the input signal. In the reverse situation, the approximation is altered by a negative increment $(-\delta)$ or a decrement by δ. Thus the accumulator pursues and keeps a constant track of the input samples. It monitors them, either incrementing or decrementing them by one step at a time, to meet the goal of delta modulation.

In receiver, Fig. 2.24 (b), positive and negative pulses of the incoming signal are generated by the decoder. These pulses are made to traverse an accumulator similar to the one at the transmitter to recover the staircase approximated signal $x_q(t)$. A low-pass filter having a bandwidth equal to that of the message signal, is employed to discard any quantising noise contaminating the high-frequency staircase approximation content.

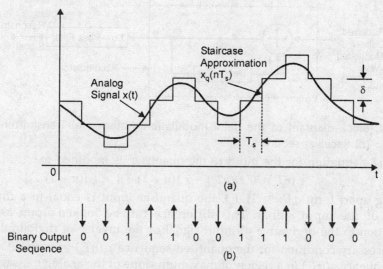

(a)

Binary Output Sequence 0 0 1 1 1 0 0 1 1 1 0 0 0

(b)

Fig. 2.23. Delta modulation : (*a*) Replacement of the analog signal by the quantised signal, and (*b*) Modulator output

2.4.4. Sources of Quantising Noise in Delta Modulation

Delta Modulation is afflicted by two types of quantising noise originating from different sources. These are called Slope Overload Distortion (or Noise) and Granular Noise.

Let us first consider *Slope Overload Distortion*. It is caused by the fact that the maximum slope that can be produced by a linear delta modulator is determined by the product of step size (δ) and sampling frequency $f_s = \dfrac{1}{T_s}$. Indeed, the correct choice of these two parameters (δ and f_s) holds the key to the effective use of delta modulation.

Let us try to understand how this distortion takes palce. The representation of quantised message signal as a summation over the quantised error signal enables us to obtain the quantised message signal as an accumulation of positive and negative increments of amount δ. This operation performed by the accumulator is equivalent to the integration process, from a digital point of view. Moreover, if $q_e(nT_s)$ is the quantising error, we have

$$x_q(nT_s) = x(nT_s) + q_e(nT_s) \qquad \qquad ...(2.46)$$

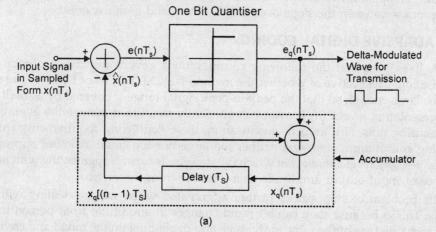

(a)

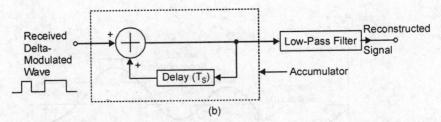

(b)

Fig. 2.24. Block diagram of the delta modulation system : (a) Transmitter section, and (b) Receiver section

The $e(nT_s)$ equation for the input to the quantiser, is modified to

$$e\,(nT_s) = x\,(nT_s) - x\,[(n-1)\,T_s] - q_e\,[(n-1)\,T_s] \qquad \ldots(2.47)$$

Leaving apart term $q_e[(n-1)\,T_s]$, the quantiser input is equal to a first backward difference of the input signal. This difference can be looked upon as the digital approximation to the derivative of input signal or the inverse of digital integration.

The necessary condition for the quantised sequence $x_q(nT_s)$ to increase as fast as the message sequence $x(nT_s)$ in a region of maximum slope of the analog message signal $x(t)$, is that

$$\frac{\delta}{T_s} \ge \max\left|\frac{dx(t)}{dt}\right| \qquad \ldots(2.48)$$

If this condition is not complied with, $|\delta|$ will be very low so that staircase approxmiation $x_q(t)$ will be unable to keep track of a steep portion of $x(t)$. Consequently, $x_q(t)$ will lag behind $x(t)$ (Fig. 2.25). This condition of lagging is called *Slope Overload* and the distortion resulting from this cause is known as *Slope-Overload Distortion*. Because the maximum gradient of the staircase approximation $x_q(t)$ is determined by the value of δ, the associated rise and fall in $x_q(t)$ occurs in straight lines. Hence, a DM system with a fixed δ value, is a linear delta modulator.

The second type of noise, viz., *Granular Noise*, is the analogue of quantising noise in PCM. It takes place when δ is too large with respect to local slope characteristics of message waveform. Then the staircase approximation is found hunting around a flat segment of the input $x(t)$ causing distortion.

From the above discussion, it is easy to visualize that a small value of δ helps in representing the low level signals, and a large value of δ is required to encompass a wide dynamic range. Therefore, an optimum value of δ which minimizes the mean square quantising error will be a compromise between the slope overload distortion and granular noise.

2.5 ADAPTIVE DIGITAL CODING

We have seen that the following considerations govern the choice of step size for quantisation, irrespective of whether the method is PCM, DPCM or DM : (i) The step size must be large enough so that the peak-to-peak signal range is covered by a small number of representation levels. (ii) It must be sufficiently small to minimize the average power of quantising noise. In uniform quantisation, these conflicting requirements are met by choosing an optimum step size, neither too large nor too small. Another approach is to employ *non-uniform quantisation* in which the step size is *variable* augmenting with increasing distance of input-output amplitude characteristic from the origin.

The problem of step size is further aggravated when we are dealing with speech signals. This is because they exhibit rapid changes in amplitude from person to person, in the speaking tone of the same individual, and depending on the mood and environment of the speaker. To accommodate such wide variations occurring both in the signal intensity and its spectral characteristics, the step size must change with the needs of the situation. A system in which the step size is adjusted to conform to the specific needs is said to be adaptive. "Adaptivity" means that one variable of a process is able to change according to the requirements of another variable. The former is called the *controlling variable* and the latter the *controlled variable*. In digital pulse modulation, the controlling variable is the step size while the controlled variable is the gradient of the input analog waveform according to which quantisation must be done to generate a matching quantised characteristic.

The applicaton of the adaptive property to pulse-code modulation results in *Adaptive Pulse-Code Modulation (APCM)*. In *Adaptive Differential Pulse-Code Modulation (ADPCM)*, not only is the step size a function of the signal changes, the prediction filter can also be made adaptive. Thus in ADPCM, a combination of adaptive quantisation with adaptive filtering can be realized to yield comparatively much improved performance for signals which vary abruptly on a broader scale. The adaptive concept can also be extended to delta modulation. Here, the step size is large for a steep segment of the signal waveform and smaller for a slowly changing segment. The resulting system is known as *Adaptive Delta Modulation (ADM)*.

2.5.1. Adaptive Pulse-Code Modulation

Reconciliation or adaptivity in PCM can be introduced in two ways. In the first method, matching of the quantiser step size to the signal power is accomplished by using the magnitude of the previous code words along with a one or two-word memory in the quantiser. Multiplication of the step size Δ by predetermined constant M_i, governed by preceding sample values, leads to the APCM algorithm:

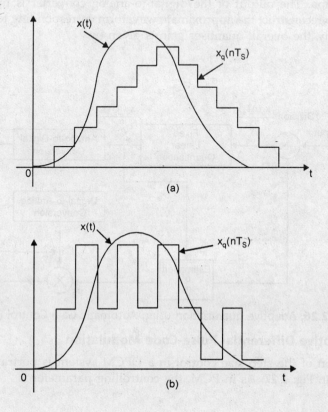

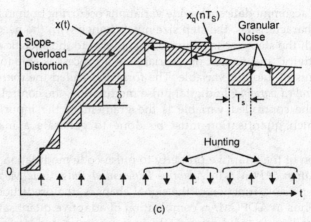

(c)

Fig. 2.25. Lack of harmony between the quantised and the continuous-time curves in delta modulation : (a) For small step size, (b) For large step size, and (c) Illustrating the two types of quantising error, slope overload distortion and granular noise

$$\Delta_{n+1} = \Delta_n M_i |H_r| \qquad \qquad ...(2.49)$$

where $|H_r|$ represents the absolute value of the previous code word.

In the second method, the short-time average power σ_n^2 at the quantiser output is determined. The σ_n value thus obtained is applied to maintain the input to the quantiser at a constant level by means of an Automatic Gain Control (AGC) circuit arrangement. Figure 2.26 presents a schematic diagram of the layout of the system. For adaptation of values, the sampled input data $x(nT_s)$ are divided by σ_n. Coding is carried out by fixed linear quantisation. The output of the digital-to-analog converter is multiplied by the same σ_n value to reconstruct the approximate waveform corresponding to the given input signal. Effectively, the overall quantiser gain is given by

$$G = \frac{1}{\sigma_n} \qquad \qquad ...(2.50)$$

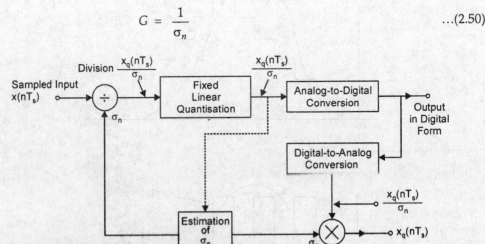

Fig. 2.26. Adaptive quantisation using Automatic Gain Control (AGC)

2.5.2. Adaptive Differential Pulse-Code Modulation

Incorporation of the step size control in a DPCM system is portrayed in the block diagram given in Fig. 2.27. As in PCM, the controlling parameter is

$$\sigma_n = \left[\left\langle \left\{ e_q(nT_s) \right\}^2 \right\rangle \right]^{1/2} \qquad \ldots(2.51)$$

The values of the step size multiplers for instantaneous adaptation are computed as in the case of PCM.

2.5.3. Adaptive Delta Modulation

The noteworthy advantage gained in a DM system is that adaptiveness of step size decreases the slope overload distortion without increasing granular noise.

In the ADM transmitter presented in Fig. 2.28, the step size in the feedback loop is adjusted by a variable gain $G(nT_s)$ such that

$$x_q(nT_s) = x_q(nT_s - T_s) + G(nT_s - T_s) e_q(nT_s - T_s) \qquad \ldots(2.52)$$

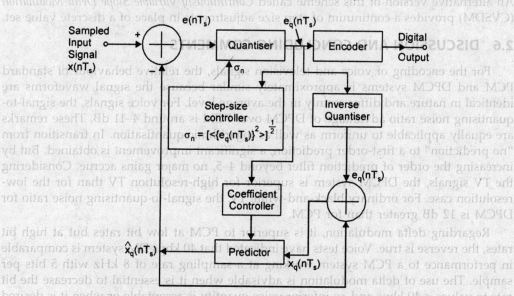

Fig. 2.27. Adaptive Differential Pulse-Code Modulation (ADPCM) system

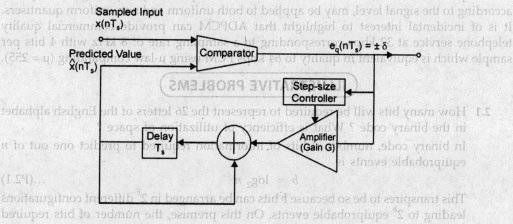

Fig. 2.28. Transmitter for Adaptive Delta Modulation (ADM)

The adjustment algorithm carried out by the step size controller is expressed as

$$G(nT_s) = \begin{cases} G(nT_s - T_s) \times K, & e_q(nT_s - T_s) = e_q(nT_s - T_s) \\ \dfrac{G(nT_s - T_s)}{K}, & e_q(nT_s) \neq e_q(nT_s - T_s) \end{cases} \quad ...(2.53)$$

where K is a constant bounded by the limits $1 < K < 2$. Thus the effective step size increases by successive powers of K during the slope overload distortion condition signified by the equation

$$e_q(nT_s) = e_q(nT_s - T_s) \qquad\qquad ...(2.54)$$

but decreases otherwise during

$$e_q(nT_s) \neq e_q(nT_s - T_s) \qquad\qquad ...(2.55)$$

An alternative version of this scheme called *Continuously Variable Slope Delta Modulation* (CVSDM) provides a continuum of step size adjustments in place of a discrete value set.

2.6 DISCUSSION AND CONCLUDING COMMENTS

For the encoding of voice and television signals, the relative behaviour of standard PCM and DPCM systems is approximately similar because the signal waveforms are identical in nature and differ mainly in the average level. For voice signals, the signal-to-quantising noise ratio advantage of DPCM over PCM is around 4–11 dB. These remarks are equally applicable to uniform as well as logarithmic quantisation. In transition from "no prediction" to a first-order prediction, a significant improvement is obtained. But by increasing the order of prediction filter beyond 4–5, no major gains accrue. Considering the TV signals, the DPCM system is superior for high-resolution TV than for the low-resolution case. For ordinary black-and-white TV, the signal-to-quantising noise ratio for DPCM is 12 dB greater than for PCM.

Regarding delta modulation, it is superior to PCM at low bit rates but at high bit rates, the reverse is true. Voice tests have indicated that 40 kbps DM system is comparable in performance to a PCM system working at a sampling rate of 8 kHz with 5 bits per sample. The use of delta modulation is advisable when it is essential to decrease the bit rate to values < 40 kbps and an inferior voice quantity is acceptable or when it is desired to simplify the circuit substantially and employ a high bit rate.

Adaptive versions of the above methods which operate by adjusting the step size according to the signal level, may be applied to both uniform and non-uniform quantisers. It is of incidental interest to highlight that ADPCM can provide commercial quality telephone service at 32 kbps corresponding to a sampling rate of 8 kHz with 4 bits per sample which is equivalent in quality to 64 kbps PCM using μ-law companding ($\mu = 255$).

(ILLUSTRATIVE PROBLEMS)

2.1 How many bits will be required to represent the 26 letters of the English alphabet in the binary code ? What is efficiency of utilization of space ?

In binary code, number of bits of information required to predict one out of n equiprobable events is

$$b = \log_2 n \qquad\qquad ...(P2.1)$$

This transpires to be so because b bits can be arranged in 2^b different configurations leading to 2^b equiprobable events. On this premise, the number of bits required to represent the 26 alphabet letters is

$$b = \log_2 26 = 4.7 \approx 5 \qquad\qquad ...(P2.2)$$

on rounding off to the nearest integer as the number of bits can only be integral. But 5 bits correspond to $\log_2 32$ allowing for a choice out of 32 different events. So, the full capacity of a 5–bit code is under-utilized. The resulting efficiency is therefore.

$$\eta = \frac{4.7}{5} \times 100 = 94\% \qquad \qquad ...(P2.3)$$

2.2 Estimate the number of bits necessary in the binary code to represent 64 different possibilities and compare its efficiency with the decimal case.

For binary system, the required number of bits $= b = \log_2 n = \log_2 64 = 6$, and the corresponding efficiency

$$\eta_b = \frac{6}{6} \times 100 = 100\% \qquad \qquad ...(P2.4)$$

For decimal system, the number of bits $= \log_{10} 64 = 1.8062 \approx 2$ bits, and the associated efficiency

$$\eta_d = \frac{1.8062}{2} \times 100 = 90.31\% \qquad \qquad ...(P2.5)$$

Obviously, $\eta_b > \eta_d$. $\qquad \qquad ...(P2.6)$

2.3 (a) The maximum frequency in an analog signal is $f_m = 2$ kHz. The information in the signal is to be conveyed over an M-level PCM system. If the number of pulse levels is $M = 8$ and the quantisation noise is restricted to be $< \pm 0.781$ % of the peak-to-peak value of analog signal, calculate the number of bits per sample (bits per PCM word) to be used in this system.

(b) What is the bit transmission rate according to the Nyquist criterion ?

(c) Find also the symbol or pulse rate for the baseband transmission of a PCM pulse having four levels for a data rate = 3200 bits/s.

(a) Specifying the quantisation error q_e to be less than a fraction α of the peak-to-peak analog voltage V_p, we have

$$q_e \leq \alpha V_p \qquad \qquad ...(P2.7)$$

If Δ is the quantum step size, the maximum value of quantising error is $\pm \dfrac{\Delta}{2}$, so that

$$|q_e|_{max} = \frac{\Delta}{2} \qquad \qquad ...(P2.8)$$

In terms of the number L of quantisation levels,

$$|q_e|_{max} = \frac{V_p}{2L} \qquad \qquad ...(P2.9)$$

Hence, $\qquad \qquad \dfrac{V_p}{2L} \leq \alpha V_p \qquad \qquad ...(P2.10)$

or, $\qquad \qquad L \geq \dfrac{1}{2\alpha}$ levels $\qquad \qquad ...(P2.11)$

But $L = 2^n$ where n is the number of bits per sample. Therefore,

$$2^n \geq \frac{1}{2\alpha} \qquad \qquad ...(P2.12)$$

or, $\qquad n \geq \log_2\left(\dfrac{1}{2\alpha}\right)$ ...(P2.13)

Here, $\qquad \alpha = \dfrac{0.781}{100}$ ...(P2.14)

$\therefore \qquad n \geq \log_2\left(\dfrac{1}{2 \times 7.81 \times 10^{-3}}\right)$ ...(P2.15)

or, $\qquad n \geq \log_2 64.02$ ...(P2.16)

or, $\qquad n \geq \log_2 64$ ...(P2.17)

$\therefore \qquad n \geq 6$ ...(P2.18)

Hence quantisation noise requirement will be met if $n = 6$ bits are used.

(b) From the Nyquist condition, the required sampling rate $= 2f_m = 2 \times 2$ kHz $=$ 4000 samples/sec, from which the bit transmission rate

$$R = n f_s = 6 \times 4000 = 24000 \text{ bits/sec} \qquad \text{...(P2.19)}$$

since each word contains 6 bits,

Employing multilevel pulses with $M = 2^k = 8$ levels,

$$k_s = \log_2 8 = 3 \text{ bits,} \qquad \text{...(P2.20)}$$

the bit stream will be divided into groups of three bits giving the symbol transmission rate

$$R_s = \frac{R}{k} = \frac{24000}{3} = 8000 \text{ symbols/sec} \qquad \text{...(P2.21)}$$

Note : The reader should mark the difference between the two types of level referred to in this problem, viz., L quantisation levels ($L = 2^n$) and the M levels of the multilevel PCM pulses; the former pertain to multiple quantisation levels and the latter to multilevel signalling.

(c) $R = 3200$ bits/sec; $M = 4 = 2^k$, $\therefore k = 2$, and the symbol or pulse rate is

$$R_s = \frac{R}{k} = \frac{3200}{2} = 1600 \text{ symbols/sec.} \qquad \text{...(P2.22)}$$

2.4 Establish a relationship between signal-to-quantisation noise ratio $(SNR)_Q$ and the number of quantum levels L for a sinusoidal signal of peak amplitude V_0 Volts, applied to a PCM system. How many quantisation levels will be required in a binary PCM system in which the quantisation noise is prohibited to be > 8% of the signal content ?

Since the amplitude of the given signal swings from $-V_0$ to $+V_0$, it covers a total range $= 2 V_0$.

Considering the general case $L \gg 1$, the step size is

$$\Delta = \frac{2 V_0}{L} \qquad \text{...(P2.23)}$$

As the mean signal power $= \dfrac{V_0^2}{2}$ and the mean quantisation noise power

$$= \frac{\Delta^2}{12} = \frac{1}{12}\left(\frac{2 V_0}{L}\right)^2 = \frac{1}{3}\left(\frac{V_0^2}{L^2}\right) \qquad \text{...(P2.24)}$$

$\therefore$ The required ratio

$$(SNR)_Q = \frac{V_0^2}{2} \bigg/ \left\{ \frac{1}{3}\left(\frac{V_0^2}{L^2}\right) \right\} = \frac{3}{2}L^2 = 1.5\,L^2 \qquad \qquad ...(P2.25)$$

In the problem,

$$(SNR)_Q \geq \frac{1}{0.08} \geq 12.5, \therefore 1.5\,L^2 \geq 1.25, \text{ or } L^2 \geq \frac{12.5}{1.5} \qquad ...(P2.26)$$

$$=8.33, \therefore L \geq 2.8867, \text{ or } L \geq 3, \text{ since } L \text{ must be an integer.} \quad ...(P2.27)$$

2.5 (a) Examine the dependence of signal-to-quantisation noise ratio $(SNR)_Q$ on the channel band-width B for a PCM system using baseband transmission of pulses.

(b) Hence obtain the bandwidth and signal-to-quantisation noise ratio for a PCM system in which the sampling rate (f_s) is 12,000 samples per second and $n = 8$ bits per word are used in the transmission of signal.

(c) By what factor does the ratio $(SNR)_Q$ improve if the bandwidth is increased by a factor 1.25 ?

(a) If n denotes the number of pulses used for representing the quantum levels, then the pulse transmission rate, i.e., the bit rate $= n f_s$ bits/sec. For baseband pulse transmission, the required minimum bandwidth $B = 1/(2\,n\,f_s)$. It may be noted that B is slightly $> n f_m$ where f_m is the maximum frequency in the signal. Hence,

$$B = \frac{n f_s}{2} \geq n f_m \qquad \qquad ...(P2.28)$$

B is referred to as the *Nyquist Bandwidth*.

From Problem 2.4, we know that

$$(SNR)_Q = 1.5\,L^2 \qquad \qquad ...(P2.29)$$

where L is the number of quantum levels. For a binary system, $L = 2^n$,

$\therefore (SNR)_Q = 1.5\,(2^n)^2 = 1.5 \times 2^{2n}$. But $n = \dfrac{2B}{f_s}$. Substituting for n we have

$$(SNR)_Q = 1.5 \times 2^{\frac{4B}{f_s}} \qquad \qquad ...(P2.30)$$

(b) Here $f_s = 12000$ samples/sec. So, bandwidth

$$B = \frac{1}{2}n\,f_s = \frac{1}{2} \times 8 \times 12000 = 48000 = 48 \text{ kbps}, \quad ...(P2.31)$$

and

$$(SNR)_Q = 1.5 \times 2^{\frac{4\times 48}{12}} = 1.5 \times 2^{16} = 98304 \qquad \qquad ...(P2.32)$$

On the decibel scale, $(SNR)_Q = 10 \log_{10} 98304 = 49.93 \simeq 50$ dB.

(c) Upon raising the bandwidth by the factor 1.25, the new bandwidth $= 1.25 \times$ 48 kbps $= 60$ kbps, and $(SNR)_Q =$

$$1.5 \times 2^{\frac{4\times 60}{12}} = 1.5 \times 2^{20} = 1572864 = 61.97 \text{ dB} \simeq 62 \text{ dB}. \quad ...(P2.33)$$

2.6 The analog signal $g(t)$ shown in Fig. P2. 6(a) is to be transmitted by pulse-code modulation. Construct the binary amplitude signal for this continuous-time signal. From the equation to a straight line passing through the points (x_1, y_1) and (x_2, y_2), viz.,

$$y - y_1 = \frac{y_2 - y_1}{x_2 - x_1}(x - x_1) \qquad \qquad ...(P2.34)$$

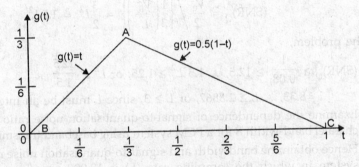

Fig. P2.6(a). Analog signal $g(t)$

we note that the equation of the straight line AB is $g(t) = t$ and that of the straight line BC is $g(t) = 0.5 (1 - t)$.

The given signal $g(t)$ being time limited, is obviously not bandlimited. But by taking the Fourier transform of $g(t)$, it can be shown that the spectral information about $g(t)$ is mainly contained in the range from 0 to 6π rad/sec. From this judgement, the Nyquist sampling frequency ω_s for signal $g(t)$ can be calculated from a low-pass filtered version $g'(t)$ of the original signal $g(t)$. Hence the Nyquist rate is $\omega_s = 2 \times 6\pi$ rad/sec $= 12\pi$ rad/sec, giving a sampling interval $T_s =$

$\dfrac{2\pi}{\omega_s} = \dfrac{2\pi}{12\pi} = \dfrac{1}{6}$ sec. The sampled values $g'(nT)$ of the signal $g'(t)$ are tabulated in

Table P2. 6(a) and the sampled signal is drawn in Fig. P2.6(b).

Table P2.6(a) The Sampling Operation

Sl. No.	Sampling Instant (T_s) sec	Equation Used	Sampled Signal $g'(nT_s)$
1.	0	$g'(t) = t$	0
2.	1/6	$g'(t) = t$	1/6 = 0.1667
3.	2/6 = 1/3	$g'(t) = t$	1/3 = 0.333
4.	3/6 = 1/2	$g'(t) = 0.5 (1 - t)$	1/4 = 0.25
5.	4/6 = 2/3	$g'(t) = 0.5 (1 - t)$	1/6 = 0.1667
6.	5/6	$g'(t) = 0.5 (1 - t)$	1/12 = 0.0833
7.	1	$g'(t) = 0.5 (1 - t)$	0

Now, in the binary system, the number of quantisation levels L can be written as $L = 2^n$ where $n =$ number of bits per sample, is a positive integer. The quantisation of amplitudes of pulses comprising the sampled signal $g'(nT_s)$ is performed in such a way that the pulse amplitudes are equal to the sample values $g'(nT_s)$ approximated to one of these L levels. The values of quantised sampled signal are denoted by $g'_q(nT_s)$. Now each pulse in $g'_q(nT_s)$ is represented by a binary word consisting of n bits. Choosing $n = 3$, $L = 8$, let the 8 quantisation levels numbered from 0 to 7 be $a_0, a_1, a_2, ..., a_7$. Then for the integer

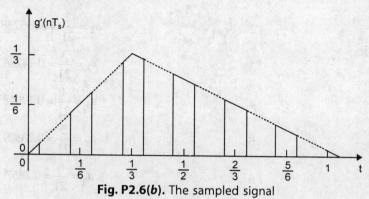

Fig. P2.6(b). The sampled signal

$$i = b_2 \times 2^2 + b_1 \times 2^1 + b_0 \times 2^0 \qquad \ldots(P2.35)$$

where b_0, b_1, b_2 are binary bits 0 or 1. The binary code word for the level a_i is $b_2 b_1 b_0$ and the 8 quantisation levels are given in Table P2.6(b)

Table P2.6(b) Encoding Parameters

Sl. No.	Quantisation Level (L)	Representation in Coded Form
1.	a_0	000
2.	a_1	001
3.	a_2	010
4.	a_3	011
5.	a_4	100
6.	a_5	101
7.	a_6	110
8.	a_7	111

Now, the peak value of the signal is $1/3$ and the maximum value of $i = 7$. Therefore, a_i can be represented as

$$a_i = \frac{i}{3 \times 7} = \frac{i}{21} \qquad \ldots(P2.36)$$

to cover the range from 0 to $1/3$ as i changes from 0 to 7. Employing this form for a_i, the values of quantisation levels are presented in Table P2.6 (c). Comparing Tables P2.6 (c) and (b), the encoded forms of the quantised samples are shown in Table P2.6 (d). For each quantised value of signal in Table P2.6 (d), we write the corresponding binary word by looking at Tables P2.6(c) and P2.6 (b). The binary representation of the signal waveform given in Fig. P2.6 (a) is sketched in Fig. P2.6 (c).

Table P2.6(c) Quantisation Level Values

Sl. No.	i Value	Value of the Quantisation Level
1.	0	$a_0 = \dfrac{0}{21} = 0$
2.		$a_1 = \dfrac{1}{21} = 0.0476$

(Contd.)

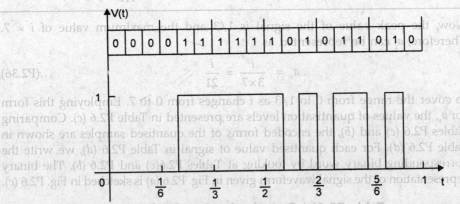

3.   2 $a_2 = \dfrac{2}{21} = 0.095238$

4.   3 $a_3 = \dfrac{3}{21} = 0.14286$

5.   4 $a_4 = \dfrac{4}{21} = 0.19048$

6.   5 $a_5 = \dfrac{5}{21} = 0.23809$

7.   6 $a_6 = \dfrac{6}{21} = 0.2857$

8.   7 $a_7 = \dfrac{7}{21} = 0.3333$

Table P2.6(d) Encoding of the Quantised Values

Sl. No.	Sample Value $g(nT_s)$	Quantised Value $g'_q(nT_s)$	Coded form Representation $(b_2 b_1 b_0)$
1.	0	0	$a_0 = 000$
2.	0.1667	0.14286	$a_3 = 011$
3.	0.333	0.3333	$a_7 = 111$
4.	0.25	0.23809	$a_5 = 101$
5.	0.1667	0.14286	$a_3 = 011$
6.	0.0833	0.095238	$a_2 = 010$
7.	0	0	$a_0 = 000$

V(t)

| 0 | 0 | 0 | 0 | 1 | 1 | 1 | 1 | 1 | 1 | 0 | 1 | 0 | 1 | 1 | 0 | 1 | 0 |

1

0    $\dfrac{1}{6}$ $\dfrac{1}{3}$ $\dfrac{1}{2}$ $\dfrac{2}{3}$ $\dfrac{5}{6}$ 1   t

Fig. P2.6(c). Binary amplitude signal for the analog signal of Fig. P2.6(a)

2.7 A compressor for a PCM system obeys the μ-law. Taking the values of the parameter μ = 75 and 200, determine the gain of the compressor for $V_i = 0.1\, V_{max}$, $0.25\, V_{max}$, $0.5\, V_{max}$, $0.75\, V_{max}$ and V_{max}. Also plot the gain characteristics of the compressor.

The μ-law may be expressed as

$$V_{out} = \frac{V_{max} \ln\left(1 + \mu\frac{V_{in}}{V_{max}}\right)}{\ln(1+\mu)} \qquad \text{...(P2.37)}$$

where the symbols have the following meanings :

V_{max} = Maximum uncompressed amplitude of the analog input signal,

V_{in} = Instantaneous value of input signal amplitude,

V_{out} = Compressed output signal amplitude, and

μ = Parameter measuring the degree of compression.

In this problem, the different input signal values are given as fractions or submultiples of V_{max}, in the form of ratios $\frac{V_{in}}{V_{max}}$. So the output signal values with reference to V_{max} expressed as $\frac{V_{out}}{V_{max}}$, will give the gain G of the compressor, written as

$$G = \frac{V_{out}}{V_{in}} = \frac{\ln\left(1 + \mu\frac{V_{in}}{V_{out}}\right)}{\ln(1+\mu)} \qquad \text{...(P2.38)}$$

Here, $\mu = 75$. Putting $V_{in} = 0.1\, V_{max}$, we get $G = 0.4942$. Putting the different values of V_{in} successively, we get the accompanying gain values. Then the calculations are repeated for $\mu = 200$. These gain values of the compressor are presented in Table P.2.7. The gain characteristics are plotted in Fig. P.2.7.

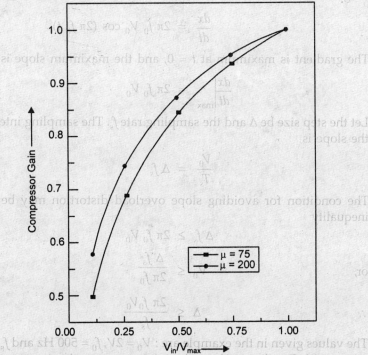

Fig. P2.7. Plots of the gain characteristics of the compressor of Problem 2.7, obeying the μ-law, with respect to input signal, for two different values of the parameter μ.

Table P2.7. Compressor Gain

Sl. No.	$\dfrac{V_{in}}{V_{max}}$	Values of gain for	
		$\mu = 75$	$\mu = 200$
1.	0.1	0.4942	0.574
2.	0.25	0.6888	0.7414
3.	0.5	0.8430	0.8702
4.	0.75	0.9346	0.9461
5.	1.00	1.0000	1.0000

2.8 If slope overload distortion is to be avoided in a delta modulation system, what should be the relation between the step size Δ, the maximum signal frequency f_0 and the highest permitted signal amplitude V_0 ? Derive this relation. Hence determine the minimum step size which does not give slope overload distortion in a delta modulation system for transmitting a sinusoidal signal of amplitude 20 V and frequency 500 Hz using a sampling rate of 25,000 samples per second.

The step size Δ should obey the relation

$$\Delta \leq \frac{2\pi f_0 V_0}{f_s} \qquad \qquad \text{...(P2.39)}$$

For deriving this relationship, let us consider a sinusoidal signal of amplitude V_0 and frequency f_0 given by

$$x(t) = V_0 \sin 2\pi f_0 t \qquad \qquad \text{...(P2.40)}$$

Its gradient is

$$\frac{dx}{dt} = 2\pi f_0 V_0 \cos (2\pi f_0 t) \qquad \qquad \text{...(P2.41)}$$

The gradient is maximum at $t = 0$, and the maximum slope is

$$\left.\frac{dx}{dt}\right|_{max} = 2\pi f_0 V_0 \qquad \qquad \text{...(P2.42)}$$

Let the step size be Δ and the sampling rate f_s. The sampling interval $T_s = 1/f_s$ and the slope is

$$\frac{V_0}{T_s} = \Delta f_s \qquad \qquad \text{...(P2.43)}$$

The condition for avoiding slope overload distortion may be expressed as an inequality

$$\Delta f_s \geq 2\pi f_0 V_0 \qquad \qquad \text{...(P2.44)}$$

or,
$$V_0 \leq \frac{\Delta f_s}{2\pi f_0} \qquad \qquad \text{...(P2.45)}$$

$$\therefore \qquad \Delta \leq \frac{2\pi f_0 V_0}{f_s} \qquad \qquad \text{...(P2.46)}$$

The values given in the example are : $V_0 = 2V, f_0 = 500$ Hz and $f_s = 25,000$ samples per second. For these values, the minimum step size is

$$\Delta_{min} = \frac{2 \times 3.14 \times 500 \times 2}{25,000} = 0.2512 \text{ V} = \frac{1}{4} \text{ V} \qquad ...(P2.47)$$

and the approximated signal will comprise $2 \times 4 = 8$ different levels.

2.9 For a sinusoidal message signal

$$x(t) = A \cos \omega t \qquad ...(P2.48)$$

having a frequency $\omega = 800\pi$, determine the sampling rate required to prevent slope overload distortion for realizing the condition $A/\delta = 10$. Compare it with the Nyquist sampling rate.

For the given sinusoidal information signal $x(t)$, using the condition for preventing slope overload distortion

$$\left| \frac{dx(t)}{dt} \right| \leq \frac{\delta}{T_s} \qquad ...(P2.49)$$

it can be readily seen that satisfactory operation demands that the signal levels obey the condition

$$\frac{A}{\delta} \leq \frac{1}{2\pi} \left(\frac{\omega_s}{\omega} \right) \qquad ...(P2.50)$$

But $A/\delta = 10$ and $\omega = 800\pi$

$$\therefore \qquad 10 \leq \frac{1}{2\pi} \left(\frac{2\omega f_s}{800 \, \pi} \right) \qquad ...(P2.51)$$

or, $\qquad\qquad f_s \geq 10 \times 800 \, \pi \geq 25.12 \text{ kHz} \qquad ...(P2.52)$

The Nyquist sampling rate is

$$= 2 f_m = 2 \times 400 = 800 \text{ Hz} \qquad ...(P2.53)$$

which is $\dfrac{800}{25120} = 0.032$ times smaller than the sample rate f_s calculated above.

REVIEW QUESTIONS

2.1 What are the three main forms of digital pulse modulation ? Draw the block diagram of a Pulse-Code Modulation System from the signal source to its destination. Explain the function of each block.

2.2 Define quantising error. What is the maximum quantising error in terms of the step size ? Derive the relationship between the average power of quantising noise P_q and the step size Δ. What inhibits us from decreasing the step size indefinitely to reduce the quantising noise ?

2.3 Explain why quantising noise degrades small-amplitude signals much more than the large amplitude ones in a PCM system ? Can tapered quantising levels counteract this effect ? Why is signal companding preferable to quantising with tapered steps ?

2.4 What are the three main types of quantisers used in PCM ? Briefly describe their working principle with the help of diagrams.

2.5 What is meant by Aliasing ? Illustrate the aliasing effect by drawing the message spectrum and its two frequency-shifted replicas. What remedial measures are adopted to combat aliasing?

2.6 Draw and explain the circuit of a Sample and Hold Circuit using MOSFET devices. Are the pulses obtained ideal samples ? Show the input and output waveforms of the circuit.

2.7 What is Companding ? Why is it necessary ? Write down the expressions for the μ-law and A-law for compression of a signal, explaining the meanings of the symbols used.

2.8 Define a Code. Why does a quantised signal need to be encoded for transmission? Give a general classification of codes and mention the characteristic features of each class.

2.9 Sketch the circuit diagram of an $R/2R$ decoder device. Use a particular setting of the electronic switches and apply Thévenin's Theorem to determine the output voltage V_0.

2.10 Provide a stage-by-stage description of a differential pulse-code modulation (DPCM) system. Include block diagrams of the transmitter and receiver sections. What primary characteristic distinguishes DPCM from a pulse-code modulation (PCM) system ?

2.11 Develope the main equations for the operation of a delta modulator. Draw the block diagram showing the elements constituting such a system. How does an input signal $x(t)$ change when routed through these blocks ?

(REFERENCES AND FURTHER READING)

2.1 S. Haykin, *An Introduction to Analog and Digital Communicatons*, Wiley, Singapore, 1994.

2.2 W Tomasi, *Electronic Communications Systems, Fundamentals Through Advanced*, Prentice Hall, Englewood Cliffs, 1988. Also, W. Tomasi, *Advanced Electronic Communications Systems*, Prentice Hall, Englewood Cliffs, 1987 and V.F. Alisoukus and W. Tomasi, *Digital and Data Communications*, Prentice Hall, Englewood Cliffs, 1985.

2.3 M.S. Roden, *Analog and Digital Communicaton Systems*, Prentice Hall, Englewood Cliffs, 1985.

2.4 F. Barker, *Communications Electronics Systems, Circuits and Devices*, Prentice Hall, Englewood Cliffs, 1987.

2.5 A.B. Carlson, *Communications Systems, An Introduction to Signals and Noise in Electronic Communication*, McGraw Hill Co., New York, 1986.

2.6 B. Sklar, *Digital Communications : Fundamentals and Applications*, Prentice Hall, Englewood Cliffs, 1988.

2.7 J. Das, *Review of Digital Communications*, Wiley Eastern Limited, New Delhi, 1988.

2.8 B. Holdsworth and L.R. Martin, *Digital Systems Reference Book*, Butterworth Heinemann Ltd., Oxford, 1991.

2.9 P.Z. Pebbles, *Jr.*, *Digital Communication Systems*, Prentice Hall, Inc., Englewood Cliffs, 1987.

2.10 K. Feher, *Advanced Communication Systems and Signal Processing Techniques*, Prentice Hall, Englewood Cliffs, 1987.

2.11 D. Dunlop and D.G. Smith, *Telecommunications Engineering*, V. Nostrand Reinhold (International) Ltd., London, 1989.

3

Digital Modulation Techniques

Digital modulation is the process of transmitting baseband digital information such as binary data over a bandpass communication channel. The frequency limits of transmission are necessarily those of the channel.

To facilitate understanding, the digital modulation schemes are discussed in a graded manner in which these methods are first introduced at an elementary level, followed by an exhaustive treatment of difficult portions. After going through this chapter, the reader will be able to get a perception of various digital modulation methods, understand their operational procedures, draw their functional block diagrams, discern their error performance and have a cognizance of their bandwidth requirements.

At the outset we present a list of acronyms for digital modulation methods in Table 3.1.

3.1 BINARY AND *M*-ARY MODULATION

3.1.1. Binary Modulation

In Binary Modulation, the information comprises binary symbols 0 and 1. These symbols are supposed to occur at a fixed rate of 1 bit per T_b seconds. Binary modulation entails *switching* or *keying* any one of the parameters: amplitude, phase or frequency of the radio-frequency carrier wave between either of the two possible values representing the symbols 0 and 1. The two symbols are described by two distinct signals $x_1(t)$ and $x_2(t)$. The method is also referred to as *Binary Switching*, *Binary Signalling* or *Binary Shift Keying*. Its three basic forms – Binary Amplitude-Shift Keying (BASK), Binary Phase-Shift Keying (BPSK) and Binary Frequency-Shift Keying (BFSK) – can be considered as special cases of amplitude, phase and frequency modulation respectively.

Table 3.1. Acronyms of Common Digital Modulation Schemes

Sl. No.	Type of Modulation	Short Form	Full Form
1.	Amplitude	APK	Amplitude-Phase Keying
		ASK	Amplitude-Shift Keying
		BASK	Binary Amplitude-Shift Keying
		M-ary ASK	M-ary Amplitude-Shift Keying
		QAM	Quadrature Amplitude Modulation
2.	Phase	BPSK	Binary Phase-Shift Keying
		DCPSK	Differentially Encoded Phase-Shift

DCQPSK	Keying with Coherent Detection Differentially Encoded Quadrature Phase-Shift Keying with Coherent Demodulation
DPSK	Differential Phase-Shift Keying using Non-coherent Demodulation
DQPSK	Differential Quaternary/ Quadrature or Quadri-Phase-Shift Keying using Non-coherent Demodulation
M-ary PSK	M-ary Phase-Shift Keying
OK-QPSK, OQPSK	Offset-Keyed or Offset Quaternary/ Quadrature or Quadri Phase-Shift Keying
PSK	Phase-Shift Keying
QPSK	Quaternary/Quadrature or Quadri-Phase-Shift Keying

3.	Frequency	BFSK	Binary Frequency-Shift Keying
		CPFSK	Continuous Phase Frequency-Shift Keying
		M-ary FSK	M-ary Frequency-Shift Keying
		MSK	Minimum Shift Keying

3.1.2. *M*-ary Modulation

To the contrary, in M-ary modulation, the information is broken down into M segments or blocks with each block consisting of m bits, thus $M = 2^m$. These constituent blocks are called *Symbols*. While in binary modulation, one bit is transmitted in every bit interval (T_b), in M-ary modulation, m bits corresponding to each block are sent in T_b seconds so that the symbol duration or signalling interval is $T_s = m\,T_b$. Further, whereas in binary transmission, any one of the possible signals $x_1(t)$, $x_2(t)$ are sent in each bit interval, in M-ary case, one out of M possible signals $x_1(t)$, $x_2(t)$, $x_3(t)$, ..., $x_M(t)$ are propagated in each signalling interval T_s. The M signals represent the M symbols in M-ary modulation. The unit of rate of signal transmission is *Baud*: one baud refers to transmission of one symbol per second in binary transmission and will be obviously = $\log_2 M$ bits per second in case of M-ary transmission.

An M-ary modulator (Fig. 3.1) forms $M = 2^m$ channel signals from $N = 2^m$ successive encoded bits. This is followed by transmission of the symbols into the set of channel signals $x_i(t) = 1, 2, 3, ..., M$. These signals are sent in a form which is more suitable for transmission over the channel. The modulator performs a one-to-one mapping of the set of symbols into the set of signals. In the receiver, the demodulator carries out the reverse operation interpreting the incoming signal as one of the N symbols. The binary sequence is decoded to yield data symbols. Assuming that there is no error in transit, the received data stream is the same as the one actually sent. Otherwise, two types of errors can take place: Word or Symbol Error and Bit Error.

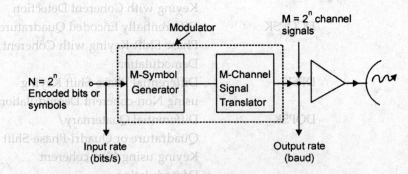

Fig. 3.1. Block schematic of an M-ary modulator system

In general, digital modulation involves the transmission of $M = 2^m$ symbols at intervals of T_s seconds through the agency of a radio-frequency modulated carrier expressed as

$$x(t) = \sum_{i=1}^{M} x_i(t)\, X(t - iT_s) \qquad\qquad ...(3.1)$$

where the function

$$X(t - iT_s) = \begin{cases} 1, & \text{if } 0 \le t \le T_s \\ 0, & \text{otherwise} \end{cases} \qquad\qquad ...(3.2)$$

and the signal $x_i(t)$ is of sinusoidal form

$$x_i(t) = A_i \cos\,(2\pi f_c t + \phi_i) \qquad\qquad ...(3.3)$$

A_i is the amplitude, f_c is the carrier frequency and ϕ_i is the phase of the ith signal.

3.2 BINARY AMPLITUDE-, PHASE- AND FREQUENCY-SHIFT KEYING: ASK, PSK AND FSK

There are three principal methods of signalling binary information, namely, amplitude-shift keying, phase-shift keying and frequency-shift keying. These are explained in the following subsections.

3.2.1. Amplitude-Shift Keying

In this method, binary symbols 1 and 0 are represented by two different signals $x_1(t)$ and $x_2(t)$ described as:

Symbol 1: By transmitting a sinusoidal wave of amplitude A, frequency f_c and phase ϕ, ...(3.4)

and   Symbol 0: By sending a signal $x_2(t) = 0$. ...(3.5)

Since $x_1(t) = 0$, symbol 0 is obtained by simply switching off the sinusoidal wave $x_1(t)$. Here in ASK, the information is in *unipolar* form. It may be noted that $x_1(t)$ is passed for a bit duration T_b seconds and switched off for the same time.

A binary ASK wave $x(t)$ can be mathematically written as

$$x(t) = \begin{cases} x_1(t) = A\cos\,(2\pi f_c t + \phi), & 0 \le t \le T_b \\ x_2(t) = 0, & 0 \le t \le T_b \end{cases} \qquad ...(3.6)$$

Figure 3.2(a) illustrates an ASK waveform for binary data.

3.2.2. Phase-Shift Keying

Here the phase of the carrier wave for the symbols 1 and 0 differs by π radians or 180°. Binary digits 1 and 0 are represented by signals $x_1(t)$ and $x_2(t)$ as

Symbol 1: $\qquad x_1(t) = A \cos (2\pi f_c t + \phi)$ $\qquad\qquad$ ...(3.7)

Symbol 0: $\qquad x_2(t) = A \cos (2\pi f_c t + \phi + \pi) = -A \cos (2\pi f_c t + \phi)$ $\qquad$ ...(3.8)

In mathematical language, a binary PSK wave is given by

$$x(t) = \begin{cases} x_1(t) = A\cos (2\pi f_c t + \phi), & 0 \le t \le T_b \\ x_2(t) = -A\cos (2\pi f_c t + \phi), & 0 \le t \le T_b \end{cases} \qquad ...(3.9)$$

A PSK wave is shown in Fig. 3.2(b).

3.2.3. Frequency-Shift Keying

In this technique, two different frequencies f_1 and f_2 are employed for conveying the symbols 1 and 0. Ignoring the initial phases ϕ_1, ϕ_2 of the signals $x_1(t)$, $x_2(t)$, we can write for continuous phase

$\qquad\qquad$ Symbol 1: $x_1(t) = A \cos (2\pi f_1 t)$ $\qquad\qquad$ ...(3.10)

$\qquad\qquad$ Symbol 0: $x_2(t) = -A \cos (2\pi f_2 t)$ $\qquad\qquad$ ...(3.11)

In mathematical terms, a binary FSK wave is expressed as

$$x(t) = \begin{cases} x_1(t) = A\cos (2\pi f_1 t), & 0 \le t \le T_b \\ x_2(t) = A\cos (2\pi f_2 t), & 0 \le t \le T_b \end{cases} \qquad ...(3.12)$$

Figure 3.2(c) shows an FSK wave.

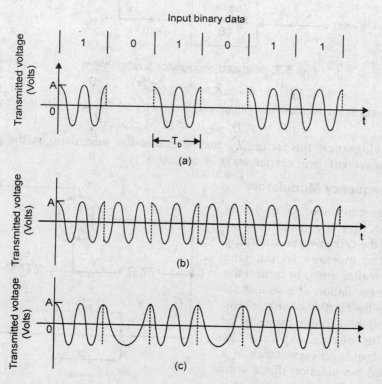

Input binary data

(a)

(b)

(c)

Fig. 3.2. Basic binary modulation techniques: (a) ASK, (b) PSK and (c) FSK

3.3 GENERAL PRINCIPLES OF PRODUCTION AND DETECTION OF BINARY MODULATED WAVES

To understand the generation schemes for binary modulated waves, let us recall from analog modulation studies, the functioning of the Product Modulator and Frequency Modulator.

3.3.1. Product Modulator

Figure 3.3 shows a Balanced Modulator Circuit. It consists of two standard similar-amplitude modulators configured in a balanced structure. Notice the sign reversal of the modulating wave applied to one input. The modulator outputs are

$$x_1(t) = A\{1 + k_a m(t)\}\ \cos(2\pi f_c t) \qquad \qquad ...(3.13)$$

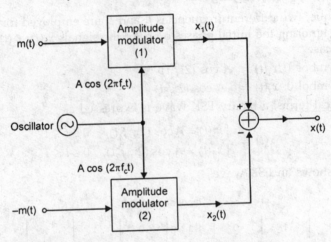

Fig. 3.3. Balanced modulator arrangement

and
$$x_2(t) = A\{1 - k_a m(t)\}\ \cos(2\pi f_c t) \qquad ...(3.14)$$

where k_a is a constant termed the *Amplitude Sensitivity* of the modulator. Now,

$$x(t) = x_1(t) - x_2(t) = 2k_a\, A\, \cos(2\pi f_c t)\, m(t) \qquad ...(3.15)$$

Thus leaving apart the factor $2k_a$, the output of the modulator is the product of modulating wave $m(t)$ and carrier wave $A\,\cos(2\pi f_c t)$.

3.3.2. Frequency Modulator

A voltage-controlled oscillator is employed to vary the instantaneous frequency of the carrier wave according to that of the message signal. One approach to realize this is to control the frequency of oscillation of a sinusoidal oscillator like the Hartley oscillator (Fig. 3.4), by a voltage-variable capacitor or varicap. The device exploits the variation of transition capacitance of a reverse-biased *p-n* junction diode with applied voltage. The frequency of a Hartley oscillator is

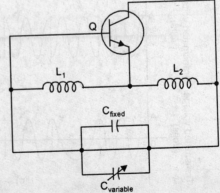

Fig. 3.4. Circuit diagram of a Hartley oscillator with voltage-dependent capacitor

$$f(t) = \frac{1}{2\pi \sqrt{(L_1 + L_2) C(t)}} \qquad \text{...(3.16)}$$

where L_1, L_2 are inductances and $C(t) = C_{fixed} + C_{variable}$. ...(3.17)

3.3.3. Generation of ASK and PSK Waves

The generation schemes for binary ASK and PSK waves are similar (Fig. 3.5). For *ASK Generation* (Fig. 3.5(a)), the binary data represented in digital format of *On-Off* or *Unipolar Signalling* (refer to Sec. 2.2.10), is applied to a product modulator along with the sinusoidal carrier wave. The output signal is obviously an ASK wave.

The *PSK Generator*, Fig. 3.5(b), differs from an ASK generator (Fig. 3.5(a)), only in the respect that in PSK, the incoming binary data are represented in polar signalling format instead of the unipolar format in ASK.

Remembering that a double-sideband suppressed-carrier (DSBSC) modulated wave equals the product of the message and carrier signals, it is readily apparent that ASK and PSK waves can be considered as DSBSC modulated waves. DSBSC is a double-sideband emission in which the virtually suppressed carrier is not used for demodulation.

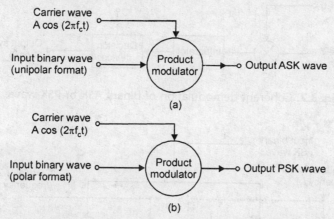

Fig. 3.5. Production of binary ASK and PSK waves: (a) ASK and (b) PSK

3.3.4. Generation of FSK Wave

For FSK waves, we employ a Frequency Modulator (Fig. 3.6), in place of Product Modulator. Binary data is applied in polar form. With each input voltage level swing from one level to another, the output changes in harmony yielding an FSK wave.

3.3.5. Coherent Detection of ASK or PSK Wave

The major components of a Coherent Detector, shown in Fig. 3.7, include: (*i*) *Multiplier* or *Product Modulator*: This multiplies the incoming signal with a sinusoidal carrier version produced by a local oscillator. (*ii*) *Integrator*: It performs the integration operation $\int_0^{T_b} dt$ on the signal emanating from the multiplier for consecutive bit intervals. This is like a lowpass filtering action. (*iii*) *Decision Device*: The output from the integrator is compared with a preselected threshold value. If this output is greater than the threshold value, symbol 1 is inferred. If it is less than threshold, symbol 0 is decided. Demodulators for ASK and PSK waves differ primarily in their threshold values.

3.3.6. Coherent Detection of FSK Wave

A coherent demodulator for an FSK wave consists of two correlators, each comprising a multiplier followed by an integrator, as shown in Fig. 3.8. These correlators are separately tuned to different carrier frequencies f_1, f_2, signifying binary symbols 1 and 0. The objective of the comparator is to look for the likeness or dissimilarity in the outputs from the two integrators and take a decision in favour of symbol 1 or 0. If, for example, the output k_1 associated with frequency f_1 is greater than output k_2 corresponding to frequency f_2, the symbol 1 is decided. In the reverse situation, the symbol is 0.

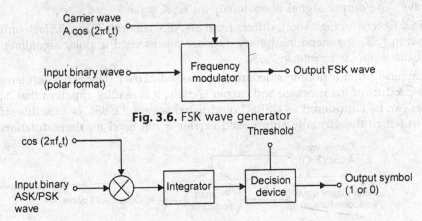

Fig. 3.6. FSK wave generator

Fig. 3.7. Coherent demodulation of binary ASK or PSK wave

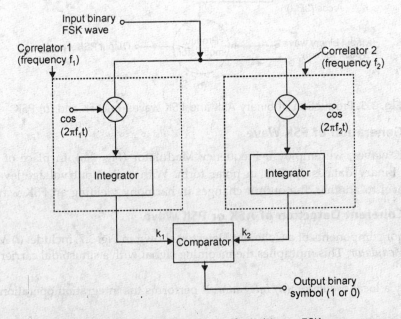

Fig. 3.8. Coherent demodulator for a binary FSK wave

Notes : (i) With regard to the coherent detectors described in Secs. 3.3.5 and 3.3.6, a general comment may be made that these detectors exclusively use *linear operations* and their function is based on the assumption that local carriers or signals are available which are ideally synchronized with the carriers at the transmitter.

(*ii*) Another important remark is concerned with explaining why these detectors are called "coherent". The operation of these detectors relies on two types of synchronization, viz., phase synchronization and timing synchronization. In *Phase Synchronization*, the carrier wave produced by the local oscillator is locked in phase with the one used in the modulator at the transmitter. For *Timing Synchronization*, the instant at which the decision is made in the receiver must be appropriately timed with respect to the switching instants between 1 and 0 in the binary signal fed to the modulator.

3.3.7. Non-coherent Detection of Binary ASK and FSK Waves

Need, Advantages and Limitations of Non-coherent Detection

Practically, a signal transmitted via a communication channel suffers a deterioration along the path not only due to channel noise but also owing to randomness of signal parameters. The major cause of this uncertainty is the distortion produced by the transmission medium. The worst-affected signal parameter is the phase, specially for narrow-band signals. The reasons are transmission over manifold variable-length paths, and rapidly changing delays in propagation medium whereby the phase variations in the received signal are not properly followed by the receiver.

A considerable simplification of circuit design is possible by altogether avoiding phase synchronization required in coherent demodulation. However, the design is made less sophisticated only at the expense of some degradation in noise performance of the receiver.

The Envelope Detection Principle

Envelope detectors are used for non-coherent detection of binary ASK and PSK waves. An envelope detector (Fig. 3.9) is so called because its output signal is the envelope of the input AM signal waveform. Referring to its circuit diagram in Fig. 3.9(*a*), during the positive half-cycle of the input signal, the diode D is forward biased. Then the capacitor C charges to peak value of the input signal. As the input signal decreases below the peak value, the diode becomes reverse biased. The capacitor then discharges through the load resistance R_L until the succeeding positive half cycle. Again when the input signal is greater than voltage across the capacitor, the diode starts conduction, repeating the above sequence of steps. For proper circuit operation, the charging time constant

$$R_s C << \frac{1}{f_c} \qquad \qquad ...(3.18)$$

where R_s is the internal impedance of the voltage source and $\frac{1}{f_c} = T$ is the period of the carrier wave. Thereafter the capacitor rapidly charges to the positive peak voltage. Also, the discharging time constant $R_L C$ must be sufficiently long for gradual discharge of capacitor between positive peaks of carrier wave. If these conditions are fulfilled, the output of the detector will be the envelope of the incoming AM wave.

Demodulation Methods

(*i*) An ASK wave can be demodulated non-coherently by straightway applying to an envelope detector.

(*ii*) For non-coherent demodulation of an FSK wave, the signal obtained at the receiver is applied to a bank of two matched filters. One of these matched filters is tuned to a frequency f_1 of the signal $A \cos (2\pi f_1 t)$ corresponding to the transmission of symbol 0, and the other is tuned to a different frequency f_2 of the signal $A \cos (2\pi f_2 t)$ pertaining to the transmission of symbol 1. The outputs from these two filters are fed to separate envelope detectors. The envelope detected waves are sampled. By comparison of the sampled outputs, it is found whether the output from the filter tuned to frequency f_1 is larger than that from the filter tuned to frequency f_2 or *vice versa*. If the tuner inequality holds, decision is taken for the binary symbol 1; if otherwise, symbol 0 is decided.

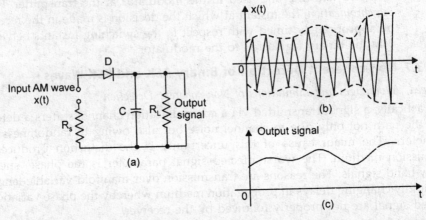

Fig. 3.9. Operation of an envelope detector: (a) Circuit diagram, (b) Input AM wave and (c) Output detected wave

(iii) A PSK wave cannot be demodulated non-coherently because its envelope is same for both symbols 1 and 0. Also, unlike an FSK wave, a single carrier frequency f_c is used for the two signal participants in a PSK wave modulation. So, a segregation of components based on frequency difference, as was done in FSK, is not possible.

Note : Non-coherent demodulation of ASK and FSK signals entails non-linear operations.

3.4 PROBABILISTIC APPROACH TO THE COHERENT DETECTION OF BINARY ASK WAVES

After surveying the elementary principles of modulation and demodulation of binary waves, both in coherent and non-coherent forms, let us now focus our attention on a more comprehensive examination of individual modulation techniques, in turn, starting with ASK.

Noise introduces two kinds of errors: (i) When the symbol 0 is transmitted and the receiver takes a wrong decision of symbol 1. Such an error is referred to as an *Error of the First Kind*.

(ii) Transmission of symbol 1 is detected as a symbol 0 by the receiver. This type of error is known as an *Error of the Second Kind*. For establishing optimization criterion of system performance, average probability of both types of error must be studied and analyzed to obtain the error minimization conditions. Such a criterion can be formulated by using statistical hypothesis testing procedures.

3.4.1. Probability of Error for a Binary PCM System

We investigate the performance of a binary PCM system. Referring to Fig. 3.7, the system is a correlation receiver which correlates the received signal $x(t)$ with stored replica of the known signal $s(t)$ {in place of $\cos(2\pi f_c t)$ in Fig. 3.7} in terms of a predetermined threshold λ. Symbol 1 is represented by the transmission of a signal A Volts, symbol 0 by switching off the signal. Symbols 1 and 0 are assumed to be equally probable. The transmission channel is assumed to be an Additive White Gaussian Noise (AWGN) channel and channel noise $n(t)$ is AWGN having zero mean and power spectral density = $N_0/2$.

Because the *a priori* probabilities of symbols 1 and 0 are equal, the probabilities of the errors of first and second kinds are same. The threshold λ is defined as

$$\lambda = \frac{1}{2} \int_0^{T_b} s^2(t)\, dt = \frac{A^2 T_b}{2} \qquad \qquad \qquad ...(3.19)$$

where T_t is the bit duration and $A^2 T_b$ represents the signal energy used in transmission of a symbol, 0 or 1.

During the transmission of symbol 0, only noise is transmitted and the received signal $x(t)$ is equal to the channel noise $n(t)$. The output of the correlator is

$$Y = A \int_0^{T_b} n(t)\, dt \qquad \qquad \qquad ...(3.20)$$

Because white noise $n(t)$ has zero mean, the mean value of output y is also zero. A *Conditional Mean* μ is then introduced. When the symbol 0 is sent, the conditional mean is

$$\mu_0 = E\left\{ \int_0^{T_b} N(t)\, dt \right\} = 0 \qquad \qquad \qquad ...(3.21)$$

where E stands for expectation, $N(t)$ represents a white noise process whose sample function is $n(t)$.

Corresponding to the conditional mean, we have the conditional variance σ_0^2 given by

$$\sigma_0^2 = E\left\{ \int_0^{T_b} \int_0^{T_b} N(t_1)\, N(t_2)\, dt \right\} \qquad \qquad \qquad ...(3.22)$$

where the double integration is used for squaring of the correlator output. The orders of expectation and integration operations can be interchanged to yield

$$\sigma_0^2 = \int_0^{T_b} \int_0^{T_b} E\{N(t_1)\, N(t_2)\}\, dt_1\, dt_2 \qquad \qquad \qquad ...(3.23)$$

$$= \int_0^{T_b} \int_0^{T_b} R_N(t_1 - t_2)\, dt_1\, dt_2 \qquad \qquad \qquad ...(3.24)$$

where $R_N(t_1 - t_2)$ denotes the ensemble averaged autocorrelation function of the white noise process $N(t)$.

Now from random theory, autocorrelation function and power spectral density of the random process constitute a Fourier transform pair. But with the proposition that power spectral density of $N(t)$ is $\frac{N_0}{2}$, the autocorrelation function R_N can be expressed as a delta function weighted by $\frac{N_0}{2}$ in the form

$$R_N(t_1 - t_2) = \frac{N_0}{2} \delta\{\tau - (t_1 - t_2)\} \qquad \qquad \qquad ...(3.25)$$

Making this substitution in the σ_0^2 equation and noting that the total area under the Dirac delta function $\delta\{\tau - (t_1 - t_2)\}$ equals unity, we obtain

$$\sigma_0^2 = \frac{A^2 T_b N_0}{2} \qquad \qquad \qquad ...(3.26)$$

Inasmuch as the white noise is Gaussian distributed, the correlator output too conforms to the Gaussian distribution function with a mean value of zero and variance

$$\sigma^2 = \frac{A^2 T_b N_0}{2} \qquad \qquad ...(3.27)$$

so that the probability density function of the correlator output for transmission of symbol 0 is described as

$$f_0(y) = \frac{1}{A\sqrt{\pi T_b N_0}} \exp\left(-\frac{y^2}{A^2 T_b N_0}\right) \qquad ...(3.28)$$

with its bell-shaped curve presented in Fig. 3.10. The hatched area represents the situation in which $y > \lambda$ so that there is a probability of a decision in favour of symbol 1.

The first conditional probability error, given that symbol 0 was transmitted, is

$$P_0 = \int_{\lambda}^{\infty} f_0(y)\,dy = \frac{1}{A\sqrt{\pi T_b N_0}} \int_{\frac{A^2 T_b}{2}}^{\infty} \exp\left(-\frac{y^2}{A^2 T_b N_0}\right) dy \quad ...(3.29)$$

Let us define

$$x = \frac{y}{A\sqrt{T_b N_0}} \qquad \qquad ...(3.30)$$

Then

$$P_0 = \frac{1}{\sqrt{\pi}} \int_{\frac{A}{2}\sqrt{\frac{T_b}{N_0}}}^{\infty} \exp(-x^2)\,dx \qquad ...(3.31)$$

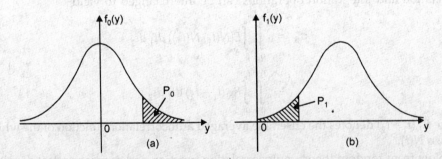

Fig. 3.10. Conditional probability of error: (a) Probability given that symbol 0 was transmitted (P_0), and (b) Probability given that symbol 1 was sent (P_1)

P_0 can be expressed in terms of the complementary error function defined as

$$erfc\,(u) = \frac{2}{\sqrt{\pi}} \int_{u}^{\infty} \exp(-x^2)\,dx \qquad ...(3.32)$$

This gives

$$P_0 = \frac{1}{2} erfc\left(\frac{1}{2}\sqrt{\frac{T_b}{N_0}}\right) \qquad \qquad ...(3.33)$$

3.4.2. Probability of Error for Binary ASK Signals

The function of a matched filter receiver, based on the correlation principle, in an AWGN ambient, is controlled by the ratio of signal energy to noise power spectral density, regardless of the signal waveform. This allows us to apply the probability expression for PCM, to the case of coherent binary ASK substituting signal energy for symbol 1 equalling $A_C^2 T_b/2$ in place of signal energy for symbol 1 in binary PCM which is $A^2 T_b/2$. This substitution leads us to the equation for average probability of bit error for binary ASK, i.e.,

$$P_b = \frac{1}{2} \, erfc\left\{\frac{1}{2}\left(\frac{A}{2}\sqrt{\frac{T_b}{N_0}}\right)\right\} \qquad \qquad ...(3.34)$$

The signal energy per bit is defined as

$$E_b = \int_0^{T_b} s_0^2(t)\,dt = \int_0^{T_b} s_1^2(t)\,dt = \frac{A_c^2 T_b}{2} \qquad \qquad ...(3.35)$$

In binary ASK, if both bits, 0 and 1, have equal probabilities, the signal energy alternates between 0, corresponding to the transmission of symbol 0, and $\dfrac{A^2 T_b}{4}$ for transmission of symbol 1. Then a more useful concept is the average signal energy per bit written as

$$E_{av} = \frac{A_c^2 T_b}{4} \qquad \qquad ...(3.36)$$

Hence the probability of bit error expression is transformed to

$$P_b = \frac{1}{2} \, erfc\left(\sqrt{\frac{E_{av}}{2N_0}}\right) \qquad \qquad ...(3.37)$$

3.5 PHASE-SHIFT KEYING

3.5.1. PSK Modulator Details

Figure 3.11 shows the elaborate block diagram of a PSK modulator. It contains several additional blocks as compared to the block diagram in Fig. 3.5(b), thus providing more functional capability. The *On-Off Signal Terminal* enables the carrier to be switched on and off depending on when it is desired to emit the PSK signal. The *Delay Adjuster* helps to compensate for the time delay when the bipolar data passes through the lowpass filter. Using this adjuster, synchronization of the switching of carrier on-off signal with input data can be effected. The *Lowpass Filter* serves to shape the spectral characteristics of the data. It also restricts the signal bandwidth preventing out-of-band emission from exceeding a prescribed value. The *Driver Amplifier*, essentially a D.C. amplifier with a temperature corrector, is incorporated in the assembly to provide proper signal level to the mixer. The *Mixer* has the role of the product modulator, giving a band-limited PSK signal. The *Bandpass Filter* is centred at the carrier frequency f_c having a wider bandwidth than PSK signal. It filters the extraneous signals produced by the mixer. The *Attenuator* is used for output level adjustment.

3.5.2. Coherent PSK Demodulator

With reference to the block diagram given in Fig. 3.12, the *Bandpass Filter* rejects unwanted neighbouring channel interferences and provides bandwidth limitation. The *Automatic Gain Control (AGC)* amplifier circuit levels the carrier over a broad dynamic range of input signal. The *Carrier Phase Recovery Circuit* extracts the carrier cos $(2\pi f_c t + \phi)$ from the input PSK wave. The *Mixer* performs the demodulation operation giving the binary bit stream. The *Lowpass Filter* sieves the out-of-band noise besides the high-frequency components of signal. *Bit Timing Recovery Circuit* obtains the bit timing clock from the PSK wave. The final stage is the *Decision Device*. Using the clock recovered by bit timing recovery circuit, the demodulated bit stream for the input PSK signal is regenerated by the decision device.

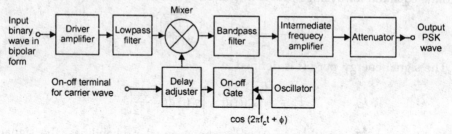

Fig. 3.11. Scheme of a PSK modulating section

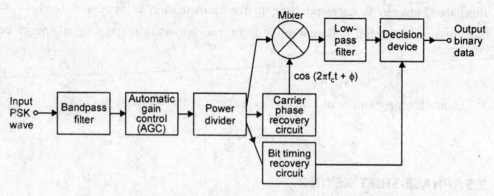

Fig. 3.12. Signal flow diagram of a coherent PSK demodulator

3.5.3. Average Probability of Bit Error

A figure of merit for assessing the performance of optimum coherent demodulator for a PSK wave over an Additive White Gaussian Noise (AWGN) channel, is the *Average Probability of Bit Error*, denoted by P_b and expressed as

$$P_b = Q\left(\sqrt{\frac{2E_b}{N_0}}\right) \qquad \qquad ...(3.38)$$

where $Q(y)$ = Gaussian integral function $- \frac{1}{\sqrt{2\pi}} \int\limits_{y}^{\infty} \exp\left(\frac{-x^2}{2}\right) dx$ and $x = \frac{z-\mu}{\sigma}$ with z

equal to the Decision variable, μ = Mean value of z, E_b = Energy per bit, N_0 = Noise

density and $y = \sqrt{\frac{2E_b}{N_0}}$.

In terms of the complementary error function erfc (y) given by

$$\text{erfc } (y) = \frac{1}{\sqrt{\pi}} \int\limits_{y}^{\infty} \exp(-z^2)\, dz \qquad \qquad ...(3.39)$$

we have
$$P_b = \frac{1}{2} \operatorname{erfc}\left(\sqrt{\frac{E_b}{N_0}}\right) \qquad \qquad ...(3.40)$$

An alternative expression for P_b as a function of bandwidth B and carrier-to-noise ratio (C/N) is

$$P_b = Q\left\{\sqrt{2T_bB\left(\frac{C}{N}\right)}\right\} \qquad \qquad ...(3.41)$$

In satellite communications, the bit duration-bandwidth product (T_bB) is chosen such that $1.1 \leq B \leq 1.4$.

3.5.4. Derivation of Error Rate Expression

To derive the expression for average probability of bit error (P_b), we consider the generalized two-path coherent correlation receiver for detection of binary PSK/FSK signals shown in Fig. 3.13 (see also Fig. 3.8).

We make the postulates that: (i) the receiver is furnished with replicas of transmitted signals $x_0(t)$ and $x_1(t)$, and (ii) the time constant of the execution of decision by the receiver coincides with the bit timing of the transmitted signal. The two assumptions tantamount to the synchronization of the receiver with the transmitter.

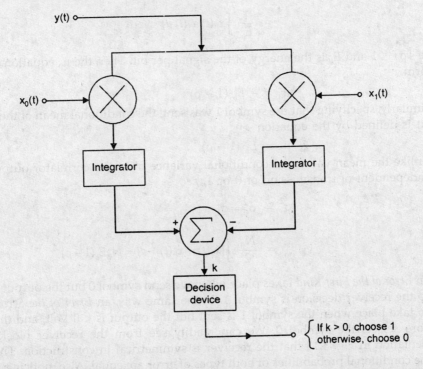

Fig. 3.13. Generalized coherent correlation receiver for binary decision making

The output of the receiver can be written as

$$k = \int_0^{T_b} y(t)\{x_1(t) - x_0(t)\}\, dt \qquad \qquad ...(3.42)$$

where $y(t)$ is the received signal plus noise, and $x_0(t)$, $x_1(t)$ are transmitted signal replicas. Assuming equal probability of occurrence of symbols 1 and 0, the output k is compared with a preselected threshold level of zero Volt. If $k > 0$, the receiver chooses symbol 1; when $k < 0$, the symbol 0 is chosen. If we assume that the channel noise is Gaussian, the output k will also obey Gaussian distribution.

The mean value of the receiver output depends on which symbol, 0 or 1, was transmitted. If we specify that the symbol 0 was sent, the conditional mean of the correlation output is defined as

$$\mu_0 = \int_0^{T_b} x_0(t) \{x_1(t) - x_0(t)\} \, dt \qquad \qquad ...(3.43)$$

We define the correlation coefficient ρ of the signals $x_0(t)$ and $x_1(t)$ as

$$\rho = \frac{\int_0^{T_b} x_0(t) x_1(t) \, dt}{\left\{ \int_0^{T_b} x_0^2(t) \, dt \right\}^{\frac{1}{2}} \left\{ \int_0^{T_b} x_1^2(t) \, dt \right\}^{\frac{1}{2}}} \qquad \qquad ...(3.44)$$

$$= \frac{1}{E_b} \int_0^{T_b} x_0(t) x_1(t) \, dt \qquad \qquad ...(3.45)$$

where $|\rho| \leq 1$ and E_b is the energy of the signal per bit. Then the μ_0 equation reduces to the form

$$\mu_0 = -E_b (1 - \rho) \qquad \qquad ...(3.46)$$

Similarly, specifying that the symbol 1 was sent, the conditional mean of the correlator output is defined by the equation

$$\mu_1 = E_b (1 - \rho) \qquad \qquad ...(3.47)$$

Unlike the mean value, the conditional variance σ^2 of the correlator output is same and independent of transmission of 0 or 1, $i.e.$,

$$\sigma^2 = \sigma_0^2 = \sigma_1^2 \qquad \qquad ...(3.48)$$

$$= \frac{N_0}{2} \int_0^{T_b} \{x_1(t) - x_0(t)\}^2 \, dt = N_0 E_b(1 - \rho) \qquad \qquad ...(3.49)$$

An *Error of the First Kind* takes place when we send symbol 0 but the output is > 0 Volt and so the receiver decision is symbol 1. In the same way, an *Error of the Second Kind* is said to take place when the symbol 1 is sent but the output is < 0 Volt, and the receiver therefore selects the symbol 0. We can readily see from the receiver block diagram representation in Fig. 3.13 that the receiver is symmetrical in construction. This implies that the conditional probabilities of both types of error are equal. Also, noticing that 1 and 0 have equal likelihood to occur, the choice of a threshold value of zero Volt is legitimate. We also recognize that the correlator output is distributed according to the Gaussian function having conditional mean $= E_b(1 - \rho)$ and variance $= N_0 E_b(1 - \rho)$. Then bearing in mind that the correlator output is a Gaussian random variable with mean μ and variance σ^2, if z denotes the decision variable, the probability of error is given by

$$P = \frac{1}{\sqrt{2\pi}\sigma} \int_{-\infty}^{0} \exp\left\{-\frac{(z-\mu)^2}{2\sigma^2}\right\} dz \qquad ...(3.50)$$

With the transformation

$$x = \frac{z-\mu}{\sigma} \qquad ...(3.51)$$

we get

$$P = \frac{1}{\sqrt{2\pi}} \int_{\mu/\sigma}^{\infty} \exp\left(\frac{-x^2}{2}\right) dx \qquad ...(3.52)$$

$$= \frac{1}{\sqrt{2\pi}} \int_{\sqrt{\frac{E_b(1-\rho)}{N_0}}}^{\infty} \exp\left(\frac{-x^2}{2}\right) dx = \frac{1}{\sqrt{2\pi}} \int_{y}^{\infty} \exp\left(\frac{-x^2}{2}\right) dx \qquad ...(3.53)$$

where

$$y = \sqrt{\frac{E_b(1-\rho)}{N_0}} \qquad ...(3.54)$$

Using the transformation $x = \sqrt{2z}$, we have

$$\text{erfc}(y) = \frac{2}{\sqrt{2\pi}} \int_{\sqrt{2}y}^{\infty} \exp\left(\frac{-x^2}{2}\right) dx = 2Q(\sqrt{2}y) \qquad ...(3.55)$$

or

$$Q(y) = \frac{1}{2}\text{erfc}\left(\frac{y}{\sqrt{2}}\right) = \frac{1}{2}\text{erfc}\left\{\sqrt{\frac{E_b(1-\rho)}{2N_0}}\right\} \qquad ...(3.56)$$

For coherent detection of binary PSK signals, $x_0(t) = -x_1(t)$ and $\rho = -1$. Such a pair of equal energy signals having a correlation coefficient $\rho = -1$, are known as *Antipodal Signals*. Effectively, the coherent receiver of Fig. 3.13 reduces to the simple one-path receiver shown in Figs. 3.5(b) and 3.12. Putting the value of $\rho = -1$, the average probability of bit error in a binary PSK receiver is given by

$$P_b = \frac{1}{2}\text{erfc}\left(\sqrt{\frac{E_b}{N_0}}\right) \qquad ...(3.57)$$

3.5.5. Direct Encoding

As we know, in binary PSK modulation, the inut data bits cause discrete changes of π radians in the phase of the carrier wave. The direct coding procedure involves a one-to-one mapping of the binary data into absolute phase of channel signal, as given below:

Binary Data Sequence: 1   1   0   0   1   1   1

Phase Sequence of

Channel Signal: π π 0   0 π π π

Because two signals $x_1(t)$ and $x_2(t)$ separated by π radians in phase, are used in PSK modulation to represent binary digits 1 and 0, it is logical to enquire how will the demodulator know as to which waveform denotes which bit. Failure to correctly judge and decide about this identity, creates confusion about whether the recovered signal is in proper form (in phase with transmitted signal) or inverted form (out of phase with this signal), leading to *Phase Ambiguity*.

The problem of ambiguous phase is solved by incorporating a known sequence of code word in the bipolar data stream, the so called *Unique Word* (UW). The demodulator circuit contains a UW detector along with a complement UW detector. For data recovery in correct state, UW detector indicates that the recovered carrier is in phase. Then data are used as such. If data are recovered in inverted form, the complement UW detector tells us that the recovered carrier is out of phase and inversion must be done.

3.5.6. Differential Encoding and Differentially Encoded Phase-Shift Keying (DCPSK)

In this method, the digital information contained in binary data is encoded in terms of signal transitions rather than absolute values. According to our convenience, we may decide to denote by symbol 0, a change of phase equal to π radians with respect to the phase in the preceding bit duration T_b or signalling interval T_s. A change of zero radians or no change will be represented by the symbol 1. These symbols can also be defined in the reverse way. Thus we have a one-to-one mapping of the bit into the phase shift between two successive signals obeying the rule:

Bit	Phase Shift
0	π
1	0

When differentially encoded, the bit sequence of Sec. 3.5.5 gives the following phase sequence and encoded binary data, assuming that the previously encoded bit was 0:

Binary Stream:	1	1	0	0	1	1	1
Phase Sequence:	π	0	π	0	π	0	0
Encoded Data:	0	1	0	1	0	1	1

Figure 3.14 presents the block diagram of a *PSK Differential Encoder*. One input to the differential encoding logic circuit is the binary data b_k and its second input is the delayed version of previous encoded bit c_k which after delay by one-bit duration T_b, becomes C_{k-1}. The logic circuit performs an exclusive OR operation on b_k and c_{k-1} giving the next encoded bit by negation according to the logic function

$$c_k = \overline{b_k \oplus c_{k-1}} \qquad \qquad ...(3.58)$$

The *PSK Differential Decoder* is shown in Fig. 3.15.

For Differentially Encoded PSK (DCPSK), the probability of error using coherent detection is

$$P_b = 2Q\left(\sqrt{\frac{2E_b}{N_0}}\right) = \text{erfc}\left(\sqrt{\frac{E_b}{N_0}}\right) \qquad \qquad ...(3.59a)$$

which is approximately double of that for PSK. This is because the decision has to be made from the signals received in two consecutive signalling intervals. Consequently, bit errors tend to occur in pairs.

3.5.7. Differential Phase-Shift Keying (DPSK)

It is a signalling technique in which differential decoding is not carried out on demodulated data but on the received signal directly, without

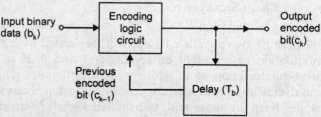

Fig. 3.14. A differential encoder for PSK signal

the aid of a carrier reference, thus providing non-coherent demodulation. This provides a perspective of DPSK as a "non-coherent" version of PSK. It operates on the assumption that the unknown phase ϕ of the received signal is maintained at a constant level over two-bit intervals.

The layout of a DPSK demodulator is shown in Fig. 3.16. The input DPSK signal is multiplied by its own version delayed by T_b, followed by integration which also lowpass filters the second harmonic in the product. If ϕ denotes the phase difference between the phase angles of the carrier in DPSK signal and its delayed version, the output of the integrator is proportional to cos ϕ. When $\phi = 0$ (symbol 0), cos $\phi = 1$ which is positive. But when $\phi = \pi$ (symbol 1), cos $\phi = -1$ which is negative. Comparison of the integrator output with a threshold or decision level of zero Volt, helps us to reconstruct the binary information sequence.

The average probability of bit error for a DPSK signal is

$$P_b = \frac{1}{2} \exp\left(-\frac{E_b}{N_0}\right) \qquad\qquad ...(3.59b)$$

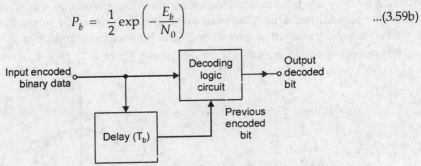

Fig. 3.15. A PSK differential decoder

Clearly, the bit error rate is higher for DPSK than for DCPSK or PSK. In so far as the noise performance is concerned, the main difference between DPSK and coherent binary PSK does not lie in the differential encoding but in the manner the reference signal is extracted for the phase detection of the received signal. During evaluation of the product of DPSK signals in successive bit duration, the AWGN contamination is also multiplied making the variance of AWGN twice as much.

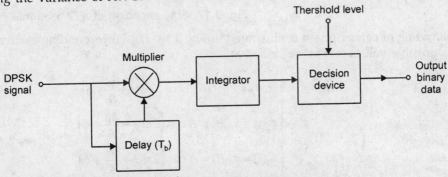

Fig. 3.16. DPSK demodulator flow diagram

3.6 QUATERNARY PHASE-SHIFT KEYING (QPSK)

3.6.1. QPSK Signal as a Linear Combination of PSK Signals

A common feature of the digital modulation techniques described above is that none of them is spectrally efficient. Lack of spectral efficiency implies that available bandwidth is not harnessed to its maximum limit. Spectral efficiency can be acquired by adopting baseband signal shaping together with bandwidth conserving linear modulation schemes. Quaternary Phase-Shift Keying, also called Quadriphase-Shift Keying with the acronym QPSK, is a spectrally efficient modulation technique for transmission of digital data.

Quaternary modulation is a special case of M-ary modulation in which $M = 4$. Since $M = 2^m$, this technique uses four blocks, each consisting of $m = 2$ bits or 1 dibit; a dibit is a pair of bits. The four dibits employed are: 00, 01, 10 and 11. The four are represented by four carrier signals. These are sinusoidal signals of constant amplitude but different phases:

$$x_m(t) = A \cos(2\pi f_c t + \phi_m + \phi), \quad 0 \le t \le T_s \qquad \ldots (3.60)$$

where we must distinguish between initial phase ϕ of the carrier and the modulation phase ϕ_m.

The dibit symbols can be mapped in several ways. In *Gray Encoding*, two symbols differing by only one bit, are represented by adjoining phases, as shown in Fig. 3.17. Since errors due to additive white Gaussian noise are likely to occur when the adjacent phase is chosen for the transmitted phase, only one-bit error is introduced in m-bit symbol.

Representing the four symbols by the phase ϕ_m, $m = 1, 2, 3, 4$, we can write

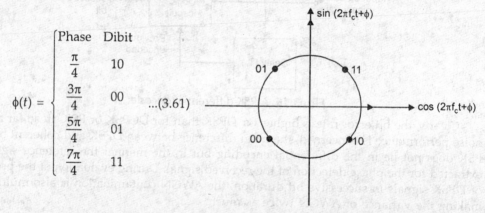

$$\phi(t) = \begin{cases} \text{Phase} & \text{Dibit} \\ \dfrac{\pi}{4} & 10 \\ \dfrac{3\pi}{4} & 00 \\ \dfrac{5\pi}{4} & 01 \\ \dfrac{7\pi}{4} & 11 \end{cases} \qquad \ldots (3.61)$$

Fig. 3.17. Gray encoding of a QPSK signal

The coding of carrier phase is illustrated in Fig. 3.18. The corresponding carrier with its four possible values can be described as

$$f(t) = \begin{cases} x_1(t) = x_{10}(t) = A \cos\left(2\pi f_c t + \dfrac{\pi}{4} + \phi\right) \\[2mm] x_2(t) = x_{00}(t) = A \cos\left(2\pi f_c t + \dfrac{3\pi}{4} + \phi\right) \\[2mm] x_3(t) = x_{01}(t) = A \cos\left(2\pi f_c t + \dfrac{5\pi}{4} + \phi\right) \\[2mm] x_4(t) = x_{11}(t) = A \cos\left(2\pi f_c t + \dfrac{7\pi}{4} + \phi\right) \end{cases} \qquad \ldots (3.62)$$

where $0 \le t \le T_s$.

Now, we may expand the cosine term and rewrite the equation for $x(t)$ as

$$x(t) = A\{\cos(2\pi f_c t + \phi) \cos \phi_m - \sin(2\pi f_c t + \phi) \sin \phi_m\} \qquad \ldots (3.63)$$

obtaining

$$x(t) = \begin{cases} x_1(t) = x_{10}(t) = \dfrac{A}{\sqrt{2}} \cos{(2\pi f_c t + \phi)} - \dfrac{A}{\sqrt{2}} \sin{(2\pi f_c t + \phi)} \\[2mm] x_2(t) = x_{00}(t) = -\dfrac{A}{\sqrt{2}} \cos{(2\pi f_c t + \phi)} - \dfrac{A}{\sqrt{2}} \sin{(2\pi f_c t + \phi)} \\[2mm] x_3(t) = x_{01}(t) = -\dfrac{A}{\sqrt{2}} \cos{(2\pi f_c t + \phi)} + \dfrac{A}{\sqrt{2}} \sin{(2\pi f_c t + \phi)} \\[2mm] x_4(t) = x_{11}(t) = \dfrac{A}{\sqrt{2}} \cos{(2\pi f_c t + \phi)} + \dfrac{A}{\sqrt{2}} \sin{(2\pi f_c t + \phi)} \end{cases} \qquad ...(3.64)$$

In this representation, $x(t)$ in each of its forms has an in-phase component equal to $A \cos{(2\pi f_c t + \phi)}$ and a quadrature component equal to $A \sin{(2\pi f_c t + \phi)}$. Thus it can be considered as a linear combination of two PSK signals in phase quadrature. This description of QPSK wave helps us to construct the block diagrams for QPSK modulator and demodulator, as shown in Figs. 3.19 and 3.20 respectively.

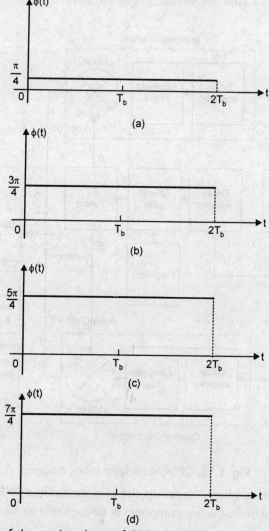

Fig. 3.18. Coding of the carrier phase of QPSK: (a) dibit 10, (b) 00, (c) 01 and (d) 11

3.6.2. Quaternary Modulation

A *QPSK Modulator*, Fig. 3.19, consists of a serial-to-parallel converter, an oscillator with a 90° hybrid supplying two carrier waves in phase quadrature, a pair of product modulators and a power combiner or summer. The *Serial-to-Parallel Converter* transforms each pair of bits of input data stream into two separate bits. One of these bits is applied to the in-phase channel to modulate the carrier $A \cos (2\pi f_c t + \phi)$ and the other to the quadrature channel $A \sin (2\pi f_c t + \phi)$, each at one half the original rate. Thus the signalling interval in QPSK is $T_s = 2 \times$ Bit duratin (T_b). Thus for a specified bit rate $\dfrac{1}{T_b}$, bandwidth requirement of a QPSK signalling scheme is $\dfrac{1}{2}$ of a PSK system. In other words, bandwidth remaining constant, the information-carrying capacity of a QPSK wave is double that of a PSK wave. This is the cause for saving in bandwidth.

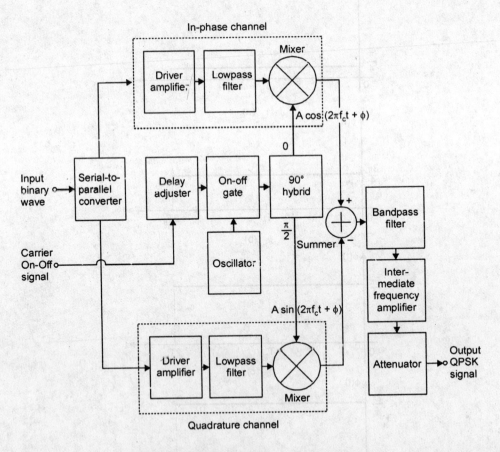

Fig. 3.19. QPSK Modulator block diagram

Finally, the power combiner sums up the two modulated PSK waves forming the QPSK signal. The function of other components is the same as described in Sec. 3.5.1.

3.6.3. Coherent Detection of Quaternary Modulated Waves

The *Coherent QPSK Demodulator* (Fig. 3.20) consists of two correlators in a parallel configuration. One correlator calculates the cosine of the carrier phase angle and the other computes its sine. The 90° hybrid supplies quadrature reference carriers to demodulate the PSK signals in the in-phase and quadrature channels. The pair of decision devices uniquely resolves one of the four transmitted phase angles. The demodulated bit streams are regenerated at the decision devices by the symbol clock obtained from the symbol timing recovery circuit. By recombination of two streams, the binary data stream is reconstructed.

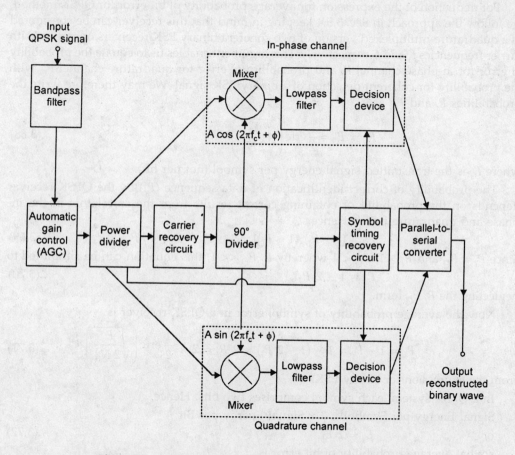

Fig. 3.20. Architecture of a Coherent QPSK demodulator

To summarize, a QPSK signalling scheme is equivalent to two binary PSK systems operating in parallel, employing two carrier waves in phase quadrature. It is a *quadrature-carrier multiplexing scheme.*

3.6.4. Probability of Error

For a coherent QPSK system, the average probability of symbol error is

$$P_s = 2Q\left(\sqrt{\frac{E_s}{N_0}}\right) \qquad \ldots(3.65)$$

where E_s is the energy per symbol (instead of energy E_b per bit in PSK) and N_0 is noise density.

Using Gray encoding, the average probability of bit error becomes

$$P_b = \frac{1}{2} P_s = Q\left(\sqrt{\frac{E_s}{N_0}}\right) = \frac{1}{2}\operatorname{erfc}\left(\sqrt{\frac{E_b}{N_0}}\right) \qquad ...(3.66)$$

In terms of carrier-to-noise ratio (C/N), we have

$$P_b = Q\left\{\sqrt{2\,T_b\,B\,(C/N)}\right\} \qquad ...(3.67)$$

which shows that for the same channel bandwidth, bit rate obtained with QPSK = 2 × Bit rate with PSK.

For deduction of the expression for average probability of bit error for QPSK method, we follow the approach in Sec. 3.5.4 keeping in mind that this receiver can be considered as a quadrature-multiplexed version of two coherent binary PSK receivers operating with carrier frequencies f_1 and f_2 respectively. This argument enables us to equate the probability of error for in-phase channel P_I and probability of error for quadrature channel P_Q with the probability for coherent detection of a binary PSK signal. We may therefore write the probabilities P_I and P_Q as

$$P_I = P_Q = \frac{1}{2}\operatorname{erfc}\left(\sqrt{\frac{E_s}{2\,N_0}}\right) \qquad ...(3.68)$$

where E_s is the transmitted signal energy per symbol (not per bit).

The probability of correct identification of data sequence (P_c) by the QPSK receiver depends on the probability of obtaining correct results from the correlators in the in-phase and quadrature paths. Hence.

$$P_c = (1 - P_I)\,(1 - P_Q) = 1 - P_Q - P_I - P_I\,P_Q \qquad ...(3.69)$$

Since $P_I = P_Q$ and $P_I > 1$, $P_Q < 1$ whereby $P_I\,P_Q \ll 1$, this equation can be simplified to

$$P_c = 1 - 2\,P_I \qquad ...(3.70)$$

neglecting the $P_I\,P_Q$ term.

Now the average probability of symbol error in a QPSK receiver is

$$P_s = 1 - P_c = 1 - (1 - 2\,P_I) = 2\,P_I = 2 \times \frac{1}{2}\operatorname{erfc}\left(\sqrt{\frac{E_s}{2\,N_0}}\right) \qquad ...(3.71)$$

from the expression for binary PSK.

In a QPSK system, each symbol comprises two bits. Hence,

Signal Energy per Symbol = 2 × Signal Energy per Bit

or $\qquad\qquad\qquad E_s = 2\,E_b \qquad\qquad\qquad\qquad\qquad\qquad\qquad\qquad ...(3.72)$

so that average probability of bit error is

$$P_b = \operatorname{erfc}\left(\sqrt{\frac{E_b}{N_0}}\right) \qquad ...(3.73)$$

3.6.5. Phase Ambiguity Resolution

Let us consider the QPSK signal

$$x_m(t) = A\cos\left(2\pi f_c\,t + \phi_n + \phi\right),\ 0 \le t \le T_s \qquad ...(3.74)$$

where $\qquad\qquad \phi_m = (2m - 1)\,\dfrac{\pi}{4},\ m = 1, 2, 3, 4. \qquad\qquad\qquad ...(3.75)$

Taking the initial phase ϕ as a reference standard, the phase of the received carrier ϕ_r follows the equation

$$\phi_r = \phi + \frac{n\pi}{2}, \; n = 0, 1, 2, 3. \qquad \qquad ...(3.76)$$

i.e., ϕ_r acquires one of the four possible values :

$$\phi_r = \phi, \; \phi + \frac{\pi}{2}, \; \phi + \pi, \; \phi + \frac{3\pi}{2} \qquad \qquad ...(3.77)$$

As a result, there is a *fourfold phase ambiguity.*

Let us denote the digits of the in-phase channel by I and those of the quadrature channel by Q. Let subscripts m and d apply to modulated and demodulated forms respectively. In this terminology, when $\phi_r = \phi$ (Fig. 3.21 (a)), $I_d = I_m$, $Q_d = Q_m$. But when $\phi_r = \phi + \dfrac{\pi}{2}$ (Fig. 3.21 (b)), the modulated signal $x_{10}(t)$, $x_{00}(t)$, $x_{01}(t)$, $x_{11}(t)$ will yield after demodulation and decoding the signal $x_{00}(t)$, $x_{01}(t)$, $x_{11}(t)$, $x_{10}(t)$. Hence the demodulated I-channel will be in phase with the transmitted Q-channel whereas the transmitted Q-channel will be π radians phase-shifted relative to the modulated I channel. Aftr resolving the phase ambiguity, the correct I and Q digits will be

$$I = I_m = \overline{Q_d} \qquad \qquad ...(3.78)$$
$$Q = Q_m = I_d \qquad \qquad ...(3.79)$$

where the bar sign denotes the complement or inversion of the respective quantity, *i.e.,* $\bar{1} = 0$ and $\bar{0} = 1$.

Proceeding on lines similar to PSK demodulation, the phase confusion can be surmounted by using either identical or different unique word patterns in I-and Q-channels. Necessary decision for unique word detection can be taken from the Hamming distances between the demodulator I-and Q-streams and the known unique word patterns stored in the I-and Q-channel unique word correlators.

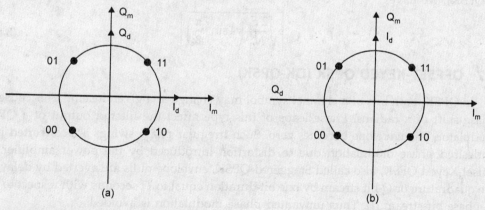

Fig. 3.21. Illustrating QPSK phase ambiguity : (a) Zero ambiguity $\rightarrow I_d = I_m$, $Q_d = Q_m$;

and (b) Ambiguity of $\dfrac{\pi}{2} \rightarrow I_d = Q_m$, $Q_d = I_m$

Another remedy to phase evasion is differential encoding and decoding (Fig. 3.22). In Fig. 3.22 (a), IQ stands for the input symbol or dibit, I_2Q_2 is the encoded symbol and I_1Q_1 the previous encoded symbol. Likewise, in Fig. 3.22 (b), IQ is the symbol in the received QPSK signal, I_2Q_2 is the decoded symbol and I_1Q_1 the preceding received symbol. The operations of encoder and decoder are similar to those described in Sec. 3.5.6.

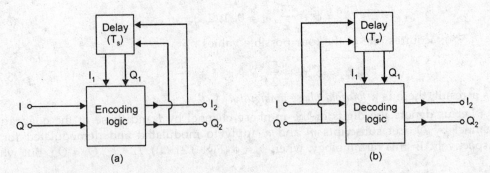

Fig. 3.22. QPSK differential systems : (*a*) Encoder and (*b*) Decoder

For Differential Encoding QPSK with coherent demodulation (DCQPSK), the average probability of symbol error is

$$P_s = 4Q\left(\sqrt{\frac{E_s}{N_0}}\right) \qquad\qquad ...(3.80)$$

using usual notation. The value of P_s is twice that for coherent QPSK. This is expected to be so because of involvement of two successive symbols in the decision making process, inducing the pairing of symbol errors.

Using Gray encoding in DCQPSK, the formula for average probability of bit error can be written as

$$P_b = \frac{1}{2} P_s = 2 Q\left(\sqrt{\frac{E_s}{N_0}}\right) \simeq 2Q\left(\sqrt{\frac{2 E_b}{N_0}}\right) \simeq \text{erfc}\left(\sqrt{\frac{E_b}{N_0}}\right) \qquad ...(3.81)$$

In the case of differential encoding QPSK employing non-coherent demodulation (DQPSK), we have

$$P_b \simeq Q\left[\sqrt{\frac{2 E_b}{N_0}\left(4\sin^2\frac{\pi}{8}\right)}\right] \qquad\qquad ...(3.82)$$

3.7 OFFSET-KEYED QPSK (OK-QPSK)

In QPSK, both bits of a channel symbol may change at a given instant. This causes a phase shift of π radians. Phase leaps of this type affect the filtered output of a QPSK modulator. The envelope becomes zero. Such irregular phase swings are converted into undesired phase modulation due to distortion introduced by the power amplifier. In Offset-Keyed QPSK, also called Staggered QPSK, envelope nulls are averted by delaying the quadrature or Q-bit stream by one bit duration equal to T_b seconds with respect to the in-phase bit stream (*I*). Thus unwanted phase modulation is avoided.

Power spectral density is not altered by creating this difference in time alignment between *I* and *Q* channel data streams. Power spectral density of OK-QPSK is therefore the same as that of QPSK. Moreover, since orthogonality between *I*- and *Q*-bit streams is protected, the average probabilities of bit error for OK-QPSK and QPSK are intrinsically equal.

3.7.1. OK-QPSK Modulator

Elementary block diagram of an OK-QPSK modulator is depicted in Fig. 3.23 to explain its working mechanism. Other components may be included as in Fig. 3.19. Notice the placement of the delay element.

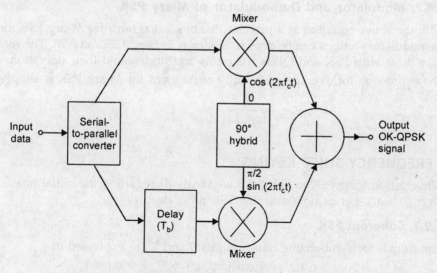

Fig. 3.23. Block diagram of an OK-QPSK modulator

3.7.2. OK-QPSK Demodulator

The detector for OK-QPSK is shown in Fig. 3.24. The reader may note the delay element in upper branch and compare this with Fig. 3.20.

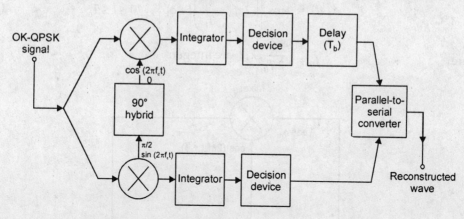

Fig. 3.24. Block diagram of an OK-QPSK demodulator

3.8   M-ARY PHASE-SHIFT KEYING

3.8.1. General Waveform of M-ary PSK

After familiarizing ourselves with the first principles of PSK and QPSK, let us now approach the general modulation technique, M-ary Phase-Shift Keying ($M = 2^m$) called M-ary PSK, epitomized by the equation

$$x_m(t) = A \cos (2\pi f_c t + \phi_m + \phi), \qquad 0 \le t \le T_s \qquad \qquad \text{...(3.83)}$$

which can be rewritten as

$$x_m(t) = \cos (2\pi f_c t + \phi) (A \cos \phi_m) - \sin (2\pi f_c t + \phi) (A \sin \phi_m) \qquad \text{...(3.84)}$$

3.8.2. Modulator and Demodulator of *M*-ary PSK

With the above equation as a premise, the block diagrams for *M*-ary PSK modulator and demodulator sections can be drawn as shown in Figs. 3.25 and 3.26. The reader may compare these with PSK and QPSK diagrams and understand their operation.

The expression for average probability of bit error for *M*-ary PSK is simply

$$P_b \simeq \frac{P_s}{\log_2 M} \qquad \qquad ...(3.85)$$

using Gray encoding

3.9 FREQUENCY-SHIFT KEYING

While introducing FSK in Sec. 3.2.3 we tacitly disregarded the initial phase ϕ_1, ϕ_2 of signals $x_1(t)$, $x_2(t)$. Let us now examine FSK more deeply.

3.9.1. Coherent FSK

The signals for symbolizing binary digits 0 and 1 are expressed as

$$x_1(t) = A \cos(2\pi f_1 t + \phi_1), \qquad 0 < t \le T_b \qquad ...(3.86)$$
$$x_2(t) = A \cos(2\pi f_2 t + \phi_2), \qquad 0 < t \le T_b \qquad ...(3.87)$$

Here $f_1 \ne f_2$. Information is borne by the frequencies, not phase. By appropriate frequency selection, signals $x_1(t)$ and $x_2(t)$ can be made orthogonal over a sampling interval. Such frequency-orthogonal waveforms can be represented as

$$x_k(t) = \cos\left\{\left(2\pi f_0 + \frac{k\pi}{T_b}\right)t + \phi_k\right\}, \qquad 0 \le t \le T_b \qquad ...(3.88)$$

where

$$f_0 = \frac{1}{2T_b}, k, l \text{ are integers} \qquad ...(3.89)$$

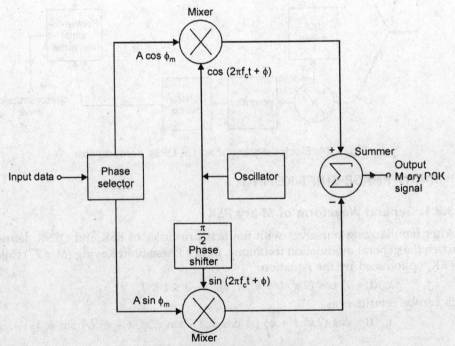

Fig. 3.25. *M*-ary PSK modulator

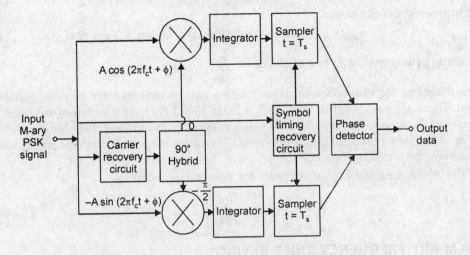

Fig. 3.26. *M*-ary PSK demodulator

For coherent orthogonal FSK, the average probability of bit error is

$$P_b = Q\left(\sqrt{\frac{E_b}{N_0}}\right) \qquad \qquad ...(3.90)$$

This expression can be straightforward deduced from the discussion of the generalized coherent receiver in Sec. 3.5.4. Since the frequencies f_1 and f_2 of the FSK signal are generally spaced far apart, the justification of treating $x_0(t)$ and $x_1(t)$ as *orthogonal signals* holds well. But the meaning of this orthogonality is that the correlation coefficient $\rho = 0$ whereby the average probability of bit error for a coherent binary FSK receiver is simply

$$P_b = \frac{1}{2} \operatorname{erfc}\left(\sqrt{\frac{E_b}{2 N_0}}\right) \qquad \qquad ...(3.91)$$

3.9.2. Non-coherent FSK

When knowledge of initial phases ϕ_1, ϕ_2 is either not necessary or cannot be accurately obtained, non-coherent demodulation is used. We assume that the initial phase is a random variable having a uniform probability density function $\frac{1}{2\pi}$ so that

$$p(\phi_1) = \frac{1}{2\pi}, \quad 0 \le \phi_1 \le 2\pi \qquad \qquad ...(3.92)$$

$$p(\phi_2) = \frac{1}{2\pi}, \quad 0 \le \phi_2 \le 2\pi \qquad \qquad ...(3.93)$$

Considering the FSK wave

$$x_m(t), m = 1, 2 \text{ with } f_1 \ne f_2, \qquad \qquad ...(3.94)$$

we may write

$$x_m(t) = A \cos (2\pi f_m t + \phi_m), \quad 0 \le t \le T_b \qquad \ldots(3.95)$$

which gives upon expansion

$$x_m(t) = (A \cos \phi_m) \cos (2\pi f_m t) - (A \sin \phi_m) \sin (2\pi f_m t) \qquad \ldots(3.96)$$

Assuming orthogonality, f_m is a multiple of $\dfrac{1}{T_b}$.

Block diagrams for non-coherent demodulators can be sketched for an orthogonal FSK signal. These are presented in Figs. 3.27, 3.28. In Fig. 3.27, four correlators are used. The purpose of the square-law detectors following integrators, is to eliminate phase dependence. In Fig. 3.28, two matched filters are used. Envelope detectors play the same role as square-law detectors in Fig. 3.27.

The average probability of bit error for non-coherent FSK is

$$P_b = \frac{1}{2} \exp\left(-\frac{E_b}{2N_0}\right) \qquad \ldots(3.97)$$

3.10 *M*-ARY FREQUENCY-SHIFT KEYING

Just as binary PSK was generalized to *M*-ary PSK, similarly we seek a generalization of orthogonal binary FSK or orthogonal *M*-ary FSK embracing $M = 2^m$ symbols designated by *M* waveforms :

$$x_m(t) = A \cos (2\pi f_c t + \phi_m), \text{ where } m = 1, 2, 3, \ldots M; \qquad \ldots(3.98)$$
$$0 \le t \le T_s \qquad \ldots(3.99)$$

and

$$\int_0^{T_s} x_i(t)\, x_j(t)\, dt = \begin{cases} E_s, & i = j \\ 0, & i \ne j \end{cases} \qquad \ldots(3.100)$$

f_m is a multiple of $\dfrac{1}{2T_s}$ and E_s is the energy per symbol.

3.10.1. Coherent *M*-ary FSK

The coherent *M*-ary FSK detector is analogous to the binary FSK demodulator described in Sec 3.3.6. The average probability of bit error is given by

$$P_b = \frac{2^{m-1}}{2^m - 1} P_s \qquad \ldots(3.101)$$

It is found that by increasing the number of waveforms, for instance from $M = 2$ onwards, the ratio $\dfrac{E_b}{N_0}$ decreases accompanied by an increased bandwidth. Thus this scheme conserves power and trades it with a higher transmission bandwidth.

3.10.2. Non-coherent *M*-ary FSK

Like the detector described in Sec. 3.9.2, the non-coherent orthogonal *M*-ary FSK consists of a bank of 2 *M* correlators, arranged as in Fig. 3.27. The minimum frequency spacing for this case is $2\pi/T_s$ radian/sec and the bit error probability is once again

$$P_b = \frac{2^{m-1}}{2^m - 1} P_s \qquad \ldots(3.102)$$

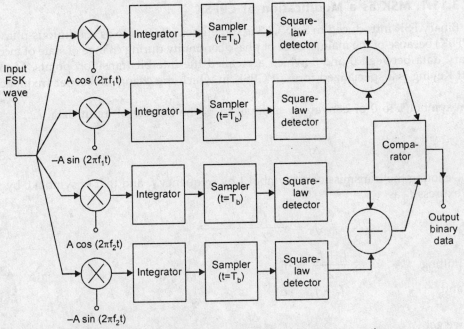

Fig. 3.27. Non-coherent demodulator for FSK using correlators

3.11 MINIMUM SHIFT KEYING

This is a power-and bandwidth-efficient quadrature carrier modulation scheme which can be treated as a special case of continuous-phase FSK (CPFSK) or QPSK.

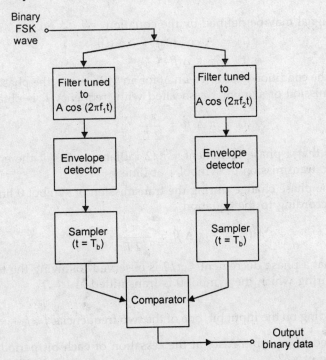

Fig. 3.28. Non-coherent demodulator for FSK using matched filters

3.11.1. MSK as a Modification of CPFSK

Binary FSK introduced in Sec. 3.2.3 is sometimes referred to as continuous-phase FSK (CPFSK) because of the maintenance of phase continuity during change of state of incoming binary data between 0 and 1 which are called the interbit transition points. Minimum Shift Keying is a specialized form of CPSK in which the change in carrier frequency (Δf) from symbol 1 to 0 or conversely is equal to $\dfrac{1}{2}$ the bit rate of input data, *i.e.*,

$$\Delta f = \frac{1}{2T_b} \qquad \qquad ...(3.103)$$

Denoting the transmission of symbol 1 by frequency f_1 and that of symbol 0 by f_2, we can express f_1 as

$$f_1 = \frac{f_1 + f_2}{2} + \frac{f_1 - f_2}{2} \qquad \qquad ...(3.104)$$

Putting $\qquad \dfrac{f_1 + f_2}{2} = f_c \qquad \qquad ...(3.105)$

and $\qquad f_1 - f_2 = \Delta f \qquad \qquad ...(3.106)$

we get $\qquad f_1 = f_c + \dfrac{\Delta f}{2} \qquad \qquad ...(3.107)$

where f_c is the unmodulated carrier frequency.

In an identical manner,

$$f_2 = f_c - \frac{\Delta f}{2} \qquad \qquad ...(3.108)$$

The MSK signal may be defined by the equation

$$x(t) = A \cos \{2\pi f_c t + \phi(t)\} \qquad \qquad ...(3.109)$$

where $\qquad \phi(t) = \pm \pi \Delta f t \qquad \qquad ...(3.110)$

Exploiting the condition laid down on Δf for an MSK wave, the phase change resulting from the transmission of symbol 1 associated with frequency f_1 is obtained from

$$\phi(t) = \pi \Delta f t = \frac{\pi t}{2T_b} \qquad \qquad ...(3.111)$$

This means that a phase increment $= \pi/2$ radians occurs at the end of the interval representing the transmission of symbol 1 at time $t = T_b$.

Similarly, the phase change during the transmission of symbol 0 linked to frequency f_2 takes place according to the equation

$$\phi(t) = -\pi \Delta f t = -\frac{\pi t}{2T_b} \qquad \qquad ...(3.112)$$

which means that a phase decrement $= \pi/2$ is observed following the termination of the time interval during which the symbol 0 is transmitted at $t = T_b$.

Thus depending on the input bit, one of the two frequencies $f = f_c + \dfrac{\Delta f}{2}$ is transmitted during the period of each bit. Also, at the cessation of each bit period, the phase is an integral multiple of $\pi/2$.

3.11.2. MSK as a Special Case of OK-QPSK

Another picture of MSK is an example of quadrature multiplexing. In essence, it can be visualized as a modified form of OK-QPSK wherein the rectangular pulse is replaced by a $\frac{1}{2}$ cycle sinusoidal pulse.

The expression for MSK wave can be cast in the form

$$x(t) = \cos(2\pi f_c t) A \cos\{\phi(t)\} - \sin(2\pi f_c t) A \sin\{\phi(t)\} \quad ...(3.113)$$

demonstrating that $x(t)$ consists of an in-phase component $I = A \cos\{\phi(t)\}$ and a quadrature component $Q = A \sin\{\phi(t)\}$. As in QPSK, MSK involves four dibits 10, 00, 01, 11. Figure 3.29 shows the coding of carrier phase for MSK. We begin with the condition $\phi(0) = 0$. Then at $t = T_b$, the phase of MSK wave $= \pm \pi/2$. It either increases by $\pi/2$ or decreases by this amount. After another interval T_b, i.e., at $t = 2T_b$, $\phi(t)$ is either 0 or π radians. Now, for the dibit 10 (Fig. 3.29 (a)), the phase of MSK wave first increases by $\pi/2$ as signified by symbol 1. Then it decreases by $\pi/2$ as represented by 0. Thus the trajectory of phase is like the one shown in the figure. Similarly, the path of phase for dibits 00, 01 and 11 can be traced out.

Now a comparison of Figs. 3.18 and 3.29 reveals the difference between QPSK and MSK. In QPSK for a given dibit, the phase of the carrier has a distinct value, which remains constant throughout the duration of the symbol. In MSK, on the other hand, depending on the dibit under consideration, the phase shift path is made up of linear segments. Thus MSK is a special form of QPSK with sinusoidal weighting instead of rectangular weighting. MSK differs from QPSK in the respect that MSK is a type of frequency modulation whereas QPSK is a form of phase modulation.

3.11.3. MSK Generation and Detection

Suppose $x_I(t)$ typifies the in-phase symbol stream and $x_Q(t)$ the quadrature symbol stream which has undergone a delay of T_b seconds. Let $r(t)$ denote a rectangular pulse of duration T_s seconds having unity amplitude. Then the two symbol streams characterizing the MSK wave are given by

$$x_I(t) = \sum_{l=-\infty}^{\infty} a_l \, r(t - lT_s), \quad a_l = \pm 1 \quad ...(3.114)$$

$$x_Q(t) = \sum_{l=-\infty}^{\infty} b_l \, r(t - lT_s + T_b) \quad ...(3.115)$$

$$= \sum_{l=-\infty}^{\infty} b_l \, r\left\{t - \left(l - \frac{1}{2}\right)T_s\right\}, \quad b_l = \pm 1 \quad ...(3.116)$$

The MSK signal in the modulated form is then expressed as

$$x(t) = \frac{A}{\sqrt{2}} x_I(t) \cos\left(\frac{\pi t}{T_s}\right) \cos(2\pi f_c t) +$$

$$\frac{A}{\sqrt{2}} x_Q(t) \sin\left(\frac{\pi t}{T_s}\right) \sin(2\pi f_c t) \quad ...(3.117)$$

This equation serves as the basis for drawing the MSK modulator and demodulator block diagrams (Figs. 3.30 and 3.31 respectively). The coherent detector consists of a pair of correlators with integrating and decision devices.

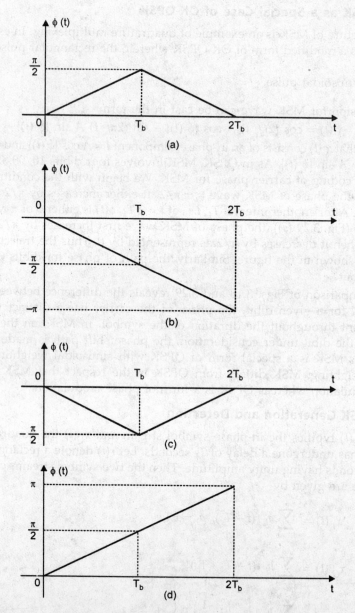

Fig. 3.29. Carrier phase coding for MSK : (a) dibit 10, (b) 00, (c) 01 and (d) 11

3.11.4. Minimum Frequency Spacing

The equation for the modulated MSK signal can be rearranged in the form

$$x(t) = \frac{A}{\sqrt{2}} \cos \left\{ 2\pi f_c\, t - x_I(t)\, x_Q(t)\, \frac{\pi t}{T_s} + \phi \right\} \qquad \qquad ...(3.118)$$

where $\qquad \phi = \begin{cases} 0, & x_I(t) = 1 \\ \pi, & x_Q(t) = -1 \end{cases}$ $\qquad \qquad ...(3.119)$

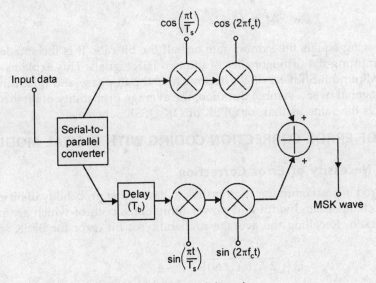

Fig. 3.30. MSK modulator layout

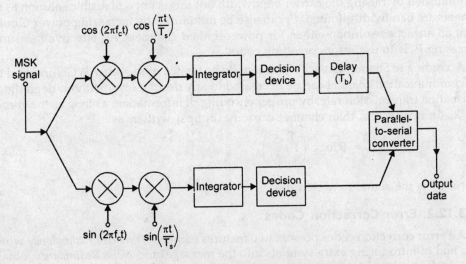

Fig. 3.31. Structure of MSK demodulator

Choosing the carrier frequency $f_c = \dfrac{\omega_c}{2\pi}$ to be an integral multiple of $\dfrac{1}{4T_b} = \dfrac{1}{2T_s}$, the phase becomes continuous at the transition instants of the bits. The MSK is a constant envelope, constant phase FSK having the signalling frequencies

$$f_1 = f_c + \frac{1}{2T_s} \qquad\qquad ...(3.120)$$

and

$$f_2 = f_c - \frac{1}{2T_s} \qquad\qquad ...(3.121)$$

from which the minimum frequency spacing is found to be

$$\Delta f = f_1 - f_2 = \frac{1}{T_s} = \frac{1}{2T_b} \qquad \qquad ...(3.122)$$

Thus spacing equals the symbol rate or half the bit rate. It is the smallest frequency distance permitting the orthogonality of the two FSK signals. This explains the origin of the name "Minimum Shift Keying". Inasmuch as the in-phase and quadrature channels remain orthogonal over a symbol duration, the average probability of bit error (P_b) for an MSK signal is the same as that for QPSK or OK-QPSK schemes.

3.12 USE OF ERROR CORRECTION CODING WITH DIGITAL MODULATION

3.12.1. Necessity of Error Correction

It is desired in any communication system to have a low probability of bit error keeping in view the channel bandwidth and power limitations, both of which are precious and must be stocked. Recalling the average probability of bit error for BPSK scheme, from Sec. 3.5.4

$$P_b = Q\left\{\sqrt{2T_b\,B(C/N)}\right\} \qquad \qquad ...(3.123)$$

which is a monotonically decreasing term with increasing value of parenthesis term, P_b can be diminished by raising the carrier bandwidth but this is not a plausible solution as most channels are bandwidth-limited. P_b can also be minimized by increasing power C but this is not an attractive solution either, for power-limited channels. An effective measure for decreasing P_b is to use error-correcting codes.

According to Shanon Capacity Theorem (to be treated in sequel), AWGN-induced error in a communication channel can be decreased to any desired level without degrading the information transmission rate, by proper encoding of information, as long as the encoding rate R_b (in bps) is less than channel capacity (in bps) written as

$$C = B\log_2\left(1 + \frac{S}{N}\right) \qquad \qquad ...(3.124)$$

where $\frac{S}{N}$ is the signal-to-noise ratio.

3.12.2. Error Correction Codes

All error correction codes possess two features namely *Structured Redundancy* which is a method of introducing extra symbols into the message, and *Noise Redundancy*, obtained by embodying dependence of extra symbols on a span of several message symbols.

Main types of encoders include :

(i) *Block or Group Encoders.* Here r parity check bits are formed by linear operations on n data bits. The formed parity bits are attached to each block of n bits. As a result, blocks of length $k = n + r$ symbols are produced. Thus the operation generates a (k, n) block code containing 2^n code words. These code words are supplied to a modulator whose output is a set of finite duration waveforms. These waveforms are transmitted over the channel. Block encoders are *memoryless devices* because each k-bit code word depends only on an information block comprising n bits.

(ii) *Convolution Coder.* This produces, for each input binary source symbol, $\dfrac{R_c}{R_b}$ encoded binary symbols, depending not only on the most recent symbols but also on preceding source symbols. It is essentially a memory device in which the information data propagate through a linear shift register consisting of several stages, shifting a specified number of bits at a time. For the various information bits stored in the register, there are a number of logic circuits which operate on the register producing the coded bits.

3.12.3. Effect of Coding

A comparison of average probability of code word error with the same for block error without encoding, subject to identical transmitted carrier and information rate R_b boundaries, tells us about the effectiveness of coding. If E_b stands for the received energy per information bit without encoding and E_c the corresponding received energy per coded bit, then

$$E_b = \frac{C}{R_b}, E_c = \frac{C}{R_c} \qquad \qquad ...(3.125)$$

Now, the code rate is defined as the ratio

$$R = \frac{\text{Number of information bits } (k)}{\text{Total number of bits in a code word } (n)} = \frac{k}{n} \qquad ...(3.126)$$

The information bit rate at encoder input (R_b) is related to the coded bit rate (R) at encoder output as

$$R_c = \frac{R_b}{R} \qquad \qquad ...(3.127)$$

By manipulation of E_b, E_c equations we get

$$E_c = \frac{C}{R_c} = \frac{C}{\frac{R_b}{R}} = \frac{RC}{R_b} = \frac{R\,E_b\,R_b}{R_b} < E_b \text{ since } R < 1 \qquad ...(3.128)$$

from which we can state that upon encoding, the energy obtained per coded bit is less than the energy per bit in the uncoded system implying a reduction of energy. However, this is offset by a net gain in overall system performance by the error correcting capability of coding/decoding scheme.

3.13 MODEMS

At this point, it will be interesting to know about Modems. The term "Modem" is the short form of "MOdulator-DEModulator". It is a device, often used with a computer, to convert the digital signals used by the computer into analog signals which can be transmitted on the telephone lines and vice versa. Connected to a computer, the modem helps in sending e-mail messages, for browsing the Internet or simple data transfer.

3.13.1. Internal and External Modems

There are two types of modems : internal and external. An *Internal Modem* is a card placed inside the computer, and drawing power from the computer for its operation. An *External Modem*, on the other hand, is connected to a free serial port on the system and is capable of functioning independently.

3.13.2. Autofall Backward and Autofall Forward

These are features which enable a modem to adjust automatically to the highest speed depending on the line quality. Typical speeds of modems ae 9.6 kbps, 14.4 kbps, 28.8 kbps, 33.6 kbps and 56 kbps.

A modem should switch to the next lower speed, witihin a defined range, if the line condition degrades and also step up to the next higher speed upon its improvement. These features to monitor line quality are called Autofall Backward and Autofall Forward.

3.13.3. Data and Error Correction Protocols

These are the systems of rules governing the speed, compression ratio and built-in error correction methods for detecting and eliminating errors. In the CCITT standard, *V.32 bis* denotes data speed of 14.4 kbps, *V.34* means 28.8 kbps and *V.34+* stands for 33.6 kbps.

Before transmitting data over the telephone line, the modem first compresses it. The frequently repeated character strings are substituted by a special character to decrease the redundant information. Similarly, the receiving modem decompresses the redundant data before passing it to the computer. The generally used protocols are : V.42 bis (1:4 compression) and MNP 5 (1:5 compression).

The noise creeping into the telephone lines may corrupt the data strings for which error correction protocols such as V.42 bis and MNP5, are utilized.

3.13.4. Modem Terms

While dealing with modems, one must know the commonly used terminology :

Analog Loopback. This is a self test for the modem using either data entered from the computer keyboard or an internally stored test pattern. This data is fed to the transmitter of the modem, converted into analog form, looped back to the receiver and reconverted to the digital domain, thus checking the overall performance of the system.

Originate and Terminal Modes. The *Originate Mode* is a state wherein the modem transmits at a pre-defined low channel frequency with reception at a high frequency. In the *Terminal Mode*, the computer acts as a teletypewriter instead of a data processor, allowing keyboard entries to be transmitted directly to the modem irrespective of whether the entry is a modem command or data. The received data are sent to the screen directly and may also be kept in memory. *Terminal Emulation* is a setting which permits the readable display of incoming information.

Xmodem, Ymodem and Zmodem. These are error control software protocols used for transferring files between modems.

3.14 DISCUSSION AND CONCLUSIONS

Various digital modulation techniques are described in this chapter. The rendition of these techniques can be quantitatively understood by comparing their error performance and spectral efficiency.

3.14.1. Average Probability of Bit Error

The error performance is adjudged by finding the average probability of bit error at given energy per bit to noise density, the latter being a function of carrier-to-noise ratio and hence signal energy. It is expedient to make the comparative study using the ideal error rate which can be considered as a goal specifying the best performance achievable. The ideal error rate is obtained under the postulates that additive white Gaussian noise is the only perturbation, that the synchronization is perfect and that error control coding is not used. In practice, the performance is degraded by several factors and these deviations can be determined by experimentation, computer simulations and analysis.

The expressions for average probability of bit error sprinkled through this chapter are compiled in Table 3.2. Using these expressions, the error probability is plotted against signal-to-noise power ratio $\frac{E_b}{N_0}$ for different modulation techniques in Fig. 3.32. Practical digital communication systems typically employ an average probability $P_e \le 10^{-4}$. The curves give the following information :

(i) For all modulation techniques under examinaton, the error rate is a monotonically decreasing function with increasing $\frac{E_b}{N_0}$ values. This means that the error rate diminishes at a high signal-to-noise power ratio.

(*ii*) At a given $\dfrac{E_b}{N_0}$ value, for the methods under consideration, coherent binary PSK gives the minimum error rate while non-coherent binary FSK yields the maximum error rate. From this viewpoint, the former can be called the best signalling method and the latter the worst method.

To obtain the same error rate, there is approximately a 4-dB difference in $\dfrac{E_b}{N_0}$ between PSK and FSK. At the first sight, this may look like a trivial improvement. But in applications like digital satellite communications where power is at a premium, even a 1-dB saving effort is worthwhile.

(*iii*) Let us compare the phase modulation systems, coherent binary PSK and DPSK with their analogues in frequency regime, viz., coherent binary FSK and non-coherent binary FSK. At a specified error rate, the phase modulation systems need an $\dfrac{E_b}{N_0}$ value which is 3 dB less than the frequency modulation systems. This capability to achieve a given error rate at a lower power ratio makes them superior in this respect.

Table 3.2. Summary of Ideal Error Rate Performance Formulae for Different Digital Modulation Schemes

Sl. No.	Modulation Technique	Average Probability of Bit Error (P_b)
1.	(*i*) Coherent Binary PSK (BPSK)	$\dfrac{1}{2}\,\text{erfc}\left(\sqrt{\dfrac{E_b}{N_0}}\right)$
	(*ii*) DPSK	$\dfrac{1}{2}\exp\left(-\dfrac{E_b}{N_0}\right)$
	(*iii*) Coherent DCPSK, Coherent QPSK, Coherent DCQPSK	$\text{erfc}\left(\sqrt{\dfrac{E_b}{N_0}}\right)$
2.	(*i*) Coherent Binary FSK	$\dfrac{1}{2}\,\text{erfc}\left(\sqrt{\dfrac{E_b}{2N_0}}\right)$
	(*ii*) Non-coherent Binary FSK	$\dfrac{1}{2}\exp\left(-\dfrac{E_b}{2N_0}\right)$
	(*iii*) Coherent MSK	$\text{erfc}\left(\sqrt{\dfrac{E_b}{N_0}}\right)$

(*iv*) Comparing the curves for (Non-coherent) DPSK with Coherent PSK and Non-coherent binary FSK with Coherent binary FSK at high $\dfrac{E_b}{N_0}$ values, we note that within a space of 1 dB, the capability of non-coherent receivers is nearly similar to that of their coherent partners. But the same is not true at low values of $\dfrac{E_b}{N_0}$.

(v) Finally, we compare coherent QPSK with coherent binary PSK. Although at low $\dfrac{E_b}{N_0}$ values, their error rates markedly differ but at higher values of $\dfrac{E_b}{N_0}$, the QPSK curve approaches the superior PSK curve. Bearing in mind that for a given bandwidth, QPSK transmits twice as many information bits as PSK, and at higher power ratio, its error rate is also like PSK, the superiority of QPSK over PSK is evident but at the same time we must not forget that this achievement by QPSK calls for increased circuit complexity, an undesirable feature.

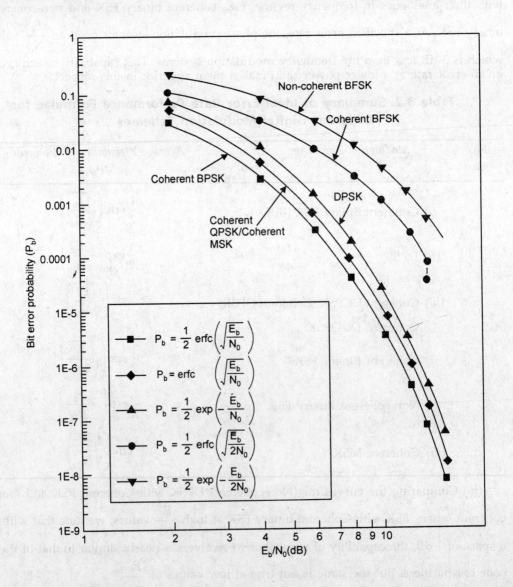

Fig. 3.32. A comparative study of noise performance of different digital modulation techniques

3.14.2. Spectral Efficiency and Trade-Offs in *M*-ary Data Transmission

Another vital parameter for evaluating the performance of a digital modulation technique is the spectral efficiency Γ defined as the ratio of transmitted bit rate to bandwidth and expressed in bits/sec-Hz. Γ defines the percentage utilization of channel bandwidth which is an invaluable communication resource. Binary modulation techniques like BASK, BPSK and BFSK are inferior in this respect as they do not utilize bandwidth efficiently. The bandwidth utilization factor is improved through the agency of *Quadrature Multiplexing*. QPSK and MSK are useful from this consideration. Similarly, *M*-ary digital modulation techniques enable us to transmit more bits per second without increasing the bandwidth proportionally. But this is accompanied by an increase in necessary power. The selection of the correct modulation technique is done by a trade-off criteria between bandwidth and power.

Our discussion of noise in digital modulation techniques will be incomplete without probing into the compromises involved in *M*-ary PSK and *M*-ary FSK on the basis of *Shanon's Channel Capacity Theorem* which may be stated as : In a bandlimited communication channel of bandwidth B (in Hz), perturbed by AWGN and subject to power limitation, the channel capacity, expressed in bits per second, is given by

$$C = B \log_2 (1 + \text{SNR}) \qquad \qquad ...(3.129)$$

where SNR is the signal-to-noise ratio for the received signal. The channel capacity C signifies an upper maximum limit on the rate of transmission of information through the channel without introducing any error.

Suppose P_s is the average power of the received signal and the channel noise has a power spectral density $= -\dfrac{N_0}{2}$. If E_b denotes the signal energy per bit and T_b is the bit duration,

$$P_s = \frac{E_b}{T_b} = E_b R_b \qquad \qquad ...(3.130)$$

where R_b, the reciprocal of T_b, defines the bit rate in bits per second.

Considering both positive and negative frequencies, in a bandwidth B, the average noise power

$$P_n = N_0 B \qquad \qquad ...(3.131)$$

Here the signal-to-noise ratio for the received signal is

$$\text{SNR} = P_s = \frac{E_b R_b}{N_0 B} = \frac{E_b / N_0}{B / R_b} \qquad \qquad ...(3.132)$$

The reader may recognize that the numerator, $\dfrac{E_b}{N_0}$, is equal to ratio of signal energy per bit to average noise power per unit bandwidth and the denominator, $\dfrac{B}{R_b}$, is equal to the bandwidth efficiency Γ in units of bits per second per Hertz.

Since the channel capacity C defined by Shanon's Theorem represents an upper limit on the bit rate R_b, obviously

$$R_b \leq C \leq B \log_2\left(1 + \frac{E_b/N_0}{B/R_b}\right) \qquad \ldots(3.133)$$

using the SNR equation. Finally, Shanon's Theorem can be brought into the form

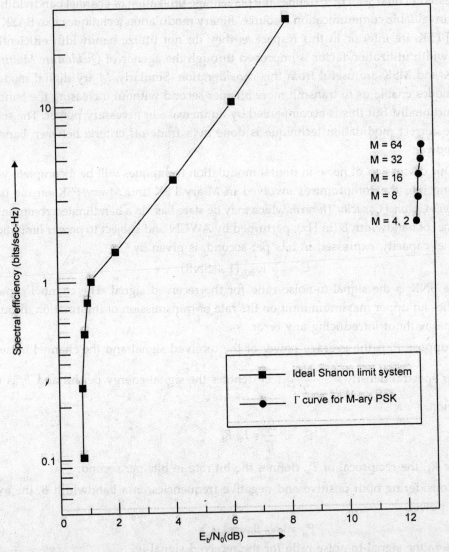

Fig. 3.33. Variation of spectral efficiency $\Gamma = \dfrac{R_b}{B}$ with signal energy per bit to average noise

power ratio $\dfrac{E_b}{N_0}$ = for M-ary PSK with M = 2, 4, 8, 16, 32, 64. Equality condition

N_0 in $\dfrac{R_b}{B}$ equation is assumed and following equations are used :

$$P_b = \frac{P_s}{\log_2 M} \text{ and } P_b = \frac{1}{2} \text{erfc}\left(\sqrt{\frac{E_b}{N_0}}\right)$$

P_s is taken to be 10^{-6}. Also shown is the Shanon limit plot of Γ as a function of $\dfrac{E_b}{N_0}$

$$\frac{E_b}{N_0} \leq \frac{2^{\frac{R_b}{B}} - 1}{R_b / B} \qquad\qquad \text{...(3.134)}$$

We have to abide by this equation for ensuring error-free transmission. This suggests that given a bandwidth efficiency $\frac{R_b}{B}$, ratio of received signal energy per bit to noise power spectral density will obey this equation. For the extreme case of an infinitely large bandwidth, $B \to \infty$, hence $\frac{R_b}{N_0} \to 0$ and $\lim \frac{E_b}{N_0} = \text{In } 2 = 0.693 = -1.6$ dB which is called the *Shanon Limit*.

The spectral efficiency for M-ary modulation schemes is calculated from

$$\text{MPSK} \qquad\qquad \Gamma = \begin{cases} 2, & M = 2 \\ \log_2 M, & M > 2 \end{cases} \qquad\qquad \text{...(3.135)}$$

$$\text{MFSK} \qquad\qquad \Gamma = \frac{\log_2 M}{M} \qquad\qquad \text{...(3.136)}$$

In Fig. 3.33, the spectral efficiency vs $\frac{E_b}{N_0}$ plot for coherent M-ary PSK is shown and compared with boundary curve for Shanon capacity. The calculations have been carried out for different values of $M = 2^m$ using $m = 1, 2, 3, ...6$. The calculations are for P_s value $= 10^{-6}$. Identical curves for M-ary FSK are given in Fig. 3.34. In PSK, an increase in M causes an improvement of spectral efficiency but the price is paid in terms of a high $\frac{E_b}{N_0}$ ratio. As opposed to this, in FSK, the bandwidth efficiency variation pattern follows the reverse trend, decreasing with increasing M value; this is also associated with a higher signal energy per bit.

ILLUSTRATIVE PROBLEMS

3.1 Assuming that the carrier frequency f_c equals the bit rate $\frac{1}{T_b}$, draw the ASK waveform for an input binary signal 11101101.

The incoming signal sequence is an 8-bit binary number. Observing that the carrier frequency and bit rate are equal, the time scale is divided into 8 segments of length T_b each at intervals of T_b, $2 T_b$, $3 T_b$, ..., $8T_b$, as shown in Fig. P3.1. The symbol 1 is represented by transmitting the sinusoidal carrier wave of fixed amplitude A Volts, constant frequency f. Symbol 0 is signified by removal or switching off the carrier.

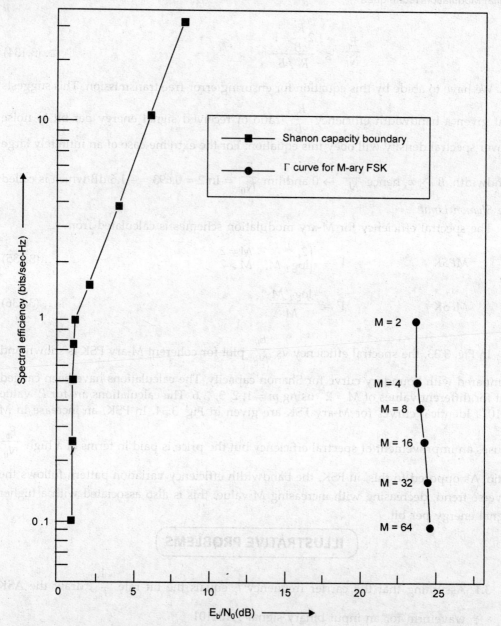

Fig. 3.34. Dependence of $\Gamma = \dfrac{R_b}{B}$ on $\dfrac{E_b}{N_0}$ for M-ary FSK with $M = 2^1, 2^2, 2^3, ..., 2^6$. Together

with the equality condition in $\dfrac{R_b}{B}$ equation, the equations used are :

$$P_b = \frac{2^{m-1}}{2^m - 1} \text{ and } P_b = \frac{1}{2} \text{erfc}\left(\sqrt{\frac{E_b}{2\,N_0}}\right)$$

P_s is fixed at 10^{-6}. The Shanon limiting curve is also displayed for comparison.

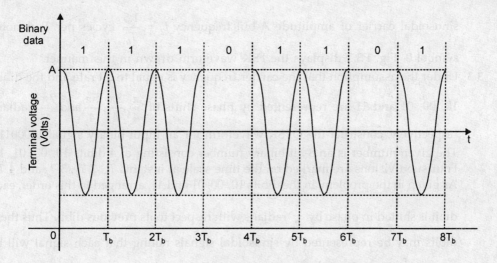

Fig. P3.1.

3.2 For the input binary sequence 110011, sketch the binary FSK waveform given that the symbol 1 is represented by a signal of frequency

$$f_1 = \frac{1.5}{T_b} \qquad \qquad ...(P3.1)$$

and the symbol 0 by the signal having the frequency

$$f_2 = \frac{1.5}{T_b} \qquad \qquad ...(P3.2)$$

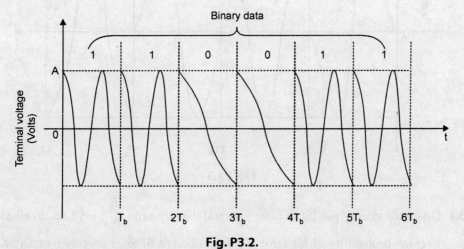

Fig. P3.2.

The given binary sequence comprises 6 bits so that the time scale is divided into 6 parts corresponding to T_b, $2\,T_b$, $3\,T_b$,..., $6T_b$. A sinusoidal carrier of amplitude A and frequency $f_1 = \dfrac{1.5}{T_b}$, i.e., 1.5 cycles per T_b represents symbol 1 while a sinusoidal carrier of amplitude A but frequency $f_2 = \dfrac{1.5}{T_b}$ cycles per T_b denotes

symbol 0. Fig. P3.2 displays the FSK waveform drawn in this manner.

3.3 Under the assumption that the carrier frequency is equal to bit rate and the dibits

10, 00, 01 and 11 are represented by phase shifts of $\dfrac{\pi}{4}, \dfrac{3\pi}{4}, \dfrac{5\pi}{4}$ and $\dfrac{7\pi}{4}$ radians

respectively, construct the QPSK waveform for an input binary signal 10000111.
The given number is an 8-bit binary number consisting of 4 dibits 10, 00, 01, 11.
Four subdivisions are marked on the time scale at instants T_b, $2\,T_b$, $3\,T_b$ and $4\,T_b$.
As given in the problem, in the dibits 10, 00, 01 and 11, arranged in this order, each

dibit is shifted in phase by $\dfrac{\pi}{2}$ radians with respect to its previous dibit. Thus these

dibits may be represented by sinusoidal signals noting that each signal will be

phase shifted by $\dfrac{\pi}{2}$ relative to its predecessor. The resulting QPSK wave is shown

in Fig. P3.3.

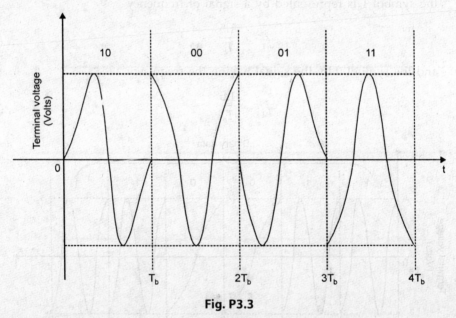

Fig. P3.3

3.4 Given the energy per bit to noise spectral density ratio $\dfrac{E_b}{N_0} = 10$ dB. Evaluate the

average probability of bit error (P_b) for coherent BPSK, non-coherent DPSK and
orthogonal non-coherent BFSK. Hence grade them in ascending order of error
rate.

For coherent BPSK

$$P_b = \frac{1}{2}\,\mathrm{erfc}\left(\sqrt{\frac{E_b}{N_0}}\right) = \frac{1}{2}\,\mathrm{erfc}\,\sqrt{10} = \frac{1}{2}\,\mathrm{erfc}\,(3.1623) \qquad \ldots (P3.3)$$

$$= \frac{1}{2}(8.82 \times 10^{-6}) = 4.41 \times 10^{-6} \qquad \text{...(P3.4)}$$

In the case of non-coherent DPSK

$$P_b = \frac{1}{2}\exp\left(-\frac{E_b}{N_0}\right) = \frac{1}{2}\exp(-10) = \frac{1}{2} \times 4.54 \times 10^{-5} \qquad \text{...(P3.5)}$$

$$= 2.27 \times 10^{-5} \qquad \text{...(P3.6)}$$

The error rate formula for orthogonal non-coherent BFSK is

$$P_b = \frac{1}{2}\exp\left(-\frac{E_b}{2N_0}\right) = \frac{1}{2}\exp(-5) = \frac{1}{2} \times 6.74 \times 10^{-3} \qquad \text{...(P3.7)}$$

$$= 3.37 \times 10^{-3} \qquad \text{...(P3.8)}$$

On the basis of the above calculations, we infer that at a specified signal energy per bit to average noise power per unit bandwidth ratio $\left(\dfrac{E_b}{N_0}\right)$,

$$(P_b)_{BPSK} < (P_b)_{DPSK} < (P_b)_{BFSK} \qquad \text{...(P3.9)}$$

3.5 If QPSK symbols are Gray encoded as follows : dibit 00 → phase shift 0 radian, 01 → $\dfrac{\pi}{2}$, 11 → π and 10 → $\dfrac{3\pi}{2}$ and if the carrier frequency is f, find the four sinusoidal transmitted signals.

The QPSK signal is succinctly written as

$$x(t) = A \cos\{2\pi f_c t + \phi(t)\} \qquad \text{...(P3.10)}$$

where A is the signal amplitude and $\phi(t)$ is the carrier phase which acquires a specific vlue for each dibit of input data stream.

In this problem we have

$$\phi(t) = \begin{cases} 0, & \text{dibit 00} \\ \dfrac{\pi}{2}, & \text{dibit 01} \\ \pi, & \text{dibit 11} \\ \dfrac{3\pi}{2} & \text{dibit 10} \end{cases} \qquad \text{...(P3.11)}$$

Accordingly, the four transmitted signals are expressed as

$$x_1 = x_{00} = A\cos(2\pi f_c t + 0) = A\cos(2\pi f_c t) \qquad \text{...(P3.12)}$$

$$x_2 = x_{01} = A\cos(2\pi f_c t + \frac{\pi}{2}) = -A\sin(2\pi f_c t) \qquad \text{...(P3.13)}$$

$$x_3 = x_{11} = A\cos(2\pi f_c t + \pi) = -A\cos(2\pi f_c t) \qquad \text{...(P3.14)}$$

$$x_4 = x_{10} = A\cos(2\pi f_c t + \frac{3\pi}{2}) = -A\sin(2\pi f_c t) \qquad \text{...(P3.15)}$$

REVIEW QUESTIONS

3.1 Name and define the basic types of digital binary modulation. Give their mathematical representation and illustrate your answer with the waveforms of the modulated signals.

3.2 What is meant by Binary and *M*-ary modulation ? Define Baud.

3.3 What is a Product Modulator ? Draw the circuit diagram of a balanced modulator and explain its operation.

3.4 How is a voltage-controlled oscillator used for frequency modulation ? Explain using a Hartley oscillator.

3.5 Reason out as to why ASK and PSK waves can be viewed as double-sideband suppressed carrier modulated waves ?

3.6 Mention the three main components of a coherent detector for binary ASK and PSK waves. Describe how is the coherent modulation of these waves done.

3.7 Draw the block diagram of a coherent demodulator for a binary FSK wave. Explain its working.

3.8 Point out the reasons for which the coherent detectors of binary modulated waves are called "coherent".

3.9 What is the motivation for non-coherent demodulation of binary ASK and FSK signals ? What is the price paid for non-coherent detection in terms of noise performance of the receiver ?

3.10 Why is an envelope detector so called ? Give its circuit diagram and input-output waveforms; describe how it performs envelope detection.

3.11 (*a*) Explain why BPSK waves cannot be demodulated non-coherently whereas BFSK waves can be non-coherently detected although both binary PSK and FSK signals have a constant envelope.

　　　(*b*) Draw the elaborate block diagrams of BPSK modulator and coherent demodulator. Define the function of each block.

3.12 Derive an expression for the probability of error for a binary PCM system. Hence deduce the error probability for a binary ASK signal.

3.13 Considering the generalized twin-path correlation receiver, derive an expression for average probability of error for the receiver. Apply this analysis to the coherent detection of binary PSK and orthogonal FSK signals to obtain the formulae for average probability of bit error in both cases.

3.14 Outline the problem of phase ambiguity in PSK systems. How is the ambiguity resolved by using a unique word ? Briefly discuss the differential encoding method for phase ambiguity resolution. Describe the functions of a PSK differential encoder and decoder.

3.15 What is Differential Phase-Shift Keying ? Using a block diagram, describe how does a DPSK modulator reconstruct binary information ?

3.16 What are the four dibits employed in Quaternary Phase-Shift Keying and what signals do they represent ?

3.17 Decomposing the carrier equation for a QPSK wave into cosine and sine components, demonstrate that a QPSK signal is a linear combination of two PSK signals. How are the phases of these component signals related ?

3.18 Sketch the block diagrams of QPSK modulator and Coherent QPSK demodulator. Discuss the role of each block.

3.19 Explain the meaning of Fourfold Phase Ambiguity in QPSK. How is the difficulty surmounted employing differential encoding and decoding ?

3.20 How do irregular phase swings degrade the performance of a QPSK system ? Explain how does Offset-Keyed QPSK eliminate these swings ? Is the power spectral density influenced by this remedy ?

3.21 For orthogonal FSK signals, sketch the block diagrams for non-coherent detection using : (*a*) correlators and (*b*) matched filters.

3.22 Does Minimum-Shift Keying represent a form of frequency or phase modulation? How does MSK differ from QPSK ?

3.23 (*a*) Introduce the idea of MSK as a modified form of continuous phase frequency-shift keying.

(*b*) Provide a conceptual development of MSK as a special case of Offset-Keyed QPSK.

3.24 Consider an in-phase symbol $x_I(t)$ and a bit-duration quadrature symbol $x_Q(t)$ in OQPSK. Express them in terms of a rectangular pulse of unit amplitude and duration equal to symbol duration T_s. Prove that the minimum frequency spacing which allows two FSK signals to be orthogonal equals half the bit rate :

$$f = \frac{1}{2\,T_b}$$

3.25 Justify the following :

(*a*) DPSK may be viewed as a "non-coherent" version of phase-shift keying.

(*b*) QPSK is a quadrature-carrier multiplexing scheme providing bandwidth conservation relative to BPSK.

(*c*) MSK may be viewed as a form of quadrature multiplexing

(*d*) BFSK wave represents a superposition of two BASK waveforms.

(*e*) BASK, BPSK and BFSK signals are special cases of amplitude-, frequency- and phase-modulated waves respectively.

(*f*) M-ary ASK and M-ary PSK modulation schemes, for all values of M and using coherent detection, are said to be linear.

(*g*) In a DPSK receiver, the bit errors tend to occur in pairs.

REFERENCES AND FURTHER READING

3.1 S. Haykin. *Digital Communications*, Wiley, New York, 1988.

3.2 S. Haykin, *Communication Systems*, Wiley, New York 1983.

3.3 B.P. Lathi, *Modern Digital and Analog Communication Systems*, Holt, Rinehart & Winston, New York, 1983.

3.4 J.G. Proakis, *Digital Communications*, McGraw Hill, New York, 1983.

3.5 L.M. Couch, II, *Digital and Analog Communication Systems*, Macmillan, New York, 1983.

3.6 K. Fisher, *Digital Communications*, Prentice Hall, Englewood, New Jersey, 1983.

3.7 K.S. Shanmugam, *Digital and Analog Communication Systems*, Wiley, New York, 1979.

□□□

4

Networking Principles

In the preceding chapter we studied how digital signals are modulated on to a carrier wave for over-the-air transmission to near and far-off places. Another method of sending and receiving messages is by physically connecting computers or devices like telephones and FAX machines, through cables. The idea of networks encompasses both types of connectivity. It includes copper wires, quartz fibre optic cables, and radio transmission like microwave and satellite links.

Networking is broadly defined as the process of building a connected configuration ranging in complexity from a congregation of a few computers, machines or other equipment, spaced some metres apart, to an assembly of millions of computers, machines, equipment, etc., spread all over the globe. The connections between these equipment may be made in whatever manner possible to be able to exchange information, and share data and processing capabilities (Fig. 4.1)

In the present chapter, we shall address the elementary networking concepts, beginning with circuit-switched and packet-switched networks, and covering Integrated Services Digital Network (ISDN), Asynchronous Transfer Mode (ATM) and the giant internetwork of networks, the "Internet". Important network issues will be raised and approaches to deal with them will be discussed.

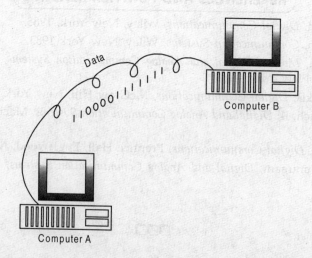

Fig. 4.1. Networking as a means of connection of computers

4.1. PRELIMINARIES

4.1.1. Network Components

A network consists of computers called *Nodes* or *Stations* which are connected to or can communicate with each other, such as by sharing files and resources, through the agency of special software (run by computers), for initiating and managing the interactions. Accordingly, a network comprises: (*i*) *Hardware Components* such as computers and interface cards, connecting cables, wires, links, etc., peripheral devices of computers like printers, storage devices and microphones, along with dialling telephone and FAX machines, and parts like hubs, switches, routers, gateways and so forth. (*ii*) *Software Components:* These include operating system and workstation software resources, tools and so on. The software aspects involved in the working of the network are looked after by the *Network Operating Software* (NOS) while the software issues of network control are dealt with by the *Network Management Software* (NMS).

4.1.2. Advantages of Networking

Networking allows the sharing of costly hardware and software resources among users accessing the network. These shared resources consist of the CPU, the hard disc, file systems and peripherals like printers and tape devices. For example, several users can take prints from a single heavy-duty laser printer connected to a network of computers.

Neworking facilitates the sharing of information. For instance, the withdrawal and credit information of a person's account may be required by many staff members. This may be kept in a main server for accessing and updating by different members, as and when necessary.

Networking allows electronic-mail transfer and also voice-mail transmission over special devices.

Networking offers the customer local processing capability by seeking the desired information from a central computer called the *Server* to the local computer, the *Client*. The data thus obtained is processed on the client's computer provided it has the requisite capability.

The above benefits of networking help in increasing the speed of communication, resulting in an improvement in productivity and skill in an organization. Accessibility of data to more staff members leads to transparency of working. Ready availability of data aids in decision-making process.

4.1.3. Common Network Terms

Node It is a device which has local processing capability with a modest graphics facility and needs additional hardware for connection to the network such as Network Interface Cards (NICs). An example of node is the Personal Computer.

Workstation It is similar to a node with built-in connectivity requirements avoiding extra attachment hardware, and possessing superior graphics capability.

Server A network device containing sharable resources which allows other devices connected to the network to share these resources. Examples are the file and print servers.

Client It is a device like a node which can access the server.

Dumb Terminal A device without local processing capability which can only access the resources of the server and use them in a restricted sense.

Network Topology It refers to the shape of the structure of the network such as Star, Ring, Tree, Bus and so on. The *logical* topology may differ from the *physical* topology.

Protocols Accepted set of rules and guidelines assuring an orderly exchange of information among two or more similar devices or processes.

Protocols establish the conventions for setting up and stopping a path of communication, lay down the parameters for data formatting, speed and sequence of transmission to eliminate compatibility problems, and define the standard data elements for exchange.

Interface Set of rules for communication among two or more dissimilar devices or processes.

In distinction to a protocol which is concerned with similar devices or processes, the interface is concerned with dissimilar devices or processes. Moreover, the protocol is a logical concept while the interface is a physical idea. We speak, for example, about the protocol between a host computer and a user computer but an interface between a computer and a switch (See Fig. 4.2)

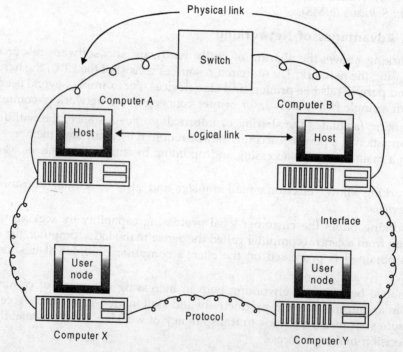

Fig. 4.2. Distinction between physical communication and logical communication, protocol and interface

Transmission Medium Physical Medium through which information is propagated, e.g., Cu wires, optic fibre cables, etc. Wireless Networks do not rely on the transmission medium.

Speed Rate of transmission of information measured in bits per sec (bps), kilobits per sec (kbps), Mega bits per sec (Mbps) and Giga bits per sec (Gbps).

Bandwidth Information carrying capacity of the transmission medium expressed in Hz and its multiples like kHz, MHz, GHz, etc.

Defined below are common network topological terms (in alphabetical order):

— *Backbone Topology* It is used to connect each pair of networks, among multiple networks, directly through a bridge.

— *Bus Topology* As a *physical topology,* a bus is a network wherein each node is connected to a common line termed the *Backbone* or *Trunk.* As a *logical topology,* the characteristic feature of a bus is that packets are broadcast so that evey node receives the information at the same time. An example is the Ethernet.

Comparatively smaller than other topologies, the bus topology-based architectures offer simplicity and flexibility, and are easily extendable.

— *Cascaded Bridge Topology* Providing a bridging method among multiple networks, this topology employs a network *Y* as an access point to a network *Z* from the network *X*.

— *Distributed Star Topology* It is a physical topology comprising two or more hubs, each being the centre of a star configuration.

— *Hybrid Topology* As the name indicates, it represents the integration of two or more differing physical topologies.

— *Logical Topology* Gives the logical layout of a network showing the manner of interconnection of network elements and the path of information transmission. Star and ring networks are the main types of logical topology.

— *Mesh Topology* It is a physical topology in which a minimum of two paths exist to and from every node.

— *Physical Topology* It gives the wiring layout of a network specifying electrical connection of elements.

— *Ring Topology* As a physical topology, it consists of a network in which every node is connected to two other nodes. As a *logical topology*, its main characteristic is the sequential transmission of packets from one node to another according to a predefined order.

— *Star Topology* It is a physical topology wherein multiple nodes join to a central component known as the "Hub"

— *Star-Wired Ring Topology* It is a hybrid topology combining the star and ring topological features.

— *Tree Topology* Also referred to as a *Distributed Bus*, it is a hybrid physical topology uniting the features of star and bus topologies.

4.1.4. Classification of Networks

(i) *By Range or Scale of Operation*, e.g., a Local Area Network (LAN), Wide Area Network (WAN), Metropolitan Area Network (MAN) and Global Area Network (GAN). The demarcation criteria is the size of the network, inter-nodal distance and the number of interconnected systems on the network. LANs are established within a building or campus premises with one or two transmission media, e.g., optical fibre for the backbone and Cu wires for nodal connections, and are based on bus, ring or star topologies. They usually have a single owner. WANs are used for long-distance or trunk communication between cities or across countries with the help of leased telephone lines and satellite links. The transmission method in WANs is "Point-to-Point" as opposed to "Multipoint or Broadcast" type in LANs. Also, the transmission is comparatively low in WANs for the land-based segment of the link. Moreover, WANs are both homogeneous or heterogeneous while LANs are homogeneous with respect to operating systems, interfaces, speed and accessing techniques. WANs have multiple owners so that tariff has to be payed to the 'service provider', either a government or private party. Unlike LANs, in the WANs, a clear definition of protocols is mandatory with the inclusion of error correction facilities and multi-vendor standards. While GANs denote big WANs, the MANs are smaller WANs connecting users in metropolises, cities and suburban areas. The above-mentioned definitions are to be considered 'relative' only because the Earth becomes a LAN when we visualize interplanetary communication.

(ii) *By Message Bearing Capacity* As examples of this group, we may cite the *Baseband Network* which can transmit only one message at a time, and the *Broadband Network* which sends multiple messages with different frequency ranges using multiplexing technique.

(iii) *By Rate of Transmission* such as 1-10 kbps, 10-20 Mbps, 100-Mbps and 1-Gbps rates.

(iv) *By Types of Nodes*, e.g., PC-based, minicomputer or mainframe computer-based networks.

(v) *According to Internodal Relationships* such as *Peer-to-Peer Network* in which all the nodes are equal in status—all are clients and all are servers so that all computers can share information with all others as well as access information from other computers; *Distributed Network*, one without any leader; *Server-based Network* having a dedicated file server; and *Client/Server Network* consisting of clients and server combinations.

(vi) *By Topology* like Bus and Ring Networks. In the former, a central bus is the backbone of the network and individual nodes are connected to this bus. In the Ring Structure, the nodes are arranged in a circle.

(vii) *By Architecture*, e.g., twisted pair, coaxial cable or fibre optic networks depending on the connecting wires used.

(viii) *By Accessing Possibilities*, e.g., a *Shared Media Network* in which only one node can transmit at a time; or a *Switched Network* which establishes temporary connections.

After this introductory survey, let us examine circuit switching which forms the basis of telephony network.

4.2. CIRCUIT-SWITCHED NETWORKS

In the traditional circuit-switched operation of a telephone network, *Circuit Switches* are employed to switch circuits from one of the several inputs to one of the many outputs, with the configuration of the switch controlled by signalling associated with the calls to be switched. Threre are two types of circuit switches: (i) *Step-by-Step* Switch in which the call is set up stagewise with each stage of the switch responding in turn to the signalling information; and (ii) *Common Control Switch* wherein the controlling parts of the switch first study the complete signalling or addressing information and utilize this to establish the optimum path through the switch.

4.2.1. Step-by-Step Switch

Using this type of switch, call setting is accomplished by consecutively setting up "Strowager" rotary switches until the called party is reached. If the call is blocked on a busy section *en route*, the call attempt is aborted. Since the network does not contain any intelligence, the call obviously cannot be directed to a different route so that a repetition of the attempt is likely to fail due to the congestion problem unless during a particular period of the day the load on the lines involved diminishes.

While a user is persevering to make a connection, alternative routes through the network may be lightly loaded and hence under-utilized. But in the absence of overall status information about the network, the other possible routes cannot be used to optimally configure the network for efficient user interconnection.

4.2.2. Digital Switching and Stored Program Control (SPC)

With the progress in digital computers, a central computer located in the telephone exchange was employed to store information regarding the status of the network. This information was analyzed to determine the possible paths through the network for materializing the call. After proper identification of the available free route, the call was set up by actuating the appropriate switches to realize an end-to-end connection. This type of operation in which signalling and control information is interchanged among computers in different exchanges, and the network intelligence is exploited for establishing user-to-user connection, is known as *Stored Program Control* (SPC).

Some of the advantages of digital switching over step-by-step switching are:

— Diversion of the traffic from heavily loaded trunks to the lightly loaded routes to relieve the burden during busy hours and for efficient connectivity.

— Flexibility of control because the stored program parameters can be easily modified to provide additional facilities, e.g., call-redirection is done by reallocation of subscriber members to different circuit connections. Similarly, call queing can be performed and alternative routing algorithms can be implemented.

Apart from the benefits accruing due to SPC, digital switching allows the use of *Electronic Logic Gates* instead of the sluggish electromechanical relay switches, the *Reed Relays*, based on the contacting principle, in conventional telephony networks.

Electronic switching drastically increases the speed of digital telephony networks. This type of switch also offers the advantage that it can be reconfigured for each individual bit in the signal.

4.2.3. Basic PCM Frame Structure for Digital Telephony

In trunk communications, any transmission path is not assigned to a single telephonic conversation. Instead, by "Time-Division Multiplexing (TDM)", several telephonic talks are multiplexed together to share a common transmission path. At the primary level, 30 speech signals are combined. Each of these signals consists of 8 bits or "Octets". Further, one additional bit is necessary for indicating the manner of assembling the bits; it is called the *Synchronization Bit*. Another additional bit is required for correctly routing the signal; it is known as the *Signalling Bit*. Thus an aggregate number of 32 time slots is needed for speech signal transmission. This group of 32 bits constitutes a PCM frame and is illustrated in Fig. 4.3. The 0'th slot plays the role of frame synchronization, slots numbered from 1 to 15 and 16 to 31 are reserved for speech signals, and the 16'th slot carries the signalling information for the network. Thus each frame contains one sample from each of the 30 speech channels, and the total number of bits in each frame = $32 \times 8 = 256$ giving an overall transmission rate = 256×8 samples per sec = 2.048 Mbits per sec. This transmission rate signifies the first level of multiplexing in *PCM Digital Hierarchy* (Table 4.1). It is therefore referred to as the "Primary Rate". In Table 4.1, the transmission rates selected at each hierarchical level are multiples of 64 kbits per sec, so that the octet structure is maintained throughout. Since each multiplexing stage requires additional bits for frame synchronization and signalling, the bit rates increase by a factor slightly > 4.

Table 4.1. Multiplexing Hierarchy of Pulse-Code Modulation

Sl. No.	Hierarchical Level	Bit Rate (Mbits/sec)	Number of Channels
1.	First Level	2.048	30
2.	Second Channel	8.448	120
3.	Third Channel	34.368	480
4.	Fourth Channel	139.264	1920
5.	Fifth Channel	565	7680

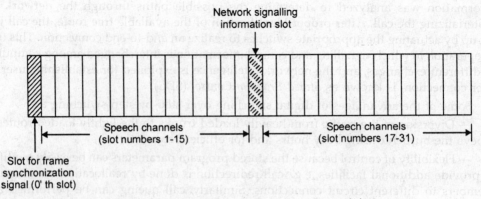

Fig. 4.3. Basic frame structure of pulse-code modulation

In time-division-multiplexed signals, two types of switching must be distinguished. The process of physical switching in the usual sense is called *Space Switching*. On the other hand, an operation similar to switching can be performed by transferring the signals associated with a given transmission circuit from one time slot to another. This operation is known as *Time Switching*. Digital telephony works by combining space and time switching modes leading to two simple configurations, viz., Space-Time-Space (S-T-S) and Time-Space-Time (T-S-T) structures.

4.2.4. Space-Time-Space Digital Switching Configuration

The structural layout of this configuration is shown in Fig. 4.4. Here, all the inlets and outlets are at the primary rate of 2.048 M bits per sec carrying 30 PCM channels of 64 kbits per sec each. Let us focus our attention on a speech signal entering the network in the x'th slot of the a'th inlet line destined for the y'th slot of the b'th outlet line. Assuming complete synchronization betweeen the time slots at the inlet and outlet lines, during the x'th slot, a cross-point in Space Switch I is enabled through which x'th slot of the a'th inlet line is directed at one of the m time switches available at that instant. A delay of the octet is made by the time switch until the time interval of the q'th slot is reached. As soon as this happens, a suitable cross point in Space Switch II is activated whereby the octet is read out into the y'th slot of outlet line b. Non-blocking operation is achievable by making provision of an adequate number of switches with the actual number of switches depending upon the mechanism of switching operation. In one method, the individual time switches contain 30 octets of storage. These octets are cyclically accessed by the Space Switch II. An octet from Space Switch I, ready to enter a time switch, is passed onto a cyclic store at the correct location from which it comes out at the needed time slot for Space Switch II. Hence switch I can use any time switch which has no entry in the concerned store situation. In this method, the number (m) of time switches is dictated by whether a given time switch can be read into and out, at the same time; otherwise more switches will be necessary.

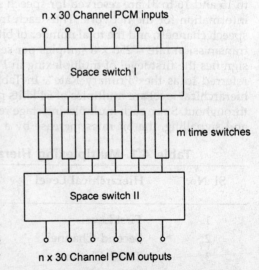

Fig. 4.4. Layout of the Space-Time-Space (S-T-S) switching configuration

4.2.5. Time-Space-Time Digital Switching Configuration

This structure (Fig. 4.5) is currently finding widespread application in telephone networks. Any signal entering the a'th time switch in time-slot x intended for the y'th time slot of outlet line b, is first subjected to time switching. Thus it gains entry into a'th inlet line of the $(n \times n)$ Space Switch in a vacant slot which does not contain any signal from any previous input stream for outlet line b. As the signals associated with the time slots corresponding to each of the outlet lines are rearranged in the time switches II, the time slot referred to above need not be the slot y. The Space Switch aligns the signal from time switch I, inlet line a to the time switch II, outlet line b.

The reason for the deployment of two stages is that two unresolvable situations may occur. First, more than one signal for a specific outlet line may arrive in the same time slot from various inlet lines. This leads to unresolvable collisions in the Space Switch with the given number of time switches (II). Secondly, more than one outlet signal for a certain time slot may reach in different time slots on the same inlet line. This again causes unresolvable collisions with the given number of time switches (I). In both instances, more time switches will be necessary.

It may be pointed out here that the synchronization and signalling bits of the PCM frame are not switched through the exchange but removed for separate processing. The signalling bits are regrouped at each exchange on the way because of the multiplexing rearrangement required after each switching step.

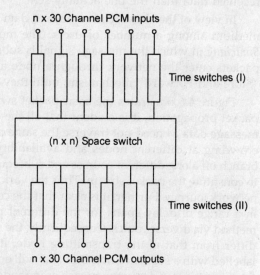

Fig. 4.5. Layout of the commonly used Time-Space-Time (T-S-T) switching configuration in digital telephony

4.2.6. Plesiochronous Nature of PCM Network

Plesiochronous operation implies that although the clock rates for each link in the network are kept same, the frame structures of the different primary rate links need not be in synchronization. Further, the small differences among the bit rates of the different primary-rate channels of a higher order multiplexed structure, call for the insertion of the so-called *Justification Bits* to maintain the interleaved structure. As justification bits are introduced into one or the other constituent bit stream, the relative positions of the frames will experience dynamical changes. As a result, no efforts are made to synchronize the frame structures above the primary rate although a global synchronization exists at the bit level.

The natural consequence of this plesiochronous nature is that for signals which are multiplexed at levels higher than the primary level, it is impossible to distinguish between octets of different channels. Therefore, one must demultiplex down to the primary rate at each switching node. This is a major bottleneck specially in situations demanding end-to-end transmission at rates greater than the primary rate of 64 kbits/sec. This shortcoming has been removed with the development of *Synchronous Digital Hierarchy* (SDH) which is being applied in high-speed optical trunk links.

4.3 PACKET-SWITCHED NETWORKS

4.3.1. Necessity of Packet Switching

The telephone network is essentially a speech conversation network in which a circuit is dedicated to the subscribers for the entire span of a call. Ascribing a circuit for the call duration is a compulsory prerequisite but highly inappropriate and undesirable for data communication inasmuch as it represents an under-utilization or inefficient operation of the network facilities. The reasons are: (*i*) The bursty nature of data traffic in which long periods of haul are intervened by short spurts of data outflow. (*ii*) Insensitivity of data to transmission delays unlike speech signals. (*iii*) Acceptance of a different sequence in the received data than the one actually sent.

In view of the above, conveyance of data is possible by sharing the same transmission medium among a number of users. The method used for this purpose is called *Packet Switching* in which the message signal is subdivided into packets of convenient size. The packets enter the network through a node and are passed on from one to another by a "Store-and-Forward" mechanism, until they reach the destination node.

Figure 4.6 illustrates the basic packet switching operation. Looking at the manner of packet propagation, it is evident that all the data packets M_1, M_2, M_3 ... M_n comprising a message data M need not traverse the same path through the network. Depending on the crowding at different nodes and availability of vacant sites, the message packets may branch off along different courses and subsequently recombine near the destination terminal to constitute the packet stream. Thus the various packets may use different circuits for their network journey. Further, it is clear that the constantly changing network traffic may result in a range of delay spans for the different packets, as they move by store-and-forward method via diverse routes. Consequently, the sequence of packets at the receiving node may differ from that at the transmitting node. It is therefore imperative that the packets be labelled with a sequence number. This will enable the receiving node to recognize whether the packets are in correct sequence or in random order. In the latter case, the receiving node may need to resequence the packets, if so desired. Suitable action has therefore to be taken by this node.

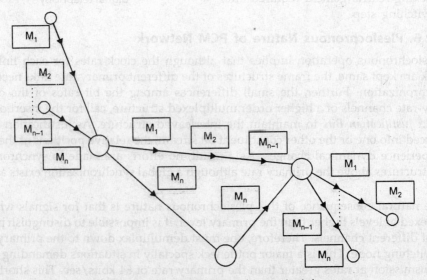

Fig. 4.6. The packet switching principle

From the viewpoint of sending and receiving nodes, a "Virtual Circuit" is established connecting these two nodes. These nodal points are hardly concerned with the circuit-switched or packet-switched modes of operation of the network. The pertinent issues of interest to them are the delays experienced by the packets in transit as well as the packet sequence.

4.3.2. Datagram and Virutal Call Operations

In applications where the sequence of packets is not of significance, each packet is considered as a separate and independent entity, complete in itself. Such packets are called *Datagrams*. The datagrams have to find their way through the network, in a single-handed and unaided manner. So, each datagram embodies information regarding source and destination addresses. This information constitutes the Overhead portion of the datagram.

In opposition to the above, are applications like digital speech telephony in which not only is the sequence of packets vital but also the transmission delay be minimized otherwise the telephonic talk will be disorganized and incoherent causing discomfiture to the subscribers. The sequencing and the delay problems are overcome by setting up an operation called *Virtual Call* wherein all the packets related to a call are made to pursue the same route through the network, seeking priority over other data packets present in the network during the period of the call. Thus the service to speech transmission is improved at the expense of a degraded service to non-priority data users. Hence a higher tariff is charged for the priority virtual call operation in comparison to datagrams.

What will happen if the virtual call operation is not invoked? Obviously, all the packets will have to be withheld for rescheduling and reorganization at the receiving node before being passed on to the receiving terminal. The delay incurred in the process will be annoying for real-time telephony but can be accepted if a person listens to pre-received or pre-recorded messages.

It will be interesting to compare datagram and virtual call operation. The datagram operation is more efficient insofar as the utilization of network facilities is concerned. However, each datagram must carry the address information tag for identification. This greatly increases the packet overhead. Moreover, datagram suffers from sequence and delay problems. These problems are avoided in virtual calls at the sacrifice of efficiency. So, the efficiency is lower for virtual calls. At the same time, packet overhead diminishes because only the first packet in the sequence needs to carry the full address information while the latter packets can be identified with a smaller number of bits.

4.3.3. Open Systems Interconnection (OSI) Protocol Model

Before examining the protocols of packet switching, let us understand the seven-layer model for Open-Systems Interconnection (OSI) laid down in the International Standards Organization (ISO) documents. OSI is an architecture of sets of protocols for unrestricted interconnection of any user equipment by the communications network. The driving force behind OSI is that customers should be able to purchase equipment from different vendors with the confidence that these equipment can be interconnected. They must also feel assured that these equipment, when connected to a network, will operate satisfactorily over the network with some other equipment connected at the other side of the network.

We know that a telecommunications system comprises the communication infrastructure and the services or applications supported. The communication functions are not only confined to the physical and network connections but also look after the transport, session control and format of information presentation. One must also distinguish between the network and physical addresses and the application identity. Therefore, the activities of the communication process need to be classified in a systematic and consistent manner which is independent of the information being conveyed. Also, it must be realized that the telecommunication systems have to be internationally-oriented calling for a minimal level of standardization at least for services like telephony and telex. Based on such considerations, the OSI identifies seven layers or levels for defining the protocols and interfaces required for Open Systems Interconnection. The seven-layer model involves communication between computers or machines but a man-machine interface acts between the human operator and a computer-based process; this interface forms a part of the model. Each of the seven model layers performs a specific task in isolation from other layers and communications occur between the same layer number at both extremities of the connection. The topmost layer interfaces with the application process. Now a brief description of the physical medium and the seven layers is given moving from the bottom upwards, with reference to Fig. 4.7.

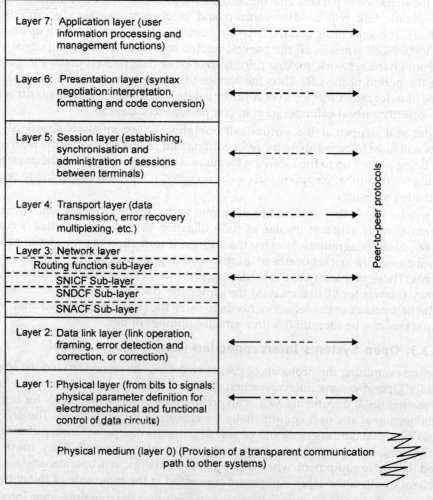

Fig. 4.7. Showing the layered structure of the OSI reference model and the functions of its seven layers; acronyms explained in the text

Physical Medium Sometimes called *Layer-0*, this layer is not part of the OSI model. Its purpose is to provide a transparent communication path to other systems. A common physical medium is wiring.

Layer-1 Physical layer As the lowest layer of the OSI model, this layer defines the physical parameters like signal voltages, line code specifications, transmission rate, etc., of the signal to be conveyed over the connection path. It transforms the bit stream received from layer-2 into a physical signal such as a voltage which is applied to the physical medium. Besides efficient data transference, it is also concerned with the synchronization at each end of the link by setting the timing of the signal sent and extracting timing from the signal received.

Layer-2: Data Link Layer It controls the operation of a *Data link* (including one or more physical media and the accompanying physical gadgetry like modems and excluding switching devices) to provide an orderly and reliable data linkage across the connection. The address mechanism furnished by this layer serves to uniquely identify each node on the local network. The main function of the data link layer is to receive messages from the upper layers and format the data into frames which are used by the network layer. These frames are described by unique flags. Bit stuffing is performed to ensure that the network layer data do not contain the bit pattern used in the flag. The header attached by the data link layer comprises an LCN (Logical Channel Number) for time-division multiplexing (TDM) of a single physical medium, flow control informaion for monitoring the movement of information to the opposite data link layer preventing storage overflow at each end, a mechanism for isolating signalling data from customer data and most importantly, information for error detection and correction. For carrying out error detection and correction, it is necessary to divide the data stream into blocks in order to identify the operational field of the error detection code. Alternatively, block delimiters are required for synchronization. Despite the assignment of specific tasks to the various digits, the transparency of the data link is not affected meaning that any data pattern can be conveyed.

Layer-3: Network Layer This layer plays the role of establishment, maintenance and release of point-to-point connections between *Network Service Access Points* (NSAPs) by specification of their addresses. These addresses are globally unique addresses to interconnect the appropriate terminal nodal points by the transport layer. In the context of OSI model, only one *Global Network* exists and the particular networks are referred to as *Sub-Networks*.

Inasmuch as the same physical pathway need not be followed by consecutive packets of the same message exchange, the above-said addresses prescribe logical connections instead of physical linkages. Over and above, control and acknowledgement fields are furnished to make sure that the data communication is correct. This control works independently of both the link level control and the higher order protocol levels.

Ascending from the bottom upwards, the network layer consists of four sub-layers with separate functions: *Sub-Network Access Control Function* (SNACF) for end-to-end service across a particular sub-network, *Sub-Network Dependent Convergence Function* (SNDCF) for mapping of a type of network service onto a given sub-network, *Sub-Network Independent Convergence Function* (SNICF) for message allocation to the suitable type of nework service, and *Routing Function* for setting up and clearing a virtual call by NSAPs by choosing the required sequence of calls across particular sub-neworks and finding the numbers for sub-network calls.

Each of these sub-layers gives its own header for peer-to-peer protocol execution. While links between various sub-networks are made by a sub-network node, those between different sub-networks are connected by a network relay which stretches upto the routing function sub-layer whereby layers upto the network layer top may communicate with intermediate node layers instead of directly interacting with equivalent layers in the far-off system. Above the network layer, all communication is with the far-off customer.

The necessity of defining these sub-layers arises from the fact that the private network/public network or terminal equipment/public network boundaries almost always occur within the network layer instead of the main network layer-to-transport layer interface.

Thus the network layer controls the data packet sequence and administers the flow with notification to the transport layer about errors and thereby maintaining the Quality of Service (QoS) to the transport layer.

Layer-4: Transport Layer Departing from the function of the three layers studied so far which were primarily concerned with the communications network, this layer sets up a transport service compatible with equipment requirements by selecting a link via the network working at a suitable data rate and quality. The user must therefore no longer bother about the data transfer mechanism in the network. The functions of the transport layer include: (*i*) Splitting the message into smaller units that can be handled by the network in the event that the message is too large for the layers 0-3 to work upon satisfactorily. (*ii*) Reliable delivery of the message by error detection and requesting for retransmission of corrupted message portions. (*iii*) Ensuring the delivery of messages to the correct processes of multitasking hosts.

Thus the transport layer optimizes the network service utilization to provide the requisite QoS economically. Five categories of service are offered by this layer as under: *Class 0* or *Basic Class* without any error correction and multiplexing; *Class 1* with error recovery but without multiplexing; *Class 2* which is the same as *Class 0* but with the inclusion of multiplexing; *Class 3*, the sum of *Class 1* and *Class 2*; and *Class 4* having the facilities of signalled and unsignalled error recovery along with multiplexing.

The transport layer represents the highest layer related to the communication medium. It can be programmed to look up tariff tables to ascertain which carrier provides the most cost-effective service for a given route length during a particular period of the day. For cost saving, multiplexing of messages is done from the higher layers onto a common bearer which is at the network layer.

Layer-5: Session Layer From this layer onwards, the layers of the OSI model are task-oriented in nature dealing with the operations of the user terminal than with any network job. The purpose of the session layer is to establish and maintain an operational session between terminals, by "signing on" to start the desired job and "signing off" to signify job completion. Dialogue co-ordination is provided by setting up, synchronizing and releasing the session between the processes in the end systems. It also decides the operational mode such as half-duplex, full-duplex and so on. As examples of session layer functions, it determines whether the transaction is of a *conversational nature* in which a reply is anticipated or of a *forward mode nature* wherein the message is simply sent without expectation for an answer.

Layer-6: Presentation Layer Having the main intent of providing a machine-independent communication process, this layer deals with the method of coding or formatting the data to be supplied to the user terminal. It carries out negotiations for the syntax or language of communication with the application layer from the available languages or defines the syntax on its own by referring to a common language like Abstract Syntax Notation (ASN). It resolves any differences in representation of information for a particular application. Hence each job can be communicated without knowledge of data code employed by a different job. When, for a given service, the syntax is fixed, the presentation layer becomes a *null layer*.

It is worthwhile pointing out that presently ASN is the only syntax available for the application layer. It is also the only means for defining the conversion from the local syntax to the presentation layer syntax.

Layer-7: Application Layer As the highest layer in the OSI model, it defines the nature of task to be carried out and provides the actual customer information processing function and terminal software for application processes such as word processing, electronic mail, banking, etc. It allows access from outside OSI to specialized communication services and the software supporting these services resides within the application layer. Any external software presently does not come in the domain of OSI standardization. According to the application, the user selects one of the established communication services or produces his/her own service. Inside the application layer, *internal interfaces* exist: the presentation layer/application layer interface on the lower side, and the interface between the application layer and a communications service like Message Handling System (MHS) on the upper side; the latter is provided by Application Service Elements (ASEs) which are mapped onto the presentation layer via three kinds of operation using different service elements: *Remote Operations Service Element* (ROSE) for asymmetric request-response interactions between end systems, *Reliable Transfer Service Element* (RTSE) for symmetric and asymmetric transference of information, *Association Control Service Element* (ACSE) for establishing, releasing and managing all application associations, and *Commitment, Concurrency and Recovery* (CCR) *Service Elements* whereby activities distributed across many open systems can be completed in the event of failures of separate transactions. Figure 4.8 shows the internal organization of the application layer.

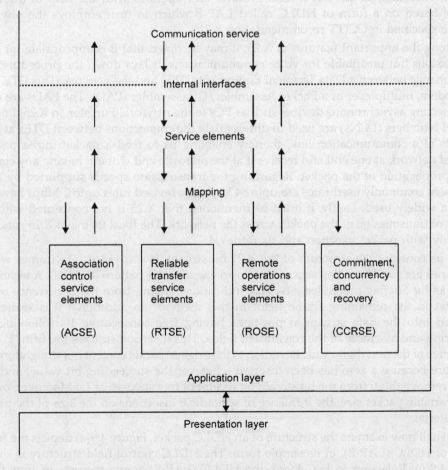

Fig. 4.8. Schematic of the internal organization of application layer

To summarize these discussions about OSI, it is a logical architecture defining a set of principles which includes protocol layering, the layer service definition, service primitives and independence. Each layer is given a definite job and offers a defined service to the layer above utilizing the service provided by the layer below it. The three higher order layers, involved in software organization, are not directly of interest to the communications engineer. These software-oriented protocols are related to the communication processes through the Transport Layer.

4.3.4. CCITT Recommendation X.25 and High-Level Data Link Control (HDLC)

X.25 consists of a set of recommendations of CCITT (International Telegraph and Telephone Consultative Committee) for data transmission over a packet-switched network. It furnishes a CCITT standard *interface* to such networks which has bcome an extremely popular interface for Wide Area Networks (WANs). This interface embodies the three lower layers of the OSI reference model, viz. : (*i*) *Physical Layer:* An X.21 interface is assumed but interfaces like V.35 can also be supported. (*ii*) *Data Link Layer:* It is postulated that Link Access Protocol-Balanced (LAP-B) is used; some older protocols are also supported. (*iii*) *Network Layer:* Packet Level Protocol (PLP) is employed.

Thus X.25 defines the OSI level-3 protocol and operates with the help of a level-2 protocol based on a form of HDLC called LAP-B which in turn employs the physical interface specified in CCITT recommendation X.21.

Among the important features of X.25, it may be noted that it is appropriate for data transmissions but unsuitable for voice communications. It lays down the procedures for data exchange between a Data Terminal Equipment (DTE) and the network. This DTE may be a modem, multiplexer or a Packet Assembler/Disassembler (PAD). The PADs are used for connecting asynchronous devices such as PCs to the network. Furthter, in X.25, Logical Channel Numbers (LCNs) are used to differentiate the connections between DTEs at both the ends of a communication link, thcreby enabling us to feed a packet into a packet-switched network at one end and receive it at the opposite end without having any control on the propagation of the packet. Regarding the transmission speeds supported by X.25, the present commonly used rates are upto 64 kbps; the revised rates upto 2 Mbps have not yet been widely used. Lastly, it must be mentioned that X.25 is not concerned with the manner of transmission of the packet across the network. The focal theme of X.25 concerns itself only with packet injection and its retrieval.

Let us consider the structure of the X.21 bit stream. It is divided into frames whose boundaries are fixed by a flag sequence comprising an octet pattern 01111110. A technique known as *Bit Stuffing* precludes false flag indications arising from the occurrence of the flag octet in the remaining frame field. In this method, an additional 0 is stuffed or crammed into the data stream at positions having five consecutive 1's following the structuring and assembly of the constituent fields. This insertion suffixes the fifth '1' digit irrespective of the next digit value. Revertion to the original packet content is a straightforward procedure because a zero has been inserted whatever the succeeding bit value, and it is easy to remove this 0 from the bit stream on receipt of five successive 1s. Moreover, owing to the variable packet size, the influence of sporadic 0 insertions on the size of the packet is immaterial.

We shall now examine the structure of an HDLC packet. Figure 4.9(a) depicts the frame format of HDLC (LAP-B), in its simple form. The HDLC control field structure is shown in Fig. 4.9(b). Referring to Fig. 4.9(a), the HDLC (LAP-B) frame consists of four fields bounded by the delimiting flags. The *First Field* is an 8-bit address field for identifying the

Called or *Secondary Party* with the calling party designated as the *Primary Party*. Messages sent by the primary party do not contain its address but response messages dispatched by other stations contain the address of the originating station.

The *Second Field* is an 8-bit *Control Field*, (Fig. 4.9(*b*)), defining three types of packets. For an information frame, the first bit of this field is a 0. Then bit numbers 2 to 4 and 6 to 8 are reserved for *Sequence Check Numbers* denoted by $N(S)$ and $N(R)$. Numbering of transmitted packets in the $N(S)$ sub-field is performed independently by the primary and secondary nodes. The $N(R)$ field gives an indication to the distant node about the number of the forthcoming packet in the sequence.

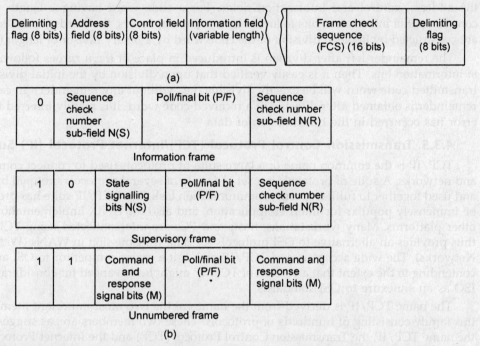

(a)

Information frame

Supervisory frame

Unnumbered frame

(b)

Fig. 4.9. Structural configuration of: (*a*) HDLC-LAP B frame, and (*b*) HDLC control field

When the first bit of the control field is 1 and the second bit is 0, the frame is known as a *Supervisory Frame*. Such frames are used to transmit $N(R)$ acknowledgement when no information is to be sent; the sequence number $N(S)$ is therefore not necessary. Then the two bits available at S are used to signal the status of the transmitting node to the distant node. These two bits can signal four different states: (*i*) *Receive Ready* indicates that after correct receipt of a packet, the node is ready for receiving the next packet in the sequence with number $N(R)$. (*ii*) *Receive Not Ready* which apart from (*i*), also indicates the temporary non-readiness of node to receive the next packet. (*iii*) *Reject* points out the erroneous reception of a packet so that $N(R)$ gives the packet number from which retransmission should begin. (*iv*) *Selective Reject* indicates the error of a particular packet for which that packet only needs to be retransmitted.

If both the first and the second bits of the control field are 1s, the frame is said to be an *Unnumbered Frame*. Frames of this type are responsible for network monitoring and control. They are exploited for sending internodal commands and responses with the intent of network housekeeping. Obviously, their non-involvement in information exchange renders packet sequence numbers unnecessary. Bit numbers 3, 4, 6, 7 and 8 are then used for command and response signals. They are labelled as *M*. A total of 32 different signalling combinations is possible with the five bits available.

A noteworthy feature is that in any control field, the fifth bit is always denoted by *P/F* standing for Poll/Final bit. In the frames produced by primary, this *P/F* bit is set to 1 to poll or instruct the secondary to give a response. For secondary produced frames, this *P/F* bit, normally set of 0, is altered to 1, to convey to the primary when the final frame in a sequence is being sent.

As we find in Fig. 4.9(*a*), the field of the HDLC frame is the *Frame Check Sequence* (FCS) consisting of 16 bits obtained by application of a *Cyclic Redundancy Check* (*CRC*) *Code* over the address, control and information fields. For a code word having a length *N* and consisting of *m* information bits followed by $n = (N - m)$ zeroes, the words for the code set are constructed by Boolean division of the code word by a binary divisor of length $(n + 1)$.

The remainder left after division is introduced in place of the *n* zeroes following the *m* information bits. Then it is easily verified that upon division by the initial divisor, the transmitted code word will be exactly divisible (i.e., without any remainder). In case any remainder is obtained after division of a received code word, it is readily inferred that an error has occurred in the transmission of data.

4.3.5. Transmission Control Protocol (TCP)/Internet Protocol (IP) Suite

TCP/IP is the common name of a large suite of protocols used to connect computers and networks. A suite of protocols is a set or family of several protocols grouped by layer and used together to fulfil a specific communication task. The TCP/IP suite has proved to be immensely popular for Internet application, and also for UNIX implementations and other platforms. Many workstations, hosts and PCs are interconnected using TCP/IP. It thus provides an alternative to OSI protocols for data transmission in WANs (Wide Area Networks). The wide acceptance of TCP/IP makes it a major competitor to OSI and it is contending to the extent that a version of TCP/IP might be advanced for consideration by ISO as an annexure to OSI standards.

The name TCP/IP is derived from the names of the two most important members of this family consisting of hundreds of protocols. These two members are, as suggested by the name TCP/IP, the Transmission Control Protocol (TCP) and the Internet Protocol (IP). TCP is a connection- and stream-oriented reliable protocol providing transport layer services. It manages the flow of data as well as ensures that the data flow is correct. IP is a connectionless technique for conveying raw data packets from one location to another. It provides this delivery of data by working at the network layer through packet switching. Thus IP transmits data from place to place and TCP takes care of the correct operation of this transference. TCP/IP is the adhesive holding together the Internet consisting of thousands of networks which in turn link millions of computers across the world.

In an IP datagram, both the source and destination addresses are included. The addresses themselves are subdivided into a network identifier (ID) and a host ID. A protocol known as the *Address Resolution Protocol* (*ARP*) is used for routing the packet to the destined station. Prior to the commencement of data transmission, an ARP request message is broadcast to all the stations. Any station recognizing its own address in the ARP request message responds by returning an ARP reply. In this way, the source node is able to acquire the necessary route information to the destination station. After the route is thus decided, the IP packets are transferred in a *best effort manner* which implies that neither this is any error correction capability built into the system nor any information that the packets have been successfully delivered, is provided. Hence IP data packet transport does not guarantee that the packets will arrive at the receiving node in the order in which they have been sent. Assurance of data integrity is given by the higher level protocol, viz., TCP.

A brief description is given now of the principal protocols included in the TCP/IP suite, besides TCP and IP.

— *Simple Mail Transfer Protocol (SMTP)* It provides electronic mail service using TCP for sending and receiving messages.

— *File Transfer Protocol (FTP)* It is a protocol for transferring files from one machine or computer to another machine or computer. It accomplishes this by using TCP at the transport layer for moving files. The *FTP Server* (or *Host)* is the remote computer on the network which allows users to download files into their own computer. This operation can also work in the reverse direction in which the user is able to transfer his/her files to another computer system on a local network or the Internet. An *FTP Account* is an account on a computer which supports transference of files between the given computer and other computers.

— *Telnet* It is a computer program which allows a computer to pretend or pose as a *dumb terminal,* and connect to and use a remote host computer, thus providing *terminal emulation* capabilities. Using Telnet, the users can log in into another computer system and avail the services they do not have on their own computers.

A user name and password is mandatory in many computer systems before permitting users to access their resources. Public Service Computer Systems have logins such as "public" or "info"; they usually prompt the user with the correct user name and password, if any.

The necessity of Telnet program arises because the host computer system may offer up-to-date versions of popular software, and services like group games, extensive newsgroups, etc.

— *User Datagram Protocol (UDP)* This is a protocol providing connectionless transport layer service. The Internet Protocol (IP) is utilized for packet delivery.

After this résumé of the main protocols constituting TCP/IP, let us now enquire about the protocol model on which TCP/IP is based. The basis of TCP/IP is a four-layer US *Department of Defence* (DoD) model known as the *DoD Model* or *Internet Model* which was developed before the formulation of the OSI standards. Although the four-layer Internet model does not fit neatly into the OSI model, nonetheless, it will be interesting to compare the two models to seek a correspondence between the four layers of the Internet model and the seven layers of the OSI model, Figure 4.10 shows the structure of the two models drawn side-by-side for the purpose of comparison.

The *Network Access Layer* of the Internet Model corresponds approximately to the Data Link and Physical Layers of the OSI Model enabling TCP/IP hosts to interact with other hosts on a network. At the network access layer, hosts are recognized by physical addresses which are used for local message delivery.

The *Internet Layer* of the Internet or DoD Model roughly resembles the Network Layer of OSI Model. It sends messages through internetworks, and is concerned with Internet Protocol exchanging information beween hosts in an internetwork. At the Internet layer, host identification is done by logical addresses called IP addresses containing both network and host identifiers which are used by IP for routing. By using an *Address Resolution Protocol (ARP),* IP addresses are mapped to the physical addresses of network access layer.

The *Host-to-Host Layer* of Internet Model is similar to *Transport Layer* of OSI Model. The function of this layer is to perform message fragmentation, assembly and multiplexing. The protocol used at this layer is either TCP (for reliability applications) or UDP (User Datagram Protocol) for applications in which a certain degree of unreliability can be tolerated.

An exact or one-to-one correspondence between the Internet and OSI models cannot be established for the Process/Application Layer. The reason is that the process/application layer supports a wide range of protocols, processes and applications like FTP, Telnet, etc.

Some of these applications are equivalent to the functions of many OSI levels. Considering FTP, for instance, this protocol plays the role of a *Session Manager,* a part which is enacted by the *Session Layer* in OSI Model. Another function of FTP is the format conversion when file transference between different systems takes place. This format conversion function is performed by the *Presentation Layer* in OSI Model. FTP does even more than that by transferring files between different systems, a task which is carried out by the Application

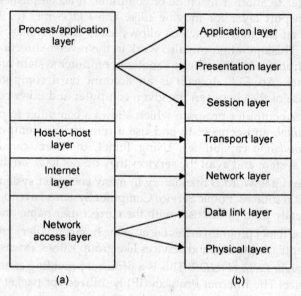

Fig. 4.10. Comparison of the Internet and OSI models: (*a*) Internet Model and (*b*) OSI Protocol Model

Layer in OSI Model. Thus a paticular application 'FTP' of the process/application layer in the Internet Model has three counterparts in the OSI Model namely, Session, Presentation and Application Layers.

TCP/IP is extensively used over the Internet. The Internet, as we know, is a network comprising several networks. These networks consist of several computers connected together. Through the Internet, our desktop computer can exchange data, messages and files with any computer linked to the Internet.

The Internet uses telephony network for this communication. When a computer is connected to the Inernet, it actually becomes part of a network which is connected to other networks through a *Network Backbone* (Fig. 4.11). Interconnections called *Gateways* exist between these backbones enabling a computer on one network to exchange messages and data with another computer which is a part of another network.

There are four methods of connection to the Internet: through a modem, by Integrated Services Digital Network (ISDN), via a Local Area Network (LAN) or directly to the Internet producing a high speed link. The choice of the method of connection depends on the performance expectations from the expenses incurred. For domestic purposes, a dial-up telephone line together with a fast modem is the best solution. Although ISDN is a high-speed network, its availability, installation complications and cost considerations presently favour connection through a modem. While selecting a modem, one should look for modem speed, modem form, whether internal or external, and modem compatibility for data communication with the network. The data communication standard for 33,600 bps modems is termed V.34 and for slower modems V.32 bis. Before connecting to the Internet through a modem, an Internet Account Number is to be obtained on any one of the many interconnected networks in the Internet through an *Internet Service Provider (ISP)* or an on-line service.

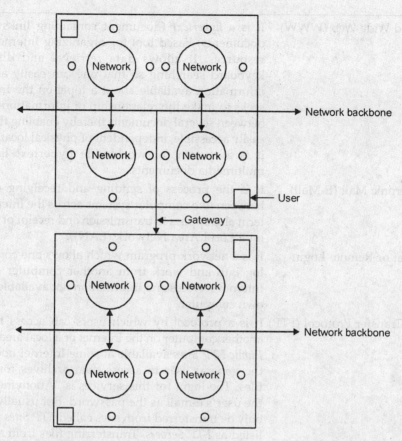

Fig. 4.11. Interconnection of networks to produce a large network

4.3.6. Services Over Internet

Internet includes many components and services, the notable among which are discussed in Table 4.2 Using these services, one can access a wealth of information on business, government documents, entertainment, sports and so on. A browser program like the Internet Explorer helps us to navigate and surf the World Wide Web, play Web page audio and video, send and receive message through e-mail over the Internet. The File Transfer Protocol and Telnet allow a computer to exchange files and programs back and forth on remote computers. With the help of a search engine or a meta-search engine, one can locate data. Learning a markup language permits us to create a simple Web page, change the size and placement of text, add graphics and organize the information into lists. One can also create a hyperlink from one Web page to another, add e-mail to our Web pages, alter the colour of text pages, search for hypertext markup language authoring tools on the Internet and transfer our self-generated documents to a Web Server. One can gain useful information by subscribing to newsgroups and using Gopher. Experiencing multimedia on the Web provides diversion and recreation. Thus the Internet is a mine of information and fun.

Table 4.2. Internet Resources

Sl. No.	Service	Brief Description
1.	World Wide Web (WWW)	It is a *hypertext* (document containing links to other documents) based tool for organizing Internet related resources. It allows data retrieval and display by keyboard searching so that one can easily access the information available about a topic on the Internet. It seeks to make the relationship of information common between several documents thereby enabling them to be easily accessible, independent of physical location. Thus it is a system for worldwide hypertext linking of multimedia documents.
2.	Electronic Mail (E-Mail)	It is the process of sending and receiving messages between two computer systems across the Internet. (The term also applies to transmission and receipt of messages on a Local Area Network (LAN)).
3.	Telnet or Remote Login	It is a network program which allows one computer to log into and work from another computer accessing Internet services and information not available on one's own computer.
4.	File Transfer Protocol (FTP)	It is a protocol by which users can access files from another computer on the Internet or a local area network. *Public FTP Sites* available at some Internet nodes allow the general user to access data archives for copying files. The login for this services is "Anonymous" with the user's e-mail as the password. But usually files can only be transferred from sites called *FTP Sites* which are listed as *FTP Servers*. Transferring files from a network computer to the local computer is called *Downloading* whereas file transfer from the local computer to a network computer is called *Uploading*. Knowledge of compression techniques is essential for downloading files because frequently a file has to be compressed for faster downloading. Threreafer, the user requires a decompression software for file restoration. Such programs are available at public FTP sites.
5	Gopher	It is an Internet software tool for accessing and retrieving information by searching computer databases. This information may be of a diverse nature consisting of reference materials, government documents, speeches, etc. The Gopher software organizes the information in a series of related menus (menu-based information) for the user to choose from, and then displays the selected item in a textual format; this can be viewed using Web browsers. Gopher thus represents a distributed service for organizing and accessing hierarchical related information in various forms.

		A *Gopher site* is a computer on the Internet offering Gopher menus. All the Gopher Servers on the Internet together constitute the *Gopher Space*.
6.	Archive	A service for information gathering, indexing and display.
7.	Archive Server	A system which makes anonymous FTP servers manageable by helping in finding their needs; this means a system for searching anonymous FTP archives.
8.	Finger Service	Facility to ask for information on a particular user recognized by a user ID.
9.	Usenet (User's Network)	A vast system of discussion groups about various topics.
10.	Talk Facility	A connection between two computers logged on to the Internet for message typing back and forth to provide real-time communication limited by transmission and routing delays.
11.	Chat Groups	Forums in which like-minded persons engage in real-time discussions.
12.	Internet Relay Chat (IRC)	Extension of talk facility to more than one peron at the same time to allow multi-party conversations.
13.	Veronica and Jughead	Tools to keep track of Gopher menus to make Gopher searches both easier and readily manageable.
14.	Wais	A service for searching indexed databases. This includes gathering information about a topic from various locations and providing easy access to the information.
15.	White Pages Directories	Resources providing listings of electronic addresses of users on the Internet. Used for searching user's electronic address.
16.	Electronic Magazines, Journals and Newsletters	Electronic publications including text and files, either scholarly or of general interest.
17.	Mailing Lists	An organized system wherein a group of people send messages on a given topic.
18.	Internet Bulletin Board Systems (BBSs)	Repositories of information usually on a particular topic.
19.	Games	Material for fun and recreation.
20.	Multiple User Dimension (MUD)	A program of multi-person virtual reality.
21.	Newsgroups	Ongoing conversations involving subscribers with similar interests, e.g., a periodical corporate newsletter.

4.3.7. Surfing the World Wide Web

For easy access to information, World Wide Web organizes resources using Internet documents called Web Pages or Web Documents. A computer storage area containing one or more Web pages is known as a *Web Site*. To reach a Web site and explore the Internet, a Web client program termed *Web Browser* is used. The browser accesses and displays the contents of a Web site and may be text-based or graphics-based depending on the type of matter displayed. Microsoft Internet Explorer and Netscape Navigator are two popular graphical browsers.

Generally, Web pages contain elements which refer the user to other pages. Such elements containing addresses which link the user to other Web pages, are termed *Hyperlinks*. The hyperlinks are also of two kinds: Textual and Graphical.

By surfing the Web, we understand jumping or moving from one Web site to another site, visiting new places and meeting new people in much the same way as a surfer on the ocean catches waves one after another. To start surfing, we visit a favourite web site and move the mouse pointer over a text or graphical hyperlink. On clicking, the browser goes to that web site to access the selected page. With the appearance of the Web page, the surfing begins. When we feel the monotony of waiting, we can click the next hyperlink and so on.

4.3.8. Internet Multimedia

Multimedia will be formally introduced in Chapter 7. Here, suffice it to say that many Web sites include audio, video, animation, etc., besides textual and graphical information. For listening to the sound files, one must download and install the audio player from the Internet. The computer must also be equipped with a sound card and self-powered *Speakers* with built-in amplifiers or *Headphones* which can be directly plugged into the sound card. Similarly, for video viewing, the video player is downloaded but no additional hardware equipment is required.

Web sites offer two types of sound, viz., *Prerecorded Sounds* such as greetings, background, audio effects and music, and *Live Sounds* like that from radio stations and other sources. Web sites providing continuous music, use compression techniques to squeeze the file size. Complementary decompression must be done at the receiver.

The standard video formats are Windows AVI (Audio Visual Interface) and MPEG (Moving Picture Experts Group) audio and video.

4.3.9. Searching and Browsing on the Internet

Browsing, for information involves movement from organized broader to narrower categories on to a specific topic. Sites offering information in these categories are called *Internet Indexes*.

The Searching operation uses a search engine which takes the help of the computer for rapidly searching a larger group of web pages. A search engine can be found at a Web site. On typing some carefully chosen words or phrases termed *Keywords* closely related to the desired topic, the search engine looks for pages in which these keywords appear. Different search engines may give different results from the same set of keywords. So, for a comprehensive and deeper search, a tool called *Meta-Search Engine* is employed. This accepts the search request and sends it to several other search engines simultaneously. The returned replies are combined to give the final response.

Specialized searches are carried out with the aid of tools known as *White Pages* containing specific directory information like the telephone book. Eventually, one goes to particular sites to locate data which are not found by a search engine.

A popular web search index is *Yahoo!* The Yahoo site is located at the address :

http://www.yahoo.com/

where 'http' stands for Hypertext Trasfer Protocol for Internet access. With the help of Yahoo, it is possible to search over 2×10^5 web sites through the keyboard. Yahoo also provides a well-organized cross-referenced hierarchical subject guide covering more than 2×10^4 organized categories. Announcement of one's own web site can also be done using Yahoo. It also provides a Search Engine. This search engine compares the entered keywords with only the pages in the Yahoo index; the entire web is not searched. Therefore, keyword matching is not possible for those web sites which have not been categorized by Yahoo editors and added to Yahoo index. Further, it may be noted that during searching, one can either search the full directory structure or confine oneself to the desired category.

Another popular search engine is *AltaVista* sponsored by Digital Equipment Corporation. Its address is:

http://www.altavista.digital.com/

It catalogues more than 4×10^7 web pages in addition to the text of 1.5×10^4 newsgroups. Gopher or FTP sites are absent. AltaVista uses its huge database for locating Web pages with the help of a computer program called 'Scooter'. An 'Advanced Search' option is also available, restricting the number of responses and ranking them according to certain rules entered in the 'Advanced Search Form'.

Lycos search engine (at Carnegie Mellon University) has the address:
http://lycos.cs.cmu.edu/

Its catalogue contains about 2×10^7 web pages, FTP and Gopher sites.

The information given in this subsection is continuously changing and needs regular updating.

4.3.10. Hypertext Markup Language (HTML)

This is a language used for creating a Web page. A markup language consists of a set of formatting commands or tags that one places around text or pictures in a document. The markup language used for the Web is called *Hypertext Markup Language* or *HTML*. These HTML documents are essentially ASCII (American Standard Code for Information Interchange) documents.

HTML Authoring Tools are programs for creation of HTML documents. There are special ways of writing, viewing, loading, editing and formatting these documents. HTML documents are produced in a text editor such as *Notepad* and rendered by a Web browser like Internet Explorer.

4.4. INTEGRATED SERVICES DIGITAL NETWORK (ISDN)

Unlike circuit-switched and packet-switched networks, ISDN is not a separate network but a network concept under which many standards and services are emerging having far-reaching impact on network design. It is an evolutionary architecture offering integrated voice and data services with the portability and cost competitiveness sufficient to bring the entire gamut of services at the customer's fingertips.

As per the preamble to CCITT-I series recommendations, ISDN is defined as a "network evolving from the telephony Integrated Digital Network (IDN) which provides *end-to-end digital connectivity* for supporting a wide range of services including both voice and non-voice services, to which users have access by a limited set of standard multi-purpose user-network interfaces." In broader terms, ISDN is a potential high-speed telecommunications standard for sending digitally encoded voice, data, video and other signals on the same lines and also for providing access to a variety of communications, information processing and auxiliary services. As ISDN is a completely digital system, an ISDN implementation must provide adapters needed to translate analog or non-ISDN compatible signals.

4.4.1. Advantages and Features of ISDN

Looking at the widespread acceptance gained by ISDN, it holds great promises as a next generation communication service offered by telephone companies woldwide, both to the business and residential subscribers. Among the benefits of ISDN, we may mention:

— It uses a *single digital link* to obtain the full group of communication facilities such as telephone voice, FAX, data, text, images, sounds and video. The use of digital technology assures a high noise immunity. The signal level at subscriber terminal equipment is not degraded by line length improving the Quality of Service (QoS) as compared to the Plain Old Telephone Service (POTS). Additionally, ISDN subscribers have full connectivity to analog subscribers either at the national or international level. Call setup time is also very short with greater accuracy and connection stability. Combined with these features is the advantage that ISDN employs the existing wiring with the same switches and transmission facilities.

— Wider bandwidth supporting capability upto 2 Mbps. Access to Internet for ISDN subscribers at 64/128 kbps improves both the response time and service quality. Using 64 kbps for internet, telephone calls can be made on the other channel. Data delivery speeds of modems today are typically ~9.6 kbps.

— Provision of *Bearer Services for Communications* such as 64 kbps (unrestricted) for circuit-switched data, 64 kbps for speech, 64 kbps for 3.1 kHz audio, alternative 64 kbps for data transfer during a speech call, 2×64 kbps (unrestricted), 384 kbps (unrestricted), etc., virtual call and permanent virtual circuit in the packet-switched mode; *Teleservices for Information Processing,* e.g., Telephony, Telefax, Teletex, Telex, Videotex, etc., and *Supplementary services for easy use of above services and additional functionality,* e.g., Calling Line Identification Presentation (CLIP), Calling Line Identification Restriction (CLIR), Multiple Subscriber Number (MSN), Malicious Call Identification (MCID), Direct Dialling In (DDI), Calling Line Identity (CLI), Call Forwarding Busy (CFB), Call Forwarding No Reply, (CFNR), Call Forwarding Unconditional (CFU), Call Deflection (CD), Call Waiting (CW), Terminal Portability (TP) and so on.

To cite a few examples of ISDN facilities, the accommodation capacity of a single ISDN line is upto 8 devices so that a person can avail multiple telephone numbers to handle the expanded volume of calls. Further, functions of serveral POTS lines can be performed by one ISDN line. Hence, one can simultaneously carry out a telephonic conversation while browsing the Internet or sending a facsimile. Also, ISDN allows talking accompanied by viewing and editing the same file. By screen sharing, two or more customers can work interactively with voice and data. Through the facility of *Internal Switching,* a call is permitted to stay within a PBX (Private Branch Exchange) or traverse across a huge network to a distant destination. For charging, *Credit Card* connection can be done via X.25 packet network.

4.4.2. ISDN Reference Configuration and Functional Devices

In many countries, the wiring for ISDN connection from the telephone company to the customer's premises will be Cu cables of POTS or PSTN with different equipment at both the ends, and powered by the end users instead of the company. An ISDN reference configuration has been defined for description of various functional blocks and access points in a user-network interface. Figure 4.12 depicts the ISDN user access reference configuration in which each component or block performs a different prescribed function. *Functional Devices* represent the definitions of the specific tasks of these components. Now, looking at Fig. 4.12, the roles of the functional devices are elucidated as under :

(i) *Network Termination Type 1 (NT1) :* This is the user's access point into the ISDN. A socket inserted into NT1 marks the end of the network and beginning of user's domain. It is therefore the boundary of ISDN from the end-user side. NT1 is the interface between the twisted pair cables of the telephone company and the eight-wire cables of ISDN equipment, to be provided as a box on the wall by the public network operator as a part of ISDN connection during the introductory phase of ISDN. As the ISDN line does not supply power like the analog line, the NT1 box will bear the responsibility of power supply for line operation. Besides termination of the line transmission, the NT1 will also carry out the tasks of maintenance and performance monitoring, multiplexing, transfer of timing and contention resolution. These functions associated with the appropriate physical and electromagnetic termination of the transmission line between the telephone exchange and the user, are broadly equivalent to Layer 1:Physical Layer of the OSI Reference Model shown in Fig. 4.7.

(ii) *Network Termination Type 2 (NT2)* : The NT2 Box, if present, is specified to allow some form of switching function like a digital Private Automatic Branch Exchange (PABX) or a Local Area Network (LAN) at the customer's premises. It is not compulsorily demanded in every ISDN installation. Its functions include OSI layers 2 and 3: Data Link and Network Layers, protocol handling and switching functions, switching and concentration along with maintenance and some other functions of Layer 1: Physical Layer. Functions of NT1 and NT2 boxes can be combined into one physical equipment but it is more likely that NT1 and NT2 will be separate.

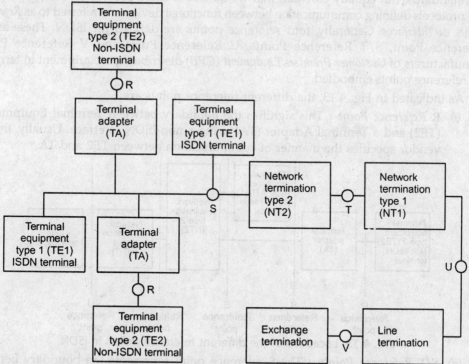

Fig. 4.12. ISDN reference model showing how the various types of components are connected to ISDN

(iii) *Terminal Equipment Type 1 (TE1)* : A TE is an end-user device in the form of an ISDN-ready or non-ISDN ready equipment, e.g., ISDN telephone or facsimile machines, ISDN integrated computer terminals, analog telephones, faxes, modems, etc.

Terminal Equipment Type 1 (TE1) represent those terminal equipment which support the standard ISDN interface directly, offering direct connectivity to ISDN without the need for terminal adapters. Examples of such equipment include digital telephones and faxes, and intergrated voice/data terminal devices.

(iv) **Terminal Equipment Type 2 (TE2)** : To the functional group TE2 belong those equipment which are not specifically designed for ISDN operation, i.e., equipment which are not ready for direct ISDN connection. Equipment complying with a non-ISDN interface are the present day analog devices such as telephones, fax machines; computers, X.25 terminals, etc., including modems, all of which require adapters to work with ISDN.

(v) **Terminal Adapter (TA)** : This is required for TE2 to adapt the equipment interface to that required for ISDN entry, allowing TE2 to be served by an ISDN user-network interface. It is not necessary if one has an ISDN ready equipment.

A terminal adapter enables analog voice and data devices to operate on an ISDN connection. It is essentially a *protocol converter* for reconciliation with all those equipment which are not designed for ISDN. The nature of TA function is determined by TE2 interface specification.

4.4.3. Reference Points

For successful working of ISDN, it is not only necessary that we lay down protocols and standards, but equally essential that we adhere to these protocols during operation. The protocols defining communication between functional devices are referred to as *Reference Points* or *Interfaces*. Generally, four reference points are defined for ISDN. These are: R Reference Point, S/T Reference Points, U Reference Point and V Reference Point. Manufacturers of *Customer Premises Equipment* (CPE) describe their equipment in terms of the reference points embodied.

As indicated in Fig. 4.13, the different reference points are:

(i) **R Reference Point** : This signifies the boundary between Terminal Equipment 2 (TE2) and a Terminal Adapter (TA) using a non-ISDN interface. Usually, the TA vendor specifies the manner of communication between TE2 and TA.

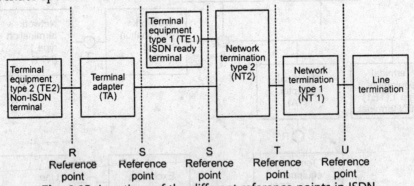

Fig. 4.13. Locations of the different reference points in ISDN

(ii) **S/T Reference Points** : The S-reference point represents the boundary between customer equipment utilizing ISDN user-network interface such as TE1 or TE2 with a TA and the device NT1. The T-reference point is a point lying between the PBX switching equipment at customer's premises and the Local Loop Termination (NT1). When NT2 functions are absent, the S and T reference points are coincident, and the user network reference point is designated as an S/T Reference Point. An S/T device needs a stand-alone NT1 device. However, when an NT2 is present, the interfaces at both the reference points may be similar at layers 1 and 2 of OSI Model but at layer 3, there may be a slight difference because the signalling protocols at the S interface are private network protocols while those at the T interface are public network protocols.

(*iii*) *U Reference Point* : It is the point of connection of the public exchange network with the equipment containing NT1 functions at the user's doorsteps. At the U interface, the form of the signals must be matched with the physical characteristics of exchange lines. The NT1 function is built into the ISDN device for U interface.

(*iv*) *V Reference Point* : Recently defined, this point lies between the line termination equipment at the public exchange extremity of the local exchange line and the exchange termination or switch, enabling the exchanges from different vendors to be used with different line transmission systems including fibre optic and copper cable links.

4.4.4. Channels

For the transference of information between any two points, a conceptual pathway may be visualized. This pathway is known as a *Channel*. A large number of channels may be operating simultaneouly without any mutual interference, on a single pair of wires constituting an ISDN connection. One channel, for instance, may be for dialogue telephony, another for data transmission and so on. Various kinds of channels under ISDN are as follows:

(*i*) *B or Bearer Channels* : There are two B channels delivering at the rate of 64 kbps accompanied by timing information but without any signalling content. These channels are used for carrying the bulk of digital information streams such as voice, data, video and audio. They provide access to a variety of communication modes within ISDN including circuit-switched services, permanently assigned connections and packet-switched services. The use of the two B channels is unrestricted and independent. However, the two channels can be combined for data transmission at speeds up to 128 kbps.

Thus the B channels are designed to transfer different types of information streams equally well. It must be remembered, however, that these channels are *Access Channels* for providing services; they must be clearly distinguished from the services themselves. But we must also note that the nature of a channel limits the services which can be offered on it. As already indicated, the B channels can support both circuit-mode and packet-mode services.

Rate Adaptation has to be performed in accordance with CCITT recommendation 1.460 in order to carry a single information stream at a bit rate < 64 kbps over a B channel. Multiplexing techniques are employed to combine several information streams from a particular customer in the same B channel, but for circuit switching, a complete B channel will be switched to a single destined user-network interface.

(*ii*) *D or Data Channel* : There is a single D channel delivering at a bit rate of 16 kbps or 64 kbps. The purpose of the D channel is to carry the signalling information for B channel switching between the user and the network. Since this signalling information is carried in packet form, the D channel can only provide packet switched services.

Thus the D channel carries the signalling bit stream whereby the switches of telephone network are enabled to handle the transmission from B Channels. This channel employs a layered protocol in accordance with CCITT recommendations 1.440, 1.441, 1.450 and 1.451.

(*iii*) *H Channels* : These channels, to be available at many bit rates, are multiples of the B channel which are circuit switched together. Among these H channels, the telecom will only support the H_0 channel in the initial phase. This H_0 channel is a 384 kbps channel comprising 6 B channels. The H_0 channels will be used for medium bandwidth applications like high-speed data transmission, hi-fi stereo and teleconferencing.

4.4.5. Interface Structures and Options

User access at reference points S and T complies with two forms of interface structures: Basic Rate Interface (BRI) and Primary Rate Interface (PRI). The main features of the two structures are:

(*i*) *Basic Rate Interface* : This interface is economical and hence useful for individuals, small commercial establishments, etc. It provides the user with a form of access to ISDN giving two 64 kbps B channels and one 16 kbps D channel, with a total bit rate = $2 \times 64 + 1 \times 16 = 144$ kbps. It is therefore commonly referred to as (2B + D) *Configuration*. These B channels offer the benefits of simultaneous availability together with independent operation. So, they can be utilized for different connections concomitantly. The D channel on BRI may also be used to carry packet switched data according to CCITT recommendation X.31.

(*ii*) *Primary Rate Interface* : This interface is costly and hence out of the reach of small business houses. It is useful for software companies. The form of access in this interface provides delivery of thirty 64 kbps B channels together with one 64 kbps D channel resulting in an aggregate bit rate = $30 \times 64 + 1 \times 64 = 1.984$ Mbps $\simeq 2$ Mbps. It may be noted that the bit rate for the D channel in PRI is higher than in the case of BRI. Thus the PRI interface has the structural configuration (30B + D) where all the constituent channels are at 64 kbps. Further, as in BRI, all the B channels can be availed of simultaneously and independently. The D channel does not carry any packet switched data. It is used only as a carrier of signalling information. In addition to the B and D channels, the PRI can also provide channels at an intermediate bit rate of 384 kbps. Such channels are designated as H_0 channels. Alternatively, a single channel at 1.92 Mbps, known as an H_{12} channel, can be provided.

Now considering interface options, they refer to the various possibilities of subscription to subsets of BRI or PRI. During implementation of ISDN, the customer will be able to exercise options about choice of channels such as one B and one D channel, 2 B and 1 D channels, and solo D channel, for the BRI. Similarly, for PRI, subscription up to a B channel subset with a maximum number of 30 B channels is possible along with a mandatory D channel.

Taking the help of different types of terminal adapter, ISDN will support non-ISDN user-network interface like those of X and V series recommendations, employing existing hardware. Some terminal adaptation examples are : Using an analog telephone as an ISDN telephone on a B channel, adapting a modem to work on the 3.1 kHz bearer service or 64 kbps unrestricted bearer service on a B channel, etc.

To prepare for using ISDN, one needs several devices, e.g., the *NT1 Device* for network termination and line powering functions; *ISDN Telephone* to take advantage of powerful call managment features offered by ISDN; *Personal Computer* having Pentium Processor, bus slots for connecting ISDN equipment, serial port for terminal adapter, etc.; *Remote Access Device* for connection to another PC or LAN via ISDN; and *Video Conferencing Equipment* including a video camera, video capture card, ISDN adapter card and associated software. Then only one can avail of the enormous benefits and services of ISDN, as discussed in the ensuing sub-section.

4.4.6. Services over Narrow-Band ISDN (N-ISDN)

Between any two ISDN subscribers, the following services are offered on a dial-up basis: Photo-telephony, Desk Top Video Conferencing (using a PC with the camera mounted on it and single ISDN line at 128 kbps), High-Quality Video Conferencing (using three ISDN at 384 kbps with the above facility), High-Speed Data Transmission at 128 kbps by inserting an add-on card in the PC, and High-Speed Facsimile consuming a quarter of transmission time. A major attraction of ISDN, however, is the provision of *Phone Plus Facilities*.

Looking at the Phone Plus Facilities, in addition to the traditional services, the following services will be available on ISDN: (*i*) *CLIP* or *Calling Line Identification Presentation* in which the telephone number of the calling party is displayed on the ISDN telephone for identifying the caller and offering the called party the choice to accept a call. (*ii*) *CLIR* or *Calling Line Identification Restriction* for CLIP prevention allowing the calling party to disallow the presentation of his/her telephone number. (*iii*) *MSN* or *Multiple Subscriber Number* wherein more than one telephone number is assigned to an interface. Upto 8 parallel terminals can be connected at the subscriber premises. (*iv*) *TP* or *Terminal Portability* in which 8 terminals can be connected to a single ISDN line in sockets on internal wiring. (*v*) *Closed Users Group* in which companies and individuals have their numbers in a closed group for barring selected calls and security purposes.

The variety of high quality voice, image, data and intercomputer file transfer and phone plus services given by the ISDN gift package, can be grouped into three broad categories :

— *Bearer Services* These are concerned with moving information from one place to another such as between two network access points, or between network-to-terminal interfaces, e.g., the 64 kbps circuit. A number of bearers are supported by ISDN including: (*i*) *Frame Relay*, a network standard for rapid packet switching which leaves checking and monitoring to higher-level protocols. (*ii*) X. 25 *Recommendation* providing packet switching at moderate speeds; and (*iii*) *Circuit-Switched Connections* for carrying voice or data upto 64 kbps and multiples thereof.

— *Teleservices* This is a complete service provided to a customer (instead of a terminal) by both the network and the terminal. It includes services like telefax, teletext, telex, videotex and *mixed mode service* allowing a combination of text and facsimile image, e.g., a mixed mode document transfer.

To illustrate the distinction between bearer and teleservices, circuit-switched and packet-switched services are two types of 'bearer services' whereas voice and data transfer fall under the heading 'teleservices'.

— *Supplementary Services* These are intended for making the use of bearer and teleservices easier. While bearer and teleservices are Basic Services for straight information transmission and are capable of independent existence, Supplementary Services can only exist in conjunction with the basic services to lend a helping hand to them. Examples of supplementary services are Direct Dialling In, Caller ID, Sub-Addressing, Call Forwarding Busy, Call Forwarding No Reply, Call Forwarding Unconditional, Call Waiting, Conference Calling, Credit Card Calling, Advice of Charge, User-to-User Signalling, Malicious Call Identification and a host of services which add to the utility of telephony.

The interrelationship among the three types of ISDN services is shown in Fig. 4.14. To be able to effectively utilize them, one should understand these services from the users' point of view, from the functional network viwpoint and from network implementation aspects, in a systematic structural organization.

4.4.7. Broadband ISDN (B-ISDN)

The initial ISDN service is commonly referred to as Narrowband ISDN or N-ISDN to differentiate it from broadband ISDN or B-ISDN which will be based on optical fibre transmission providing bit rates ~ 10^9 bps enabling digital video services like Cable TV and Videophone to be commonplace household items dramatically influencing the lifestyles of future generations.

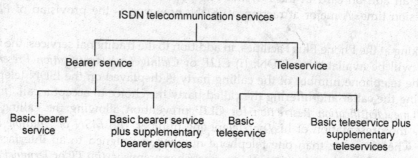

Fig. 4.14. Branching of the ISDN telecommunication services

As we know, the POTS network is essentially architectured to carry voice. The increase in traffic on POTS resulting form the popularization of the Internet may lead to a 'traffic jam' on the POTS. To prevent this clogging on the POTS, a high-speed Broadband-ISDN or B-ISDN has been conceptualized. Preparations for B-ISDN are being made. As a prelude to B-ISDN, Asynchronous Transfer Mode (ATM) technique has been developed. So, current progress in B-ISDN is closely tied to ATM. The ATM methodology is based on *Asynchronous Time Division (ATD)*, a multiplexing technique in which information is transmitted in the form of *Cells* containing an information field and header for channel identification. Cell assignment is done on a demand basis with connections established for a call duration. Individual channels bear the signalling and user information. Presently, ATM provides 155 Mbps, thus falling in the speed category of Fibre Distributed Data Interface (FDDI). ATM seems to be strongly poised to meet the requirements of Wide Area Networks (WANs) and a few specialized Local Area Network (LAN) environments. The main applications of ATM and hence B-ISDN are likely to be in the areas of using and manipulating high-quality images. A detailed presentation of ATM will be made in Sec. 4.5.

B-ISDN will be gradually adopted keeping in tune with the evolution of networks from their current state to one in which broadband services form an intergral part of a multiservice environment including *Interactive Services* such as conversational (video telephony, video conferencing, high-speed data transfer, etc.), messaging (film or image mailing), and retrieval (both film and image); and Distribution Services, e.g., audio and TV distribution.

4.4.8. Synchronous Digital Hierarchy (SDH)

It was briefly remarked in Secs 4.2.3 and 4.2.6 that the plesiochronous operation of PCM Digital Hierarchy (PDH) has inherent limitations. With the widespread deployment of high-speed optical networks and the increasing demand for end-to-end services at rates≥ 64 kbps, the need of Synchronous Digital Hierarchy (SDH) has been felt. In SDH, the multiplexing structure begins at the high levels and the participating primary rate channels are systematically inserted into the high-level frame structure. The obvious implication is that the frame structures of the primary rate channels must be in step with each other so that one can recognize the separate octets belonging to the same basic rate 64 kbps channel within the high-level multiplexed signal.

Plesiochronous switching also suffers from the drawback that the construction of a channel having an end-to-end bit rate >64 kbps by the combination of two or more basic rate channels into a single unit, may cause a reordering of the octets into an incorrect sequence, as shown in Fig. 4.15. The same cannot occur when the frame structures are organized all over the network.

Figure 4.16 illustrates the Synchronous Transport Module Level-1 (STM-1) frame from which the SDH multiplexed structure is built. For higher level multiplexing, the STM-1 frames are byte inter-leaved. A bit rate of 155.52 Mbps forms the basis of the STM-1 signal. To achieve a higher bit rate of STM-n Mbps, n STM-1 signals must be combined together. The n values specified are $n = 1$ and $n = 4$ resulting in the transmission rates = 155.52 and 622.08 Mbps. The time slot ascribed to each STM-1 frame is 125 µsec corresponding to the PCM sampling interval. Hence, the number of bits in the PCM frame = 19440 leading to $19440 \div 8 = 2430$ bytes which are arranged into 9 sub-frames like rows in a matrix. Thus there are 9 rows with 270 bytes in each row representing 270 columns. The bit transmission is done sequentially from top left to bottom right with the first 9 columns allocated for Section Over Head (SOH) containing the framing and maintenance information and the remaining frame carrying the STM-1 information payload in administrative units (AU). The beginning of an AU may not necessarily be coincident with the start of the payload field in the STM-1 fame. The starting point of AU is given by the AU pointer kept in the 9 bytes assigned to section overhead in the fourth row. The data carried by AU is enclosed in Virtual Containers (VC) for which three sizes have been specified to carry services at different rates: VC-31 for 34 Mbps, VC-32 for 45 Mbps and VC-4 for 140 Mbps. Likewise, three kinds of administrative units have been specified: AU-31, AU-32 and AU-4. While in AU-4, a single VC occupies the full payload, in AU-31 and AU-32, the VCs are byte inter-leaved into the STM-1 payload. To fill a higher rate VC, primary rate channels at 1.544 Mbps and 2.048 Mbps are merged together to form a Tributary Unit (TU). A *Frame Synchronous Scrambler* helps in preventing the occurrence of long sequences of ones and zeroes. The information necessary for STM-n multiplexing and demultiplexing, monitoring line and section, and for providing embedded communication channels, is supplied by the Section Overhead.

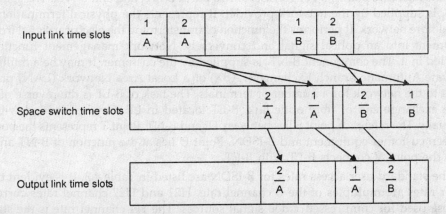

Fig. 4.15. Incorrect sequence reordering of octets in plesiochronous switching

Synchronous Transfer Mode (STM) has its foundations in *Time-Division Multiplexing* (TDM). Time slots are assigned to a service within a recurring frame structure for the entire duration of a call. A minimal header information is necessary and there is no need to collect the full cells of user information before transmission begins. Therefore STM-based networks

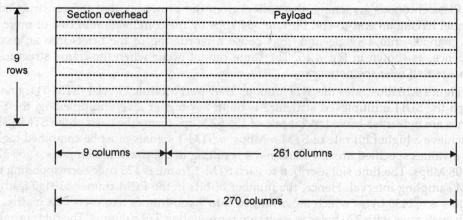

Fig. 4.16. Structure of the STM-1 frame

yield efficient performance for specific continuous bit-rate services but there is a lack of flexibility for networks required to carry a dynamically changing mixture of services at various fixed channel rates. As the future broadband services are expected to be of this dynamically altering nature, most broadband networks will resort to an alternative packet-oriented transfer mode based on an asynchronous TDM technique and referred to as the Asynchronous Transfer Mode (ATM) which is discussed in detail in Sec. 4.5. As ATM packets called *Cells* can be easily carried within the STM payload, the ATM and STM networks can work together in harmony.

4.4.9. User Access to B-ISDN

Figure 4.17 shows the user access reference configuration for B-ISDN. Comparing it with the configuration for N-ISDN given in Fig. 4.12, we immediately notice the strikin; resemblance between the two. Symbols in the diagram have the following meanings: TE: Terminal Equipment, B-NT: Broadband Network Termination, B-LT: Broadband Line Termination, B-ET: Broadband Exchange Termination, and LE: Local Exchange. S, T, U and V are the reference points. B-NT consists of two parts: B-NT$_1$ and and B-NT$_2$. The component B-NT$_1$ is supplied by the network provider. It represents the physical termination to the optical fibre network. It performs the function of transforming the electrical signal from user equipment into an optical signal and conversely. Network management functions are included in it. The component B-NT$_2$ is supplied by the customer. It may be a multiplexer, a Private Automatic Branch Exchange (PABX) or a Local Area Network (LAN) provding access to the network for a number of terminals. The task of B-LT is the reverse of B-NT$_1$ at the exchange end of fibre optic link. B-ET located in LE may be blended with B-LT eventually. The reference point S lies between TE and B-NT. Point T represents the boundary between customer equipment and B-ISDN. Point U lies at the junction of B-NT and B-LT while the point V connects B-LT with B-ET.

The standard user access rates for B-ISDN are listed in Table 4.3. It is evident that the higher rates are multiples of the B channel rate. H21 and H22 channel rates correspond to those used for compressed video signal sources. The H4 channel rate is the standard for PCM Colour TV signals and compressed HDTV signal. There is a direct mapping of the rates H21, H22 and H4 into the virtual containers VC-31, VC-32 and VC-4 respectively. However, suitable mixtures of the channels can be formed to fill any VC. It must be borne in mind that the H channels do not carry any signalling information. Hence common channel signalling must be provided within the VC through an appropriately dimensioned D channel.

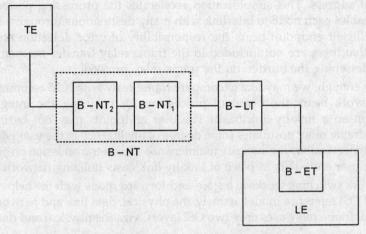

Fig. 4.17. User access reference configuration of B-ISDN
(Symbols are defined in the text)

4.5. ASYNCHRONOUS TRANSFER MODE (ATM)

4.5.1. Frame Relay

In the beginning, Frame Relay was considered to be an efficient data transport mechanism but was found to be unacceptable even for toll quality speech due to inherent delays and echo. Today with technological advancements, frame relay is gaining acceptance as the optimum solution in multimedia networks, both for voice and data transmission. Frame Relay is basically a variable frame structure signalling and data transfer mechanism across intelligent user endpoint devices having the ability to access and process stored information, such as LAN routers, fornt-end processors, etc. It is touted as a low-cost alternative to 64 kbps leased line circuits. Applications of frame relay range from interconnection of multiple LANs to fast data communications like medical image transfer or computer-to-computer file transfer. Frame Relay embodies the features of packet switching (e.g., using the transmission capacity only when traffic is to be sent) and circuit switching (transparency to data communications protocol and high-speed switching capability).

Table 4.3. Recommended User Access Channel Rates to B-ISDN

Sl. No.	Channel Designation	Bit Rate (kbits/sec)	$r = \dfrac{\text{Channel Bit Rate}}{\text{B Channel Bit Rate}}$
1.	B	64	1
2.	H0	384	6
3.	H11	1536	24
4.	H12	1920	30
5.	H21	32,768	512
6.	H22	44,160	690
7.	H4	135,168	2112

In frame relay, the initiating nodal point assigns a destination identification number to each data frame. The frame is then sent to the frame relay switching node. This node interprets the identification number as a real network address, thereby sending the frame to its destined address. This simplification accelerates the processing performed by the switch and enables each node to interlink with many destinations through a single access link. The intelligent endpoint bears the responsibility of error detection and correction processes so that these are not included in the frame relay transfer mechanism, thereby considerably lessening the burden on the frame relay protocol.

Curiously enough, we may like to compare frame realy with X.25 recommendation. In X.25, the network bears the brunt of processing for ensuring the integrity of data communication on a link-by-link basis. The user endpoints may not be intelligent. In contradiction, frame relay postulates some degree of intelligence in the user endpoints (e.g., a LAN interconnect router) for integrity maintenance of data transmission on an end-to-end basis between user endpoints in place of link-by-link basis utilizing network intelligence.

X.25 network switching works in a store-and-forward mode with the help of the bottom three layers of OSI reference model, namely, the physical, data link and network layers. On the other hand, frame relay uses only two OSI layers, viz., the physical and data link layers only.

With the progress in the field of logic circuitry having fast switching speeds upto Gbps, the technology of *Fast Packet Switching* has become a reality so that extremely short packets of constant length can be sent not only for data communication but also for voice transmission. This method based on fast packet switching using short fixed-length packets, is known as Asynchronous Time Division (ATD) multiplexing which is compared with the conventional Time-Division Multiplexing (TDM) in Fig. 4.18. ATD technique is a kind of statistical multiplexing which can significantly improve the transmission capacity utilization of a network determined by the nature and quantity of traffic being controlled. Further improvement can be effected if the *silence* samples of the speech signal are scissored off prior to sending the signal, and instead the information about the successive suppressed silence samples is conveyed to enable the reconstruction of the original signal. A form of ATD popularly known as Asynchronous Transfer Mode, with acronym ATM, has been standardized as a broadband ISDN transport vehicle.

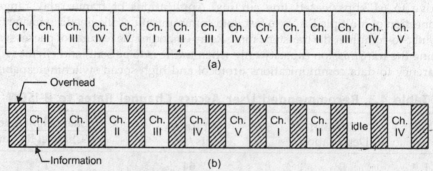

Fig. 4.18. (*a*) Time Division Multiplexing (TDM), and (*b*) Asynchronous Time-Division (ATD) Multiplexing (Ch. = Channel)

4.5.2. ATM Cell Format

The fundamental structural and functional unit of ATM is the *Cell*. The ATM Cell, shown in Fig. 4.19, consists of two parts called the Header and Information Fields. The *Header Field* contains 5 bytes or octets; it identifies the connection number of the sequence of cells constituting a virtual channel for a particular call. The *Information Field* consists of 48 bytes or octets in which the user information is placed. Thus the total number of bytes or octets in the ATM cell = 5 + 48 = 53. The size of the ATM cell has been deliberately chosen to be small to minimize the temporal delays. For example, considering a situation in which a high-priority cell arrives immediately at the instant at which a low-priority cell has gained access to the resource, it is readily seen that the waiting time for the high-priority cell will be smaller for a miniature size cell than for a bigger cell.

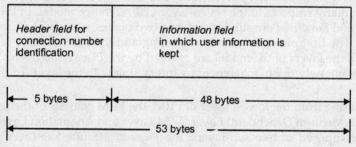

Fig. 4.19. Structure of an ATM cell showing its two parts: the Header and the user information fields

Further, ATM offers a flexible operating environment. The information to be carried is decomposed into constant-length cells. The cell transmission rate is regulated by the user application. It can vary within wide limits from a single cell sent after gaps of several minutes to the maximum network transmission capacity bearing in mind that the network is shared among a number of customers. The number of cells per unit time reflects the bandwidth requirement of the application. Any variations in their rate of arrival indicate the bursty nature of traffic on the network. The cell transfer rate may change in multiples or sub-multiples of 64 kbps channels or in an entirely random manner such as for packets in transaction processing.

4.5.3. Features of ATM

ATM, also called *Cell Relay* (to distinguish it from Frame Relay) is a packet-switched network (in distinction to a circuit-switched network) which forms the core of a broadband-ISDN (B-ISDN) architecture, extending the digital transmission capabilities defined by narrowband-ISDN (N-ISDN) to allow data, voice and multimedia transmissions on the same lines. The primary motivation for ATM is to evolve a real-time architecture which can provide very high bandwidths as demanded by the user. Initially, the ATM implementation will operate at 155.52 Mbps. Then it is likely to be upgraded to 622.08 Mbps and therefore to 2.488 Gbps.

Principal features of ATM include:

(*i*) Transmission over fibre optic cables, whether local or turnk connections.

(*ii*) Parallel Transmission Capability: This modality can be realized because ATM is a switching architecture in which each nodal point can be connected to any other nodal point in a dedicated manner.

(*iii*) Maximum speed of operation in all circumstances provided the network traffic is sufficient to yield the required throughput.

(*iv*) Usage of *fixed* cell lengths permitting incorporation of error correction and routing in hardware.

(*v*) Ease of load balancing due to the fact that switching capabilites enable us to establish multiple virtual circuits between transmitter and receiver.

(*vi*) Ability to simultaneously transmit many signals like audio, video and data which is essential for multimedia applications.

4.5.4. B-ISDN Protocol Model for ATM

Since ATM is envisaged to be the standard transport vehicle for B-ISDN, a Protocol Reference Model (PRM) has been put forward for B-ISDN as shown in Fig. 4.20. This model is analogous in many respects to the seven-layer OSI reference model. In PRM, the *Higher Layer Protocols* and *Functions* are subdivided into two planes, namely, the *Control Plane* and the *User Plane.* The first plane is used for signalling and the second plane for transferring information. All the layers of the model are covered by the *Plane Management Function.* This function carries out network management by interacting with the layers of the control and user planes.

Now beginning from the lowest layer of PRM, the PRM consists of the following three layers: Physical (Medium Dependent) Layer, ATM Layer and Adaptation Layer. The *Physical Layer* itself is composed of two sub-layers: the *Physical Medium Sub-Layer* providing the basic bit transmission ability at the chosen bit rates 155.52 and 622.08 Mbps, and including medium-dependent functions with different formats being adopted for optical fibre and coaxial cables; and *Transmission Convergence Sub-Layer* for transferring the bits supplied by the physical medium sub-layer as valid cells for ATM transmission and conversely. Options can be exercised within this sub-layer for using either the SDH physical layer or a cell-based physical layer.

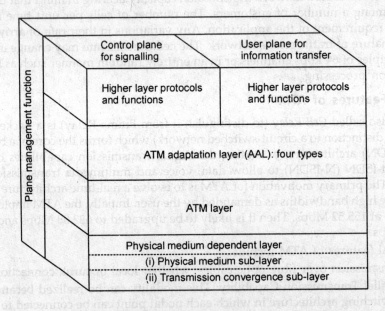

Fig. 4.20. B-ISDN protocol reference model for ATM

The ATM *Layer* deals with the 5 bytes representing the header, carrying transparently the message in the 48 bytes of information field. The ATM header serves to recognize the cells associated with a particular virtual call. Since the cells are assigned on request, governed by the activity of the source and the resource availability, the cells allocated to a channel may recur randomly.

ATM transmission works at the ATM layer by providing connection-oriented virtual connections between the two points concerned. An ATM layer connection basically comprises a concatenation of ATM layer links to achieve an end-to-end transmission. When a call is set up, header values are ascribed to every section of a connection. The connections identified by a header remain the same for the entire duration of a call. The header values are liberated as soon as their task is accomplished and their need is no longer felt. The format of an ATM header is shown in Fig. 4.21.

Looking at the ATM header structure, Byte 1 consists of Generic Flow Control (GFC) and Virtual Path Identifier (VPI) fields. Byte 2 is divided into VPI and VPI/Virtual Call Identifier (VCI). Byte 3 is fully dedicated to VCI. Byte 4 has four components including VCI, Payload Type (PT), Reserved (Res) and Cell Loss Priority (CLP) fields. Finally, the fifth byte is devoted to Header Error Control (HEC).

GFC is a four-bit field used for controlling the volume of information from a given source across the User Network Interface (UNI) to assure an impartial and legitimate support of the various services on the UNI.

Byte 1	Generic flow control (GFC) field	Virtual path identifier (VPI) field		
Byte 2	Virtual path identifier (VPI) field	Virtual path identifier (VPI)/virtual call identifier (VCI) field		
Byte 3	Virtual call identifier (VCI) field			
Byte 4	Virtual call identifier (VCI) field	Payload type (PT) field	Reserved (Res)	Cell loss priority (CLP) field
Byte 5	Header error control (HEC) field			

Fig. 4.21. Header format of asynchronous transfer mode

While setting up a call, a 12-bit or 16-bit Virtual Call Identifier (VCI) is assigned to the call. This helps in identifying and associating a packet with a particular virtual call. In practice, it is convenient to multiplex together a large number of virtual calls which can be routed unitedly from node to node. Then this multiplexed signal is conveyed along a single virtual path, defined as the logical direct link between the two nodes. For each virtual path, the route is predefined and tagged with an 8- or 12-bit Virtual Path Identifier (VPI). The reason for using the term "Virtual Path" is that the virtual calls related to a given virtual path may be transmitted by whatever route is available, subject to the network capacity and route vacancies. At the same time, these virtual calls also maintain their identity as components of a single unified multiplexed signal.

The role of the two-bit Payload Type (PT) is to identify whether the packet is a user information or one required for network functionality. One bit of PT constituting the Reserved (Res) Field, is kept for subsequent specification. The second bit of PT indicates Cell Loss Priority (CLP). Such cells may be rejected when the input traffic exceeds the network capacity. The HEC field of byte 5 gives error protection to the header but not to the payload.

Finally, as the name suggests, the *Adaptation Layer* of PRM accommodates or adjusts the data from a service into the cell structure of ATM. To consider an example, the traffic from a packet-switched network will consist of packets of different sizes. The adaptation layer carries out a segmentation of these packets to fit them into cells as per ATM standard, for transmission over the network. At the receiver, the ATM cells are assembled together to reconstruct the original packet structure. More details of the adaptation layer will be given in the next section. Signalling and user information is normally carried on separate virtual connections at the ATM layer.

Figure 4.22 shows the procedure followed for setting up an ATM call. Translation tables are compiled at the switching and multiplexing nodes to map an incoming call header to an outgoing link and header; this enables the so-called "Virtual Call". For this purpose, the suitable outgoing link for any call is determined from the call VPI with the help of the nodal routing table at each transit node. At such nodes, the VCI is not considered. However, the VCI is used to determine the outgoing link or final station at the terminal node of the virtual path. Here, it must be noted that for establishing an ATM call, one proceeds on similar lines to a narrowband ISDN approach. The main distinguishing feature is that channel capacity is allocated to the virtual connections on ATM linkages. When a call is set up, the users negotiate for network capacity and must restrict themselves within the prescribed limits. If the capacity given cannot cope with the user's requirement, a request for capacity reallocation can be made.

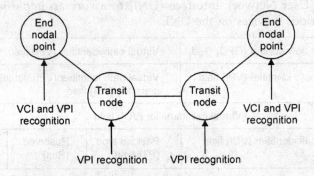

Fig. 4.22. ATM call transmission and set-up procedure

4.5.5 ATM Adaptation Layer

To examine the ATM Adaptation Layer (AAL) in finer details, we recall that this layer acts as the link between the service-independent ATM network and the manifold services supported by B-ISDN. In accordance with the four categories of service, four kinds of AAL have been standardized: (*i*) *Type 1 AAL:* This type of AAL is used to support fixed bit-rate, connection-oriented services, referred to as *Class A Services*, which have a stringent timing requirement form the origination point to the destined station. Among the Class A Services, mention may be made of speech telephony and constant bit-rate video. The various flexibilities offered by ATM are exploited by Type 1 AAL but no effort is made to utilize its potential transmission efficiencies. (*ii*) *Type 2 AAL:* This supports variable bit-rate, connection-oriented services, known as *Class B Services* having a timing requirement between the source and destination points. An example of Class B Service is variable bitrate video for interactive and distributive purposes. (*iii*) *Type 3 AAL:* It supports variable bit-rate, connection-oriented services without any constraint of timing relationship falling under Class C Services, such as packet data services, e.g., X.25, frame relay, signalling, etc. (iv) *Type 4 AAL:* This type of AAL is used to support connectionless data services belonging to the Class D, e.g., LAN and MAN (Metropolitan Area Network) and their interconnection via B-ISDN.

The above four types of AAL are used to relate the virtual connection to the network service being carried. They relate the virtual connection of the ATM layer to the virtual connection between terminal access points such as the exchange lines.

4.5.6. Quality of Service (QoS)

Certain parameters must be defined to express the Quality of Service (QoS) provided to a user. While these parameters help the user to quantify his/her expectations from a service, by ascribing numerical magnitudes to the requirements of the application at hand, they also guide the network operator in allocation of resources to the service. Crucial parameters include the time spent in call set up, the probability that an attempt to establish a call will meet with success and the probability that once a call has been set up, it will not be disconnected. It is also of interest to know how the delays experienced by ATM cells in a connection are distributed. Probability of loss of an ATM cell is another important parameter. No less significant are the end-to-end jitter and error rate.

It transpires that QoS demands of various services differ by wide margins. In the case of telephonic speech transmission, delay and jitter are critical parameters but error rate and packet loss can be tolerated to some extent. To the contrary, data transfer is relatively insensitive to delay and jitter but there should not be any errors or packet loss. So, the steps adopted for QoS control are decided keeping in view the intended application. Higher is the QoS desired, more is the resource allocation and consequently, the tariff charged from the customer increases in proportion to the access to extra privileges and priorities.

QoS is regulated by Call Acceptance Control (CAC) and policing functions. CAC takes a decision about whether a request by a customer for a call may be granted or disallowed. This is done to obtain the maximum output from the given resources and prevent any crowding at the connection level. In particular, variable bit-rate services are frequently bursty in character exhibiting wide variations in peak and average bit-rate values which do not lend themselves to easy estimation and prediction. In such situations, it is convenient to assign an "Effective Bandwidth" to the connection as a measure of the transmission capacity necessary. This assignment is done on the basis of a declaration from the customer regarding the expected peak and mean values of bit rates for the connection. The charges levied to the customer are decided according to these specifications. The CAC will then forbid any calls after exceeding the declared capacity.

Source Policing seeks to provide a preventive control of congestion on the network for protection against excessive or accidental behaviour by the customer. To this end, contractual parameters are laid down and any breach of contract, when detected, leads to suitable remedial action to protect the network from overloading.

When the demand for services from a network is greater than the resource availability, a network congestion invariably takes place. The natural cure for congestion is either a dynamic demand dimunition or a dynamic resource augmentation. In the former scheme, the users or the control ports must get updated information about load conditions in the network for traffic readjustments, as and when needed. In the latter scheme, the network has to create more resource to meet with the extra load.

Demand can be decreased by: *Service Denial* where new sessions are prohibited during rush hours; *Service Degradation* in which all customers are asked to shed their loads by reducing the number of packets outstanding in the network; and *Demand Scheduling* in which the customers have to schedule their demands to keep the total demand below the capacity.

The strategy of *Reactive Congestion Control* operates on a feedback mechanism wherein the data flow changes in response to messages from the network. This strategy is not conducive to ATM because neither audio nor video services can cease to generate cells in the event of network congestion. *Preventive Congestion Control* seems to be a better solution to ATM traffic control. Here the traffic is restrained from increasing to unacceptable magnitudes. Thus the desired QoS level is maintained for the duration of the call.

4.6. CONCLUDING REMARKS

In this chapter, all the preliminary material necessary for understanding networks was presented. Two basic network models, viz., the Open Systems Interconnection (OSI) Model and Internet Model were introduced. The overwhelming complex of INTERNET was reviewed in the context of its structure, services and protocols. The platform of digital network standards was provided through ISDN. Broadband concepts were discussed in the light of the carrying vehicle, "Asynchronous Transfer Mode".

ILLUSTRATIVE PROBLEMS

4.1. How is the 64 kbps channel of ISDN derived?

It is derived from the 3.4 kHz voice telephony practice. According to the Sampling Theorem, the sampling frequency is chosen as 8k samples per sec. Now, satisfactory speech quality is obtained by quantising at 256 amplitude levels. This gives $\log_2 256 = 8$ bits per sample. Hence, the required bit rate = 8 k samples per sec × 8 bits per sample = 64 kbits per sec.   (P4.1)

4.2. Given the gross bit rate = 2048 kbps, find the structural compositions of mixtures of the following for primary rate access interface of ISDN: (i) B and D channels, (ii) H^0 and D channels, (iii) H^{12} and D channels. Bit rates for B, D, H^0 and H^{12} channels are 64 kbps, 64 kbps, 384 kbps and 1920 kbps respectively.

(i) Primary rate access provides several B channels (x, suppose) plus a single D channel. It must be remembered that along with these B and D channels, there is an additional channel at 64 kbps for network and frame synchronization. Therefore, the structure of the composite channel is expressed as

$$xB + D + 64 = 2048 \text{ or, } 64x + 64 + 64 = 2048 \qquad (P4.2)$$

from which $x = 30$ so that the required structural composition is written as $(30B + D)$.   (P4.3)

(ii) and (iii) Writing similar structural equations, the compositions of the mixtures are obtained as:

$5H^0 + D$ for H^0 and D mixture   (P4.4)

and $H^{12} + D$ for H^{12} and D mixture.   (P4.5)

4.3. The burstiness for data transmission varies from 1 to 50. If the peak bit rate is 130 Mbps, what are the limits of variation of average bit rate? What are the corresponding limits for HDTV distribution which has a burstiness of unity?

Burstiness is defined as

$$\text{Burstiness} = \frac{\text{Peak Bit Rate}}{\text{Average Bit Rate}} \qquad (P4.6)$$

Hence, Lowest Average Bit Rate = 1 × 130 = 130 Mbps,   (P4.7)

and Highest Average Bit Rate = 50 × 130 = 6500 Mbps.   (P4.8)

Therefore, the average bit rate of data traffic swings between the limits 130 Mbps and 6500 Mbps.

For HDTV signal, the burstiness being 1, it is clear that the peak and average bit rates are equal. The lower and upper limits of bit rates are therefore both 130 Mbps.

4.4. A frame has a size of 802 bytes in which 7 bytes are the overhead bytes. How many ATM cells can its payload carry?

Subtracting the 7 overhead bytes, the number of bytes in the payload = 802 – 7 = 795. Since an ATM cell contains 53 bytes, the number of ATM cells carried by the payload of the given frame = 795/53 = 15.   (P4.9)

4.5. In ATM telephony, speech samples are collected until the information field of a cell is completely filled. If a delay of 0.8 ms occurs during depacketization, what delay would a speech signal experience in a 64 kbps channel?

ATM information field is composed of 48 bytes. We know that for the 64 kbps channel, the sampling frequency is 8 kHz (Problem 4.1). So, for packetization of speech, the delay incurred = 48/8 kHz = $48/(8 \times 10^{-3})$ = 6 ms. Including a delay of 0.8 ms for depacketization, the total delay of the signal = Packetization Delay + Depacketization Delay = 6ms + 0.8ms = 6.8 ms.   (P4.10)

4.6. Performance parameters of an ATM connection are: Cell loss ratio = 10^{-10} and Cell error ratio = 10^{-9}. If the number of errored cells is 50, how many cells were lost?

From the definition of Cell error ratio, viz.,

$$\text{Cell Error Ratio} = \frac{\text{Number of Errored Cells}}{\text{Number of Cells Transmitted}} \qquad (P4.11)$$

we get $$10^{-9} = \frac{50}{\text{Number of Cells Transmitted}} \qquad (P4.12)$$

$\therefore$ Number of Cells Transmitted $= \dfrac{50}{10^{-9}} = 5 \times 10^{10}$ (P4.13)

Now, applying the definition of Cell Loss Ratio, as

$$\text{Cell Loss Ratio} = \frac{\text{Number of Cells Lost}}{\text{Number of Cells Transmitted}} \qquad (P4.14)$$

we have $$10^{-9} = \frac{\text{Number of Cells Lost}}{5 \times 10^{10}} \qquad (P4.15)$$

$\therefore$ Number of Cells Lost = $10^{-10} \times 5 \times 10^{10}$ = 5.   (P4.16)

Note : On Errored and Lost Cells: If a cell arrives at the receiving node within a maximum allowed time interval τ but there are one or more bit errors in the information field of the received cell, the cell is said to be an *Errored Cell.* When the cell arrives after time τ, it is lost constituting a *Lost Cell.* Reasons for cell loss are: (*i*) Errors in ATM header which cannot be corrected; and (*ii*) Cell buffer overflows in the network.

$$\boxed{\text{REVIEW QUESTIONS}}$$

4.1. What do you understand by Stored Program Control (SPC)? Draw and explain the operation of: (*i*) Time-Space-Time Switching Matrix and (*ii*) Space-Time-Space Swtching Matrix.

4.2. How does circuit switching differ from packet switching? What difficulties are encountered in sending packetized speech?

4.3. What is OSI? What is the advantage of developing such a framework? Draw the structural configuration of OSI reference model and elaborate the functions of its seven layers. Is TCP/IP based on a seven-layer model?

4.4. What does TCP/IP stand for? Give a correspondence between the layers of the OSI reference model and those of the Internet model.

4.5. List the following: (*i*) Two main places form where one can get an Internet account, (*ii*) Three ways of connecting to the Internet, and (*iii*) Two important considerations in selecting a modem.

4.6. What do you understand by Surfing the World Wide Web (WWW)? What is a Hypertext Document? Name its main elements.

4.7. What kinds of sounds are offered by Web sites? How are these sounds played?

4.8. What is meant by a markup language? What does HTML stand for?

4.9. Explain the following terms with reference to the Internet:

(*a*) Telnet,   (*b*) FTP,   (*c*) Telnet,   (*d*) Finger,

(*e*) Archive,   (*f*) Talk, and   (*g*) Gopher.

4.10. Is ISDN a separate discrete network? Comment on the statment, "The title 'ISDN' is slightly misleading."

4.11. (a) What is the difference between a service and an application? Is connecting together two LANs a service or an application?

(b) Distinguish between an interactive service and a distributive service giving suitable examples.

(c) Explain the following terms for ISDN: (i) Telecommunication Services, (ii) Bearer Services, (iii) Teleservices and (iv) Supplementary Services.

4.12. Draw the structural schematic of ISDN reference model and describe the function of each box.

4.13. What is the difference between the TE2 and TE1 categories of terminal equipment for ISDN? Between which two types of terminals, device or network, does a terminal adapter (TA) mediate?

4.14. What are the two forms of user access to ISDN? How many different channels and at what bit rates are defined for each user access?

4.15. What are reference points in ISDN? How many reference points have been defined? What interfaces or connections are represented by these points?

4.16. Explain the meaning of the term "Broadband". Describe the concept of B-ISDN. What target transfer mode has been developed for implementing B-ISDN? Why?

4.17. Sketch the structure of B-ISDN protocol reference model. Explain the functions of the three planes in this model. Name the sublayers of the physical layer in B-ISDN model.

4.18. What is meant by ATM? What does the qualifier "Asynchronous" in ATM refer to? Is ATM a real-time architecture? Highlight some features of ATM.

4.19. What are the fixed-size slots used in ATM called? Draw and explain the structure of an ATM cell. Why is the ATM cell selected small and fixed in size?

4.20. (a) What user requirement is indicated by the number of ATM cells per unit time?

(b) If the number of ATM cells arriving at a node per unit time is varying within wide limits, what nature of traffic does it suggest?

4.21. Describe the roles of the ATM layer and the ATM Adaptation Layer in B-ISDN protocol reference model.

REFERENCES AND FURTHER READING

4.1. M. Orzessek and P. Sommer, *ATM and MPEG-2, Integrating Digital Video into Broadband Networks*, Prentice-Hall PTR, New Jersey, 1998.

4.2. F.E. Froehlich and A. Kent, *The Froehlich/Kent Encyclopaedia of Telecommunications*, Vols 12 & 13, Marcel Dekker, Inc., New York 1997.

4.3. D. Heywood, *Novell's Guide to Integrating NetWare and TCP/IP*, Novell Press, San Jose, 1996.

4.4. R. Stout, *The World Wide Web, Complete Reference*, McGraw Hill, Berkeley, 1996.

4.5. D.E. Comer and D.L. Stevens, *Internetworking with TCP/IP, Vols I-III*, Prentice-Hall of India, New Delhi, 1995.

4.6. R. Handel, M.N. Huber and S. Schroder, *ATM Networks: Concepts, Protocols, Applications*, Addision-Wesley Publishing Co., Inc., Wokingham, 1995.

4.7. W. Feibul, *Novell's Complete Encyclopaedia of Networking*, Novell Press, San Jose, 1995.

4.8. (a) W.R. Stevens, *TCP/IP Illustrated, Vol. 1, The Protocols*, Addison-Wesley Publishing Co., Reading, 1994.

(b) G.R. Wright and W.R. Stevens, *TCP/IP Illustrated, The Implementation*, Addison-Wesley Publishing Co., Reading, 1995.

4.9. B. Eager, M.A. Pike, D. Chandler, D. Cook, B. Kirkner and J. Minatel, *Using the World Wide Web and Mosaic*, Que Corporation, Indianapolis, 1995.

4.10. A.N. Tantawy, *High Performance Networks: Technology and Protocols*, Kluwer Academic Publishers, Boston, 1994.

4.11. H. Hahn and R. Stout, *The Internet Complete Reference*, Osborne McGraw Hill, Berkeley, 1994.

4.12. R.L. Brewster, *ISDN Technology*, Chapman & Hall, London, 1993.

4.13. R.J. Horrocks and R.W. A Scarr, *Future Trends in Telecommunications*, John Wiley & Sons, Chichester, 1993.

4.14. P.J. Fortier, *Handbook of LAN Technology*, Intertext Publications, McGraw Hill, Inc., New York, 1989.

4.15. R. Reardon (Ed.), *Networks for the 1990s*, Online Publication, London, 1988.

4.16. E. Cooper, *Broadband Network Technology: An Overview for Data and Telecommunication Industries*, Prentice-Hall, Englewood Cliffs, 1986.

5

Digital Satellite Communications

The canopy of sky studded with little 'man-made' moons or satellites can simultaneously link all terrestrial stations, providing distance-independent point-to-multipoint telecommunication. This mode of communication is called *Satellite Communication*. Spinning off from the advancing frontiers of space programme such as rocket launchers, attitude control, etc., and progress in the field of microwaves and radio communication, satellite communication is a proven technology with a wide variety of far-flung applications in broadcasting, meteorology, aeronautical and maritime radio navigation, earth exploration, space research and so forth.

Frequency division multiplexing-frequency modulation-frequency division multiple access (FDM-FM-FDMA) has been the major workhorse of commercial analog satellite systems. In the digital arena, coherent PSK, coherent QPSK and coherent MSK have been primary cynosures. Quadriphase-Shift Keying-Time Division Multiple Access (QPSK-TDMA) can oblige a large number of earth stations with minimal loss in transponder capacity and rapidly adapt to traffic changes. Digital methods constitute a supple technology which can be easily moulded to varied functions such as on-board switching and signal processing, multiple spot beams, beam hopping, error correction coding to barter bandwidth for power and Code-Division Multiple Access (CDMA) serving the needs of low data rate applications. In view of this, it is easy to surmise that the future trend is towards digital satellite communications.

5.1. PRELIMINARIES OF SATELLITE COMMUNICATIONS

In this section, we reconnoitre the overall field primarily with a view to acquaint ourselves with the key terms and definitions.

5.1.1. Frequency Allocations for Satellite Communications

The frequencies assigned for this purpose lie in the ultra-high frequency (UHF), 0.3-3 GHz, upper extremity; super-high frequency (SHF), 3-30 GHz; and extremely high frequency (EHF), 30-300 GHz segments of the electromagnetic spectrum. These are broken into frequency bands : L band (1 to 2 GHz), S band (2 to 4 GHz), C band (4 to 8 GHz), X band (8 to 12 GHz), Ku band (12-18 GHz), K band (18-27 GHz), Ka band (27-40 GHz) and millimetre waves (40-300 GHz).

5.1.2. Orbital Mechanics of Communication Satellites

Newton's and Kepler's Laws : The motion of a satellite orbiting the earth is governed by Newton's laws of motion and Newton's law of universal gravitation. Satellites are placed in circular or elliptical orbits obeying Kepler's laws of planetary motion.

Geosynchronous Satellites : The time taken by earth to rotate once around its axis, with respect to stars is called the *Sidereal Day* = 23 hours 56 min 4.09 secs = 86164.09 secs of mean solar time. A *Geosynchronous Satellite* is one having a period of revolution equal to the period of rotation of earth = 1 sidereal day. The radius of its orbit = 42, 164.2 km. A satellite moving in the direction of earth's rotation over the equator, will appear to be at rest at one point on earth's surface and is said to be in a *Geostationary Orbit.* Since the mean equatorial radius = 6378.155 km, the distance between the geostationary satellite and subsatellite point where the equator intersects the line joining the earth's centre with the satellite is = 42, 164.2 km – 6378.155 = 35, 786.045 km.

Why Most Commercial Satellites are Placed in Geostationary Orbits? Firstly, the earth station antenna can be precisely targeted towards the satellite dispensing with the expensive and cumbersome tracking equipment. This drastically cuts down the earth station costs.

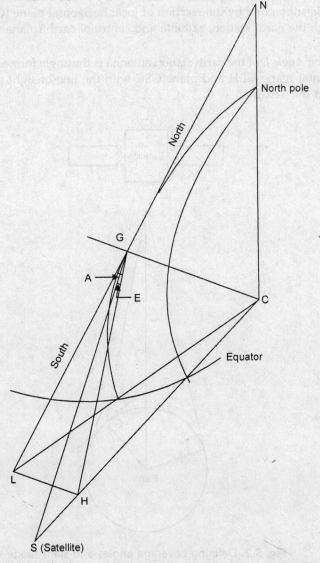

Fig. 5.1. Definition of Azimuth (A) and Elevation (E) angles

Secondly, using a 50° minimum elevation angle of earth antenna, 38 per cent of the earth's surface can be covered by a single satellite. Moreover, a trio of satellites, spaced 120° apart can embrace the whole surface of the earth with some intersection regions; exceptions include polar areas above latitude 76° N and 76°S. Thirdly, the Doppler shift due to the drift of the satellite under the influence of the lunar and solar gravitational fields, is relatively insignificant for all terrestrial stations. This is a desirable feature for synchronous digital systems.

Inclination of Orbit : This is particularly done to cover polar regions and to provide higher elevation angles for earth stations located at high northern and southern latitudes. The inclination imparts the satellite an apparent "figure of eight" motion. Satellite needs to be continuously tracked. Also, one has to switch from a rising satellite to a setting satellite.

Azimuth and Elevation Angles : The *Azimuth Angle A* of an earth station antenna (Fig. 5.1), is the angle subtended by intersection of local horizontal plane (GLH) and the plane passing through the earth station, satellite and centre of earth (plane GSC), with the true north direction.

The *Elevation Angle E* of the earth station antenna is the angle formed by the intersection of local horizontal plane GLH and plane GSC with the line-of-sight path connecting the earth station to the satellite.

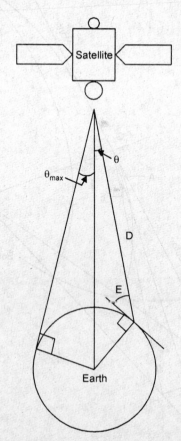

Fig. 5.2. Defining coverage angles and slant range

Coverage Angles and Slant Range Earth Coverage Angle $(2\theta_{max})$ (Fig. 5.2) is the total angle subtended by the earth as viewed from the satellite. *Communication Coverage Angle* (2θ) is defined in the same way except that the minimum elevation angle E_{min} of the earth station antenna is considered. The *Slant Range (D)* decides the satellite roundtrip delay to the earth station. Maximum slant range D_{max} = 41,127 km for a geostationary orbit with E_{min} = 5° for which the satellite roundtrip delay is calculated as $\Delta t = \dfrac{2D_{max}}{c}$ where c is the velocity of light = 2.997925×10^5 km/s giving the interval Δt = 0.274 sec.

Launching and Positioning a Geostationary Satellite : First, the rocket places the satellite in an elliptical orbit whose apogee distance = radius of geosynchronous orbit = 42, 164.2 km and perigee distance = 6678.2 km, around 300 km above earth's surface. Then the satellite is spin-stabilized. With the satellite orbit and attitude accurately determined by telemetry, exactly when the satellite is located at the apogee, the rocket motor called *Kick or Boost Motor* is fired to make the orbit circular. This impulsive manoeuvre, if performed at equator (0° lattitude) propels the satellite in a circular orbit of desired radius = 42, 164.2 km.

5.1.3. Satellite Subsystems

Although their design is dictated by goals of the mission, a typical communication satellite consists of the following subsystems:

(i) **Communication Subsystem :** (containing antenna and repeater) The *Antenna* is the link between the ground station and various satellite subsystems. The *Repeater* has several modules including a *Wideband Receiver/Downconverter* to work within the 0.5 GHz bandwidth prescribed for C- and Ku-bands; an *Input Multiplexer* isolating the 0.5 GHz bandwidth into transponder channels; Channelized Travelling Wave Tube Amplifiers (TWTAs) for amplification of feeble down link signals to be transmitted to earth; and an *Output Multiplexer* for recombining the downlink signals.

(ii) **Telemetry, Tracking and Command (TTC) Subsystem :** In *Telemetry*, data supplied by on-board sensors to ground station is used to determine satellite's attitude, status and performance and to monitor the satellite subsystems.

Tracking is carried out using telemetry signals and ranging measurements for finding the slant range.

Command Subsystem executes remote controlled operations by decoding the received commands.

(iii) **Attitude Control Subsystem :** It maintains the current satellite position, antenna pointing direction and orbit manoeuvres.

Satellites are generally spin-stabilized or three-axis body stabilized in the geostationary orbit. *Spin Stabilization is* a method of maintaining the orientation of a space object by virtue of *inherent gyroscopic stiffness* of a rotating body to disturbances. It is achieved by rotating the satellite body between 30 and 120 RPM and thereby imparting an initial stiffness to it which preserves the satellite spin motion with the rotational axis perpendicular to the equatorial plane. In the *Three-Axis Body-Stabilized Satellites*, the satellite body is maintained at a fixed attitude with respect to earth. Gyroscopic stiffness is imbibed by controlling attitude about three axes called the yaw, pitch and roll axes. Thus the requirements of attitude control system depend upon whether the satellite is spin-or body-stabilized.

(iv) **Electric Power Supply :** It is usually an array of Si solar cells. During eclipse, Ni-Cd or Ni-H$_2$ batteries are used.

5.1.4. Earth Station Subsystems

A typical earth station comprises two major subsystems:

(i) *RF Terminal* consisting of an upconverter, a downconverter, high-power and low-noise amplifiers, and antenna for transmission of modulated RF carrier to satellite and receipt of RF carrier from it. (ii) *Baseband Terminal* which includes the encoder/decoder and modulator/demodulator circuits apart from baseband equipment.

The *Antenna* must hae a *highly directive gain, a low noise temperature* and *easy steerability*. Paraboloid antenna with focal point feed and Cassegrain antenna are popular.

The *Gain* of an antenna is given by

$$G = \eta \frac{4\pi A f^2}{c^2} \qquad \qquad ...(5.1)$$

where η is the antenna aperture efficiency, A is the antenna aperture area, f is the frequency of radiation and c is the velocity of light.

The transmitted power of an earth station or a satellite is expressed in terms of the *Effective Isotropic Radiated Power* (EIRP) dfined as

$$EIRP = P_T G_T \qquad \qquad ...(5.2)$$

where P_T denotes the input power at antenna feed and G_T is the transmit antenna gain.

Among the commonly used high power amplifiers in earth stations, mention may be made of Travelling Wave Tube Amplifier (TWTA) based on velocity modulation principle, Klystron tube, IMPATT diode and GaAs FET.

The widely used low-noise amplifiers are the parametric amplifier and GaAs FETs with short gate lengths ~ 0.5 µm.

The *Upconverter* (UC) transforms the intermediate frequency (IF) ω_0 of the modulator to the uplink RF frequency ω_h in the satellite uplink frequency spectrum by mixing ω_0 with a frequency ω_l from the local oscillator (LO). Likewise, the Downconverter (DC) translates radio-frequency ω_d of satellite downlink spectrum received from the low-noise amplifier, to the intermediate frequency ω_0.

5.1.5. Satellite Link Analysis

In a digital satellite link, the signal received at an earth station is evaluated in terms of average probability of bit error which is determined by the carrier-to-noise ratio (C/N) of the satellite link.

The uplink carrier-to-noise ratio in decibels is expressed as

$$\left(\frac{C}{N}\right)_u = EIRP_{sat}(dBW) - 20\log\left(\frac{4\pi f_u d_u}{c}\right) + \frac{G_u}{I_u}(dB/K) - 10\log k$$

$$- 10\log B - BO_i \; (dB) - L(dB) \qquad ...(5.3)$$

where $EIRP_{sat}$ (dBW) is equal to carrier EIRP required to saturate TWTA in satellite transponder

$$= \Omega_{sat} \; (dBW) + 10\log (4\pi d_u^2) + L(dB) \qquad ...(5.4)$$

the parameter Ω_{sat} is the saturation power flux density, d_u is uplink slant range, L is the loss due to tracking and atmospheric effects, f_u the uplink carrier frequency, c the velocity of light, G_u/T_u is the satellite antenna gain-to-noise temperature ratio, k the Boltzmann's constant, B the noise bandwidth of satellite channel and BO_i the input back-off of TWTA.

The downlink carrier-to-noise ratio is written as

$$\left(\frac{C}{N}\right)_d = \text{EIRP}_{s,sat}(dBW) - 20\log\left(\frac{4\pi f_d d_d}{c}\right) + \frac{G}{T}(dB/K)$$

$$- 10\log k - 10\log B - BO_0\ (dB) - L'(dB) \qquad \text{...(5.5)}$$

where $\text{EIRP}_{s,sat}$ is the satellite saturation EIRP, f_d the downlink carrier frequency, d_d downlink slant range, (G/T) the antenna gain-to-noise temperature ratio of earth station, BO_0 the output backoff of TWTA and L' the antenna tracking loss and atmospheric attenuation including precipitations and clouds.

5.2. MULTIPLE ACCESS TECHNIQUES

A satellite can be compared with one shop serving several customers. To exploit its broadcasting capability (Fig. 5.3), a large number of scattered earth stations must simultaneously establish connection with the satellite through two-way links. In turn, the earth stations themselves are connected to many users. Such multiple two-way links can be made by using a large number of transponders. But as the number of transponders becomes excessively high, it is more beneficial to employ a single wide-band transponder with suitable multiple access techniques.

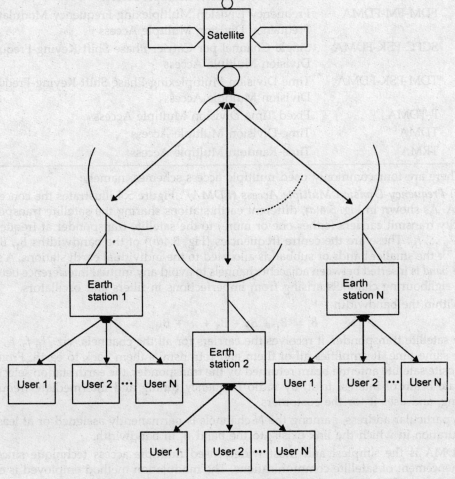

Fig. 5.3. Accessing an earth station and a satellite

Actually, the problem consists of two parts. In the first part, a wide community of users on earth access an earth station by multiplexing and demultiplexing techniques. In the second part, the various earth stations access a satellite through a technique which is specific to satellite communications called Multiple Access Technique.

Multiple access is a form of multiplexing in which a large number of earth stations form simultaneous links with the satellite through one or more radio frequency channels. It is essentially the multiplexing of RF signals in the satellite communication channel.

The study of multiple access technique involves the use of many abbreviations. It would be worthwhile to become conversant with the abbreviations given in Table 5.1.

Table 5.1. Abbreviations of Multiple Access Techniques and Allied Terms

Sl. No.	Abriged Form	Complete Statement
1.	CDMA	Code-Division Multiple Access
2.	DA-FDMA	Demand Assignment-Frequency Division Multiple Access
	DAMA	Demand Assignment Multiple Access
	DA-TDMA	Demand Assignment-Time Division Multiple Access
3.	FDMA	Frequency-Division Multiple Access
	FDM-FM-FDMA	Frequency Division Multiplexing-Frequency Modulation-Frequency Division Mulitple Access
	SCPC-PSK-FDMA	Single Channel per Carrier-Phase Shift Keying-Frequency Division Multiple Access
	TDM-PSK-FDMA	Time Division Multiplexing-Phase Shift Keying-Frequency Division Multiple Access
4.	F-TDMA	Fixed Time Division Multiple Access
	TDMA	Time-Division Multiple Access
	TRMA	Time-Random Multiple Access

There are four commonly used multiple access schemes, namely:

(i) *Frequency-Division Multiple Access (FDMA)* : Figure 5.4 illustrates the concept of FDMA. As shown in Fig. 5.4(a), different earth stations sharing the satellite transponder capacity transmit carriers (either one or more) to the satellite transponder at frequencies $f_1, f_2, f_3, ..., f_N$. These are the centre frequencies (Fig. 5.4(b)) of the bandwidths $B_1, B_2, B_3, ... B_N$ for the smaller bands or subbands allocated to the individual earth stations. A small Guard Band is inserted between adjacent channels to avoid any mutual interference between two neighbouring channels arising from imperfections in filters and oscillators.

Within the bandwidth

$$B = B_1 + B_2 + B_3 + ... + B_N \qquad ...(5.6)$$

of the satellite transponder, it receives the carriers for all the channels, viz., $f_1, f_2, f_3, ..., f_N$ at the same time. It amplifies all of them and retransmits them back to earth. From the composite satellite antenna beam returned by the transponder, the earth station selects the separate beam of interest to it, by radio frequency tuning and intermediate frequency filtering, and uses it for the customers.

A particular address, i among the N channels is permanently assigned or at least for the duration in which the link exists, to the band B_i in bandwidth.

FDMA is the simplest and most widely used multiple access technique since the commencement of satellite communications. The modulation method employed is either analog such as FM or digital like PSK.

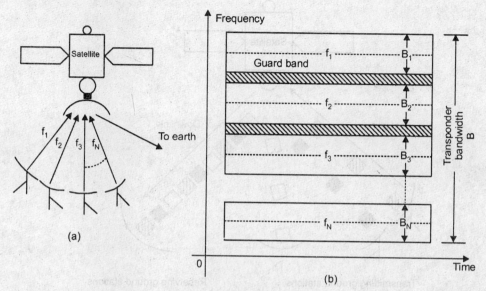

Fig. 5.4. Principle of FDMA

A major bottleneck of FDMA results from the fact that the carrier bandwidth produced by amplification of multiple carriers by a single TWTA in a satellite transponder, contains intermodulation products. These products originate from the amplitude and phase non-linearities of TWTA. The difficulty is further intensified as the number of carriers increases because then the TWTA has to be operated near saturation to supply the requisite power per carrier for decreasing the influence of downlink thermal noise. However, close to saturation, the transfer characteristic of TWTA becomes more non-linear introducing still more intermodulation products and worsening the situation.

(ii) Time-Division Multiple Access (TDMA) : Firstly, we note that this method works on a time division basis as opposed to frequency division in FDMA. Secondly, the entire transponder bandwidth is available to all carriers. Thirdly, as we shall see later, TDMA is well suited for digital communications. So, the modulation scheme is invariably a digital one. Figure 5.5(*a*) depicts the concept of TDMA and Fig. 5.5(*b*) shows the TDMA frame structure in a simplified form.

In TDMA, a number of ground stations can access the satellite by making their transmissions reach the satellite in closely spaced but *non-overlapping time slots*. They do so by transmitting finite sequences of bits called *Bursts* in a periodic time frame known as the TDMA time frame. *N* bursts constitute a frame. Besides the frame structure, the TDMA also needs a *global timing mechanism* establishing coordination among the ground stations to synchronize the transmission instants of the bursts. A *Guard Time* is introduced between successive bursts to account for variations in satellite range.

The transponder in the satellite receives the bursts one by one. Each burst is amplified and sent back to earth.

Thus in TDMA, each link is set up during a time slot t_j for a section of length T_F sec called the *Frame Period*. The position of t_j within T_F defines the link address. When all links occupy equal t_j, a total of $N = \dfrac{T_F}{t_j}$ links can be established.

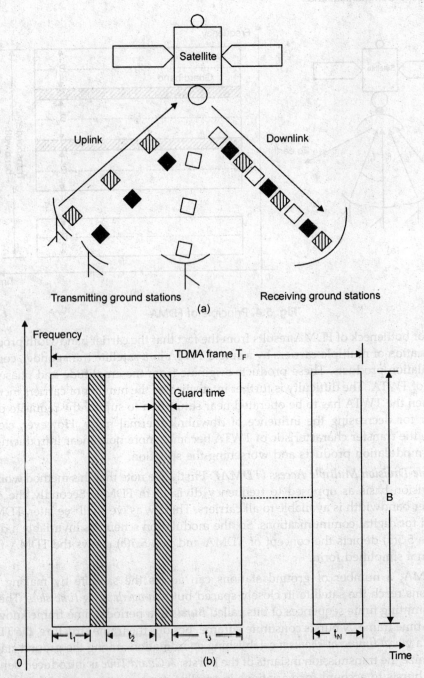

Fig. 5.5. TDMA: (*a*) Concept and (*b*) Frame structure

Compared with FDMA, TDMA provides improved performance and is particularly useful in medium crowded to highly crowded traffic networks. Here, efficient techniques like demand assignment and digital speech interpolation inherently befitting to TDMA, augment the traffic handling capability of the satellite transponder. Nonetheless, in low traffic links, FDMA with demand assignment is preferred due to economical reasons.

The major reason for the superiority of TDMA over FDMA is that only modulated carrier is present in the transponder at a given instant avoiding intermodulation product generation. Absence of intermodulation products in the transponder precludes crosstalk between individual transmissions. It permits the maximization of power efficiency by allowing the TWTA to operate at or near saturation output power level thus helping in optimization of noise performance of the receiver.

(*iii*) *Time-Random Multiple Access (TRMA)* : This is a simplification of TDMA wherein signals are transmitted from earth stations in a burst mode without any scheduling between the transmitting stations. As shown in Fig. 5.6, impingement or collision of data packets from different stations A, B may corrupt their information content. In the event of destruction of data, the packet needs to be retransmitted at a *randomly selected time* so that a collision is averted.

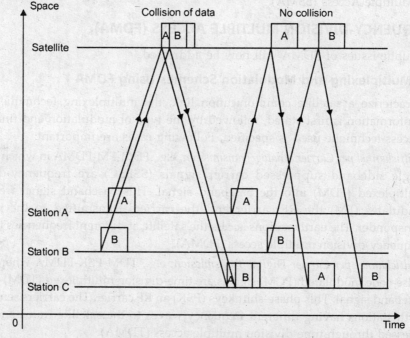

Fig. 5.6. Space-time graph of a TRMA scheme

The method is useful for serving a large population of users at a low duty cycle traffic. Important performance indices are the *Throughput* measured by the ratio of information bits delivered to the customer, to the number of bits sent which is the same as ratio of successful bursts to the total number of bursts sent; and the *Time Delay* that occurs between the transmission of signal and its delivery to the user.

(*iv*) *Code-Division Multiple Access (CDMA)* : The previously described multiple access techniques predominantly find commercial applications. In military satellite links, the signal may be subject to intentional interference or jamming by the enemy. Protection against jamming can be built in the access method by a technique called *Spread Spectrum Communications*. The principle of the method is to vastly expand the carrier spectrum with respect to the information rate with the help of *Direct Sequence* (DS) spreading, *Frequency Hopping* (FH) and hybrid techniques. As compared to the bit duration-bandwidth product $T_b B = 1.2 - 1.4$ commonly used in PSK satellite communications, this product is ~ 1000 or more for the spread spectrum case. Hence the signal jammer has to deploy the jamming power over a comparatively broad bandwidth in order to be successful. Over and above, the signal appears pseudorandom in nature like noise, making it difficult for the enemy to interrupt. Thus the signal is made invulnerable to harm.

The noteworthy feature of CDMA is that all users operate simultaneously in the same frequency band. Also, each user occupies the full transponder bandwidth throughout the operation time. Then it is curious to know how the receiver is able to separate the different signals. By a code transformation, each user combines the signal to be sent with a signature sequence. This sequence has two correlation properties, viz., it is easily distinguishable from any of its time-shifted replicas, and each sequence can be readily differentiated from every other in the site. These properties are exploited by the receiver to isolate the signals.

As we find, the occupied bandwidth in CDMA is much larger than the minimum bandwidth required to transmit information. It is therefore often referred to as Spread Spectrum Multiple Access (SSMA).

5.3. FREQUENCY-DIVISION MULTIPLE ACCESS (FDMA)

More subtle issues of FDMA will now be addressed.

5.3.1. Multiplexing and Modulation Schemes Using FDMA

To characterize a satellite communication link, the multiplexing technique of the baseband information is first stated, followed by the type of modulation and finally the multiple access technique used is specified. Following cases are important:

(i) *Multichannel per Carrier Analog Transmission*, e.g., FDM-FM-FDMA in which several single sideband suppressed carrier signals (SSBSC) are frequency-division multiplexed (FDM) into the baseband signal. This baseband signal frequency modulates (FM) the RF carrier and the carriers transmitted to the satellite transponder. The earth stations access the satellite at different frequencies through frequency-division multiple access (FDMA).

(ii) *Multichannel per Carrier Digital Transmission*, e.g., TDM-PSK-FDMA where many pulse-code modulated (PCM) signals are time-division multiplexed (TDM) into the baseband signal. This phase-shift keys (PSK) an RF carrier. The carriers sent by the earth stations having different frequency waves to the satellite transponder, are accessed through time-division multiple access (TDMA).

(iii) *Single Channel per Carrier Transmission* (SCPC): The modulation is either analog such as SCPC-FM-FDMA or digital like SCPC-PSK-FDMA.

Unlike methods (i) and (ii) which serve large capacity links, method (iii) is suitable for applications requiring only a few channels per link.

5.3.2. Intermodulation Products

Several frequency-separated signals are simultaneously amplified by the satellite repeater. These signals remain completely separated at the repeater output if the repeater is perfectly linear. But the high power amplifier TWTA in a repeater possesses non-linear input-ouput characteristics. Due to this non-linearity, the output contains the input carrier signals together with linear combinations of input frequencies called *intermodulation products*. The occurrence of these products leads to wastage of a percentage of available power. Also, odd intermodulation products appear within the transponder bandwidth vitiating the desired signals.

The spectral density of intermodulation products is approximately constant within the bandwidth. Hence they can be considered as filtered white noise having constant power density.

Debilitation of intermodulation products is accomplished by using a linearizer or by driving the high power amplifier with a signal power less than that required to work at saturation (Input Backoff), whereby the amplifier operation becomes more linear. The resulting relative decrease of output power is known as "Output Back-Off".

With increase in the number of carriers at the transponder input, several degrading effects act unitedly to reduce the transponder capacity. Among these effects may be mentioned: Reduction of total power at transponder output due to back-off operation, decrease in useful power for carriers because a portion of the total power is converted into intermodulation noise power, and contribution of intermodulation noise towards increasing the noise power density at the earth station receiver input.

5.3.3. FDMA Merits and Pitfalls

The following advantages of FDMA are worthy of mention: Synchronization between different ground stations is not necessary unlike TDMA. It utilizes well-established techniques and equipment developed for terrestrial microwave links.

Among the disadvantages, we may point out the requirement of linearity using either a linearizer or back-off operation. Another problem is the deterioration of transponder capacity as compared to a single access with back-off operation. Further, there is a lack of flexibility due to intricate procedure involvement while changing the frequencies assigned to different stations. Finally, it is also obligatory that all the carriers access the transponder with a prefixed equal power. This calls for transmitted power control at ground stations.

5.4. TIME-DIVISION MULTIPLE ACCESS (TDMA)

In its simplest form, the TDMA frame time is divided into slots of fixed duration. Also, the slots are equally divided amongst the stations. This scheme is called *Fixed Assignment TDMA* or *F-TDMA*.

5.4.1. TDMA Frame Structure

Figure 5.7 shows the structure of a typical TDMA frame. The frame is defined as the elementary signal format which is periodically repeated. This format occupies the time duration of a few milliseconds termed the frame duration T_F, $0.75 \leq T_F \leq 20$ ms for voice service.

The frame consists of reference bursts, traffic bursts and inter-burst guard time. From reliability considerations, two reference bursts are generally used. The first one, either RB_1 or RB_2, called the *Primary Reference Burst* (PRB) is transmitted by the *Primary Reference Station* (PRS). The second one (RB_1 or RB_2) known as the *Secondary Reference Burst* (SRB) is sent by the *Secondary Reference Station* (SRS).

The remaining N-2 bursts out of the total number N are the *Traffic Bursts* allocated to ground stations with one or more bursts per TDMA frame per station according to a *burst-time plan* co-ordinating traffic between stations. Thus each station may transmit once or many times as decided. The traffic burst length is determined by the amount of information transmitted. It can be altered if required. A short time gap G between bursts from different ground stations accessing a transponder guarantees that there is no chance of interference between their signals. It must be sufficiently long to make room for difference in transmit time accuracy and the satellite range rate variation. Transmission of information does not take place during the guard time. It only occurs during traffic bursts.

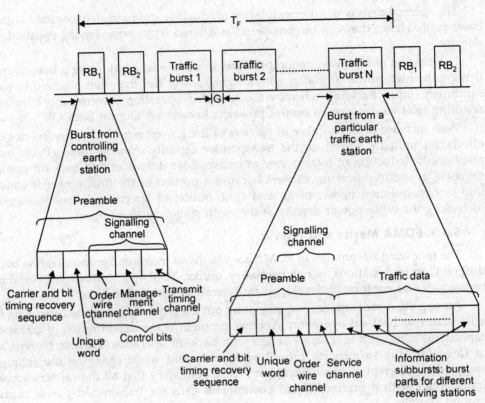

Fig. 5.7. Structural organization of TDMA frame

The Reference Burst This burst consists of only the *Header* or *Preamble* made up of three parts, namely, the *Carrier and Clock Recovery* (CCR) sequence, the *Unique Word* (UW) and the *Signalling Channel*. The aim of reference burst is to synchronize and recognize the frame. This burst is emitted by the *Controlling* or *Reference Earth Station*.

The carrier and clock recovery sequence helps the earth station demodulator to recover the phase of the carrier and regenerate the bit or symbol timing clock for demodulation of data.

The uniqe word is a sequence of 1's and 0's with good correlation properties marking the time of occurrence of traffic burst and providing the receive burst timing which enables the station to obtain only the desired subbursts within a traffic burst. It is detected at the demodulator by a unique word detector. This detector is a digital correlator which correlates a stored pattern of the unique word with the incoming signal. For a unique word of length N, the digital correlator (Fig 5.8) consists of two N-stage shift registers, N modulo-2 adders, a summer and a threshold detector with a preset threshold level ε. As the received data are translated in the register, the output of modulo-2 adder is 0 when the data bit agrees with stored unique word bit. Summing up the modulo-2 adder outputs and comparing with preset threshold, the summer output is a step function expressing the extent to which the input data agrees with the unique word pattern in memory. When the maximum number of permissible errors is $\leq \varepsilon$, the unique word has been detected.

Three subbursts constitute the signalling channel, viz, an *Order Wire Channel* which bears voice and data traffic through which instructions are exchanged with earth stations; *Traffic Management Channel* which is transmitted by the controlling station to all traffic stations and carries frame management instructions identifying the burst positions, the position, length and source or destination stations for the subbursts, and also the burst time plan alterations, if any; *Transmit Timing Channel* providing acquisition and synchronization information to traffic stations. In effect, the signalling channel contains control bits meant for station identification and housekeeping functions.

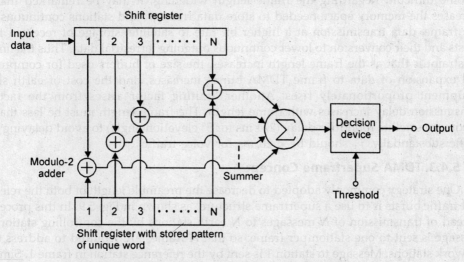

Fig 5.8. Principle of unique word detection

The Traffic Burst Like the reference burst, this burst consists of two parts, viz., the *Header* containing a carrier and bit timing recovery sequence, a burst code word or unique word and control bits including the order wire and service channels, and *Traffic Data* comprising as many subbursts as there are destinations of subbursts. The length of a subburst is determined by the service type: voice, video, data or FAX and the total number of channels ascribed to each service in the burst. Normally, each constituent station of a TDMA network can transmit several traffic bursts. In general, the number of subbursts per frame may also be different. Also, each station has the capability of reception of many traffic bursts or subbursts per frame.

5.4.2. TDMA Frame Efficiency

It is easy to recognize two functionally different components in each TDMA frame: a *Revenue Earning Component* represented by information portions, and a *System Overhead* which includes the remaining portion leaving the message part, viz., guard times, reference bursts, preambles and postambles, if incorporated. In practice, the efficiency of a TDMA system is measured by the ratio of time interval dedicated to information bits (as traffic data) to the total frame length T_F, and is expressed as

$$\eta = 1 - \frac{\sum_i t_i}{T_F} \qquad\qquad ...(5.7)$$

where the summation includes the entire overhead portion in different forms like guard times, reference bursts, etc.

The value of η is usually ~0.9. Efficient TDMA system design calls for a trade-off between efficiency requirement and system implementation complexity. Needless to say that an efficient system requires that $\sum t_i$ should be small and T_F should be large. Considering the components of t_i, the length of guard time is governed by accuracy of synchronization while the preamble duration is controlled by demodulation and signalling requirements. Thus $\sum_i t_i$ can be lowered only upto the limit upto which design does not become difficult. Regarding the frame length widening, it may be remarked that this increases the memory space needed to store data from ground stations continuously for one frame, data transmission at a higher bit rate to satellite, storage of received traffic bursts and their conversion to lower continuous outgoing terrestrial data. Thus the limiting constraint is that as the frame length increases, the size of buffers used for compression and expansion of data to frame TDMA bursts increases, and the cost of earth station equipment proportionately rises. Another limiting factor arises from the fact that transmission delay increases with frame length. The frame length must be less than the maximum satellite roundtrip delay (274 ms for 5° elevation angle) to avoid delaying voice traffic substantially. T_F should be < 20 ms for voice traffic.

5.4.3. TDMA Superframe Concept

One strategy commonly adopted to decrease the preamble length of both the reference and traffic bursts is to use a superframe structure, as shown in Fig. 5.9. In this procedure, instead of transmission of N messages to N earth stations by the controlling station, one message is sent to one station per frame, so that N frames are required to address the N network stations. Message to station 1 is sent by the reference station in frame 1. Similarly for frame 2 and upto N frames. This is followed by repetition of procedure for the N frames until completion. In a like manner, the status report submitted by the traffic station to the reference station is transmitted over N frames and the procedure is repeated till completion. These N frames can be clubbed together into one group known as the *Superframe* where N is the total number of earth stations addressed. Identification of individual frames comprising a superframe is done using a frame identification number borne by the management channel. Usually the identification number of frame 1 acts as the number for the superframe. During demand assignment, the N stations send a *Superframe Short Burst* (SSB) once every superframe. The messages are transmitted in the Service Channel of traffic bursts and demand assignment messages in superframe short burst.

The idea of superframe greatly enhances the frame efficiency of TDMA.

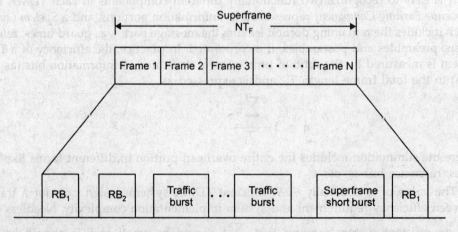

Fig. 5.9. Superframe organization

5.4.4. Frame Acquisition and Synchronization

Frame Acquisition is defined as the process by which a station is brought into harmonious operation with a working TDMA network. *Synchronization* is the procedure by which timing information is provided at all stations for controlling the TDMA bursts whereby they are confined to their prescribed slots.

Temporal reference in TDMA is provided by the primary reference burst. Detection of the unique word of this burst enables us to determine the *Receive Frame Timing* (RFT)–The instant at which the last bit of this unique word occurs. Similarly, the last bit of the unique word of traffic burst defines the *Receive Burst Timing* (RBT).

The traffic station must also set up a *Transmit Frame Timing* (TFT) marking the beginning of transmit frame of concerned station, and a *Transmit Burst Timing* (TBT) at which traffic burst to satellite commences. The process of acquiring RFT is called *Receive Frame Acquisition* (RFA). Getting TFT is known as *Transmit Frame Acquisition* (TFA). Maintenance processes of these timings are termed *Receive Frame Synchronization* (RFS) and *Transmit Frame Synchronization* (TFS) respectively. It is mandatory that all stations in a TDMA network must undergo the four operations: RFA, RFS, TFA and TFS.

Acquisition and synchronization are accomplished by detection of the reference burst unique word, by the search and track modes. In the former, the unique word sequence is matched with its stored pattern. As soon as matching is completed, one switches over to track mode to find the unique word position. This is done by using a narrow aperture window greater than or equal to guard time and increasing the threshold from 0 in the search mode to ε.

Frame Acquisition Methods There are two main approaches to frame acquisition: closed-loop acquisition and open-loop acquisition.

In *Closed-Loop Acquisition*, a low power burst or a pseudonoise (PN) burst is transmitted; a PN random sequence has specific auto-corrlation properties. Wideband signals are employed at a low power to avoid interference with other signals. Auto-correlation properties are exploited to harmonize the entrant station with the network.

In *Open-Loop Acquisition*, the newcomer station is informed about the time shift D_N with respect to the reference burst at which the station should transmit a short burst containing a preamble and a unique word. This delay must be computed such that the burst falls at the middle of the assigned time instant of TDMA frame. Thus the error due to doubtful range between satellite and earth station is avoided.

Frame Synchronization Methods Figure 5.10(a) depicts the procedure of synchronization. First, using the reference burst, each station establishes a local TDMA frame. This is a fictitious frame starting at time t_{RN}. But this local frame must be aligned with the actual frame, i.e., the one at the satellite transponder input. This misalignment is obviously due to time delay incurred during transmission. For this purpose, a delay D_N is introduced relative to the reference burst reception time as estimated by detection of its unique word sequence. From Fig. 5.10(b),

$$D_N = mT_F - \frac{2s_N}{c} \qquad \qquad ...(5.8)$$

where T_F is frame duration, S_N is distance between satellite and earth station and c the velocity of light. Obviously, $\frac{2s_N}{c}$ is a round-trip propagation time; m is an integer chosen so that D_N is minimum but > 0 when s_N is calculated for the earth station farthest from the satellite.

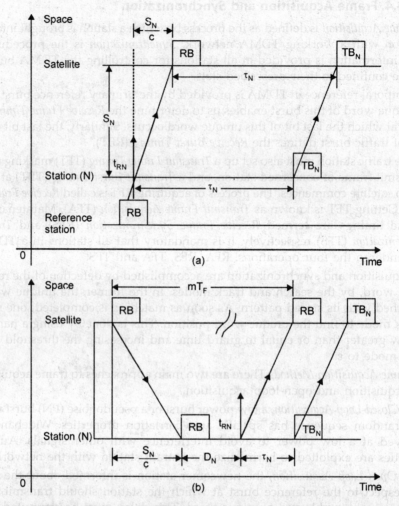

Fig. 5.10. Method of synchronization : (a) Setting up a fictitious frame, and
(b) Introducing delay D_N for synchronization

Synchronization methods can be classified as: *Closed-Loop Synchronization* in which the distance D_N is ascertained by the earth station directly from its own transmission, and *Open-Loop Synchronization* wherein the distance D_N is determined without requiring that the earth station receives the bursts transmitted by it.

In *Closed-Loop Synchronization*, the earth station records the time interval separating the unique word of reference burst and that of traffic burst sent by it. The difference between the two is the error $\varepsilon_N(j)$. The delay is then corrected to the value

$$D_N(j + 1) = D_N(j) - \varepsilon_N(j) \qquad \qquad ...(5.9)$$

In *Open-Loop Synchronization*, the traffic burst position is determined from the knowledge of distance d_N between satellite and earth station. s_N is obtained from satellite position measurements, knowing the exact location of earth stations. D_N is calculated as before.

5.4.5. TDMA Earth Terminals

These are the terminals which interface with the terrestrial facilities and equipment preparing speech, video or data. They contain different modules for dealing with different types of signals, e.g., data requires error-correction codes which may not be necessary for speech. An example module is *Echo Control Unit* which nullifies the return signal of a telephone speaker. Another example is *Digital Speech Interpolation* (DSI) facility which condenses the telephone traffic for frugal utilization of transponder capacity by allowing transmission of a larger number of bits per sec per unit bandwidth. It achieves this by accommodating in the idle time separating calls as well as in the pauses between conversation.

The speech and data bit streams are sent to the multiple access facility which buffers and scrambles the traffic. Scrambling entails modulo-2 addition of a pseudo-noise random sequence to obviate long sequences of ones and zeroes. Before modulation, a preamble is added to each burst.

Upon reception, the signals are demodulated by detection of unique word in burst preamble. Various control digits are extracted and a clock signal is provided for different units. The signals are submitted to appropriate processing operations.

5.4.6. Benefits and Drawbacks of TDMA

Principal advantages of TDMA are:

(*i*) TDMA permits maximization of power efficiency in satellite transponder by allowing TDMA operation at or near saturation.

Intermodulation products are not generated in the transponder. Notwithstanding their absence, non-linear effects still persist causing intersymbol interference. This deteriorates the demodulation process increasing the bit error rate.

(*ii*) The TDMA transmissions contain independent provisions for carrier and bit timing synchronization to occur simultaneously. Thus the overhead due to recovery time in the receiver is restricted to a minimum.

(*iii*) Precision adjustments of carrier power transmitted by different earth stations is not imperative.

(*iv*) Simplification of RF timing is achieved because all stations transmit and receive on a single frequency.

(*v*) Signals are amenable to digital signal processing and can gainfully use digital facilities like storage, coding, digital speech interpolation, etc.

Chief shortcoming of TDMA is the stringent synchronization requirement whereby bursts from different stations do not intermingle with each other. This raises the intricacy and hence expenditure on ground station equipment.

5.4.7. Digital Modulation Requirements for TDMA

From the discussion in Sec. 5.4.6, we understand that only limited set of digital modulation techniques can be used for satellite communications with TDMA scheme. Point (*i*) compels the modulation format to have a constant envelope; ASK is thus debarred. Point (*ii*) makes it practicable to use coherent detection. Hence in digital satellite communications with TDMA, attention is concentrated on coherent binary PSK, coherent QPSK and coherent MSK. TDMA systems generally employ *M*-ary PSK.

Power efficient systems employing coherent demodulation require a local carrier reference closely resembling the received carrier in frequency and phase. Moreover, for proper detection of data symbols, a local clock is needed strictly time aligned with received data pulses. But in power efficient modulation techniques, transmitted power is devoted solely to data while carrier and symbol clock are completely suppressed. Hence the demodulator has to regenerate the symbol and clock from the received signal.

Carrier Recovery for M-ary PSK Figure 5.11 shows the method of obtaining the reference carrier for M-ary PSK using frequency multiplication. The circuit consists of three main parts, viz., the M th Harmonic Generator, the Tracking Filter and the Frequency Divider. The bandpass filter BPF_i of Harmonic Generator is essentially the same as the bandpass filter in PSK demodulator (Fig. 5.12) or the one in QPSK demodulator (Fig. 5.10); it determines the input carrier-to-noise ratio C/N. If $|H_i(j2\pi f)|^2$ is the gain response of BPF_i, and f_c is the carrier frequency, the noise bandwidth B of BPF_i is written as

$$B = \int_0^\infty \frac{|H_i(j2\pi f)|^2}{|H_i(j2\pi f_c)|^2} df \qquad ...(5.10)$$

The symbol duration (T_s) – noise bandwidth (B) product of the filter $= T_s B = r$ where $1 \le r \le 1.5$. BPF_i is followed by a frequency multiplier. The bandpass filter at the output of (Time – M) frequency multiplier is a filter of very narrow bandwidth $= B_n$, with its centre frequency turned to the frequency $M(2\pi f_c)$ for a high signal-to-noise ratio at this frequency, i.e., $M(2\pi f_c)$. The phase tracking circuit provides carrier adjustment for phase coherence. Finally, the coherence reference carrier is obtained from the divide-by-M frequency divider.

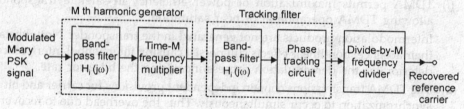

Fig. 5.11. Block diagram of a carrier recovery cicuit

Practically, a phase-locked loop (PLL) or a narrow-band filter having an automatic loop for frequency control are used for implementation of tracking filter.

Symbol Timing Recovery Circuit The reference clock is obtained by performing a non-linear operation on the received modulated signal. A second-order non-linearity is adequate for the M-ary signal.

Block diagram of symbol timing recovery circuit is given in Fig. 5.12. The circuit consists of a bandpass filter BPF_i tuned to $f_c = \frac{\omega_c}{2\pi}$ followed by a squarer and then a bandpass filter BPF with a centre frequency $f_0 = \frac{\omega_c}{2\pi} = R_s = \frac{1}{T_s}$ where R_s, T_s denote respectively the symbol rate and symbol duration.

The modulated M-ary PSK carrier signal is given by

$$r(t) = Re\{A\, a(t) \exp (j2\pi f_c t + \phi)\} \qquad ...(5.11)$$

where A is the amplitude and ϕ the phase of the carrier, $a(t)$ is the data signal, $|a(t)| = 1$.

The BPF_i output is

$$y(t) = Re\{Am(t) \exp (j\, 2\pi f_c t + \phi)\} \qquad ...(5.12)$$

where $m(t)$ is the envelope of $y(t)$. Then the output of the squarer is

$$y^2(t) = \frac{A^2}{2}|m(t)|^2 + \frac{1}{2}Re\{A^2 m^2(t)\exp(j2\pi f_c t + 2\phi)\} \qquad ...(5.13)$$

Assuming that $f_c = \dfrac{\omega_c}{2\pi} > R_s$ as is practically the case, the second term is rejected by

BPF delivering $\dfrac{A^2}{2}|m(t)|^2$ which can be shown to contain the clock component.

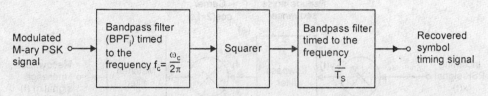

Fig. 5.12. Block diagram representation of symbol timing recovery circuit

5.5. CODE-DIVISION MULTIPLE ACCESS (CDMA)

The CDMA operation is based on the principle that when two unrelated signals are multiplied together, the spectrum of the product signal equals the convolution of the spectrum of multiplicands. Thus if the baseband message signal is narrower in bandwidth than the spreading sequence, the product signal spectrum will be approximately the wider spectrum of the spreading sequence. In the demodulator of the receiver, the received signal is multiplied by an in-phase replica of the same spreading sequence used at the transmitter modulator. This operation disperses the jamming signal over the spreading signal bandwidth. It is evident that the jammer should not know about the spreading signal. When the resultant multiplied signal is lowpass filtered, the original message signal is recovered. There are two methods widely used in CDMA practice, viz., Direct Sequence (DS) and Frequency Hopping (FH). We shall briefly discuss these methods.

5.5.1. Direct Sequence Method (DS-CDMA)

The major steps involved are shown in Fig. 5.13. At the transmitter (Fig. 5.13(a)) the binary baseband message $m(t)$ at a rate $\dfrac{1}{T_b}$, is multiplied with a pseudo-noise (PN) random sequence or pseudorandom sequence $p(t)$ represented by a bipolar waveform at a chip rate $\dfrac{1}{T_c}$ where $T_c \ll T_b$. When the composite signal formed is used to PSK modulate a carrier using the same frequency for all stations, the transmitted signal can be written as

$$x(t) = m(t)\,p(t)\cos(2\pi f_c\,t) \qquad\qquad ...(5.14)$$

where $$m(t) = \pm 1, p(t) = \pm 1 \qquad\qquad ...(5.15)$$

In the receiver (Fig. 5.13(b)), demodulation is performed by multiplying the modulated carrier with its coherent replica producing the signal

$$y(t) = m(t)\,p(t)\cos(2\pi f_c t) \times 2\cos(2\pi f_c\,t) \qquad\qquad ...(5.16)$$
$$= m(t)\,p(t) + m(t)\,p(t)\cos(4\pi f_c\,t) \qquad\qquad ...(5.17)$$

The first term represents the low-frequency component which is retained by the lowpass filter. Multiplying this low-frequency component by a local pseudo-noise sequence, the same as at transmitter and in phase with the received signal sequence, the ouput signal from the matched filter equals

$$m(t)\,p(t) \times p(t) = m(t)\,p^2(t) = m(t) \qquad\qquad ...(5.18)$$

which is the required message.

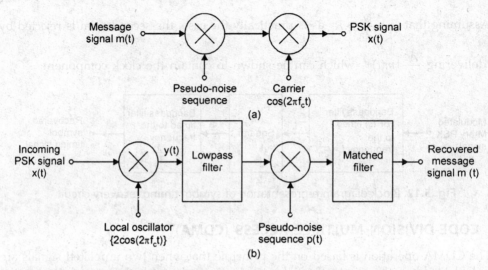

Fig. 5.13. CDMA implementation using coherent PSK-DS spectrum spreading

5.5.2. Frequency Hopping Method (FH-CDMA)

Figure 5.14 presents the block diagram schematic of frequency hopping operation. Here, the binary baseband message signal $m(t)$, rate $\dfrac{1}{T_b}$, PSK-modulates the carrier (Fig 5.14(a)). Under the supervisory control of a pseudo-noise (PN) sequence having chip rate $\dfrac{1}{T_c}$ > message bit rate $\dfrac{1}{T_b}$, the frequency of the PSK-modulated carrier is hopped over the total available bandwidth. For this, the PN sequence-controlled hopping generator feeds a frequency synthesizer giving the output signal cos $\{2\pi f_c(t)t\}$ where f_c is the instantaneous carrier frequency. Then the transmitted signal is given simply by

$$x(t) = \cos \{\cos (2\pi f_c(t)\ t + \phi(t)\} \qquad \qquad ...(5.19)$$

where $\phi(t)$ is the phase related to the message $m(t)$. For BPSK,

$$\phi(t) = m(t)\frac{\pi}{2} \text{ and } m(t) = \pm 1 \qquad \qquad ...(5.20)$$

In the receiver (Fig. 5.14(b)), demodulation is carried out on the received carrier by multiplication with an in-phase replica of the carrier. This replica is supplied, as before, by a frequency synthesizer in the receiver controlled by the same pseudonoise sequence. This operation yields the signal $y(t)$ given by

$$y(t) = \cos\{2\pi f_c(t)\ t + \phi(t)\} \times 2 \sin \{2\pi f_c(t)t\} \qquad \qquad ...(5.21)$$

$$= \sin \phi(t) + \sin \{4\pi f_c(t)t + \phi(t)\} \qquad \qquad ...(5.22)$$

The first term sin $\phi(t)$, representing the low-frequency component, is retained by the lowpass filter. With the assumption that the locally generated pseudonoise sequence is in phase with the frequency hopping sequence in the received signal, the lowpass filter output is the message $m(t)$ which had actually been sent, e.g., for BPSK, the output is

$$= \sin \phi(t) = \sin m(t)\frac{\pi}{2} = m(t) \qquad \qquad ...(5.23)$$

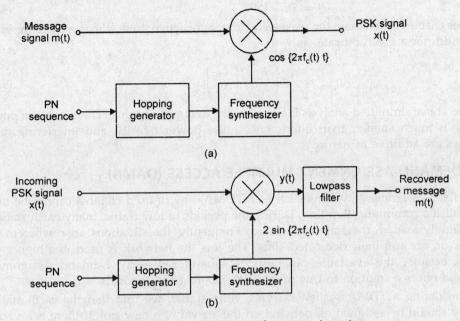

Fig. 5.14. CDMA operation by frequency hopping

5.5.3. CDMA Performance Analysis

If I is the power and B the bandwidth of the undesired interfering signal, the average noise power density N_0 is given by

$$N_0 = \frac{I}{B} \qquad \qquad ...(5.24)$$

The ratio of energy per bit to noise power density is

$$\frac{E_b}{N_0} = \frac{PB}{IT_b} \qquad \qquad ...(5.25)$$

where P is the power of the received carrier and T_b is the information bit rate. Then the ratio of undesired to desired signal power is

$$\frac{I}{P} = \left(\frac{B}{T_b}\right)\bigg/\left(\frac{E_b}{N_0}\right) \qquad \qquad ...(5.26)$$

The denominator is fixed for a given bit error rate. Hence larger the $\dfrac{B}{T_b}$ ratio, higher

is the level of acceptable interference. So $\dfrac{B}{T_b}$ is often referred to as *Processing Gain*.

In military satellite communications, the interfering signal is an intentional jamming signal. Here, the hostile interferer may transmit, for example, a high power RF signal. The

ratio $\dfrac{I}{P}$ expressing the capability of the system to function in a hostile environment, is

called the *Jamming Margin*.

In commercial satellite communication systems, the interfering signal is an additive broadband noise originating from the other users sharing the RF bandwidth. Considering n users with equal power P each, the interfering power is

$$I = (n-1)P \qquad \qquad ...(5.27)$$

This enables us to obtain the maximum number of active users who can share the given bandwidth for a given bit rate, as

$$\eta_{max} = 1+\left(\frac{B}{T_b}\right)\bigg/\left(\frac{E_b}{N_0}\right) \qquad \qquad ...(5.28)$$

The above simplified analysis is based on the assumptions that: Thermal noise power density is much smaller than interference noise power density, and interfering noise densities are additive in nature.

5.6. DEMAND-ASSIGNMENT MULTIPLE ACCESS (DAMA)

In fixed assignment systems such as F-TDMA, any unused channel cannot be used to establish a communication link. During the periods of low traffic, many earth stations being lightly loaded, the slots are wasted. Frequently, the situations arise wherein the stations do not use their dedicated slots. The less the network is used, the higher the penalty because the available capability is squandered away. Demand Assignment technique offers a solution to this problem by pooling the channels.

Considering a TDMA system carrying voice traffic, we find that the earth station capacity should be assigned on demand on the arrival of a new call. If there is a vacant channel in the burst of the station, the call connection is established. After the call is completed, the same channel can be offered to other incoming calls. In the same way, the satellite transponder capacity, i.e., the TDMA frame capacity can be assigned depending on the traffic requirements. Variable duration slots can be allocated to earth stations. Also, a station can be alloted more slots per frame.

The aforesaid measures of pooling capacities of earth station and the frame for use only when a demand arises, help in improving the efficiency of the system. They constitute Demand-Assignment Multiple Access (DAMA). The DAMA method associated with FDMA gives birth to DA-FDMA or *Demand Assignment-Frequency Division Multiple Access*. Similarly, DAMA in conjunction with TDMA leads to DA-TDMA or *Demand Assignment-Time Division Multiple Access*.

5.6.1. The Erlang *B* Formula

For a voice traffic system having a capacity of n channels, any new arriving call will be blocked when all the n channels are busy. The phenomenon of call congestion is described by the Erlang B formula which gives the probability that an arriving call will be intercepted by finding all channels busy, as

$$P_n = \frac{\dfrac{a^n}{n!}}{\displaystyle\sum_{k=0}^{n}\dfrac{a^k}{k!}} \qquad \qquad ...(5.29)$$

where a is the traffic intensity $= \dfrac{\lambda}{\mu}$, λ is the call arriving rate, $\dfrac{1}{\mu}$ the average service time or holding time and k is a random variable denoting the number of calls in a given interval of time, $k = 1, 2, 3, ... n$.

The Erlang B formula forms the basis for judging the *grade of service* of a voice traffic network.

5.6.2. Types of Demand-Assignment Multiple Access

These fall under four headings:

(i) *Variable-Capacity Demand Assignment :* Here the reference station of the TDMA network assigns the length and position of the burst and subburst along with the identification number of subburst in the TDMA frame. Since the changeover from an old burst time plan to a new burst time plan consumes several minutes, this method is suitable for networks in which each station has a large area of gradually changing traffic intensity serving only a few destination stations.

(ii) *Per-Call Variable Capacity Demand Assignment :* This method requires the reference station of TDMA network to assign only the burst length and position. The position and the length of the channel ascribed to the calling party are transmitted to the destination through a special *Common Signalling Channel.* Bearing in mind the rapid allocation of burst length and position, this method is sometimes known as *Real-Time* or *Dynamic Frame Reconfiguration.* It is partially useful in situations where each station serves several destination stations at a small but quickly changing traffic intensity.

(iii) *Per-Call Demand Assignment :* The use of variable capacity techniques is troublesome with FDMA because when we alter the frequency and capacity of the carriers, the carrier-to-noise intermodulation ratio changes. So, only per-call demand assignments are employed with FDMA. The satellite capacity for all network stations is pooled and exploited on a single channel per carrier (SCPC) basis. This method is called SCPC-DAMA. In TDMA networks, the per call demand assignment is used when each station serves many stations and the traffic intensity is low.

(iv) *Fully-Variable Demand Assignment :* Corresponding to the SCPC-DAMA method in FDMA we have Single Channel per Burst-Demand Assignment Multiple Access or SCPB-DAMA method in a TDMA network. Techniques like SCPC-DAMA and SCPB-DAMA, for pooling the satellite capacity and sharing by all terrestrial stations belong to the class of Fully-Variable Demand Assignment. This class of methods is used in situations where each station serves a large number of destination stations with a rapidly varying traffic intensity and the total traffic at each station is light.

5.6.3. Demand Assignment Control

There are two strategies for assigning demands: centralized control and distributed control. Accordingly, we have two types of demand assignment: Centralized Control Assignment and Distributed Control Assignment. In the former, all assignment transactions take place under the supervisory control of a central master controller keeping track of vacant satellite channels as well as those at earth stations. In the latter, there is no unique master controller and all traffic stations have equal status.

In a *Centralized Control DAMA System* (Fig. 5.15(a)), the master controller senses that a traffic station is initiating a call. It locates the station to which the call is addressed and ascertains the channel availability at the satellite or at the two stations. Then it assigns a duplex circuit and allows the two stations to communicate via the satellite.The end point of the call is detected when the duplex circuit is liberated and returned to the station or satellite making it available for another caller.

In a *Distributed Control DAMA System* (Fig. 5.15(b)), each traffic station maintains a continuously updated database or idle-busy table.

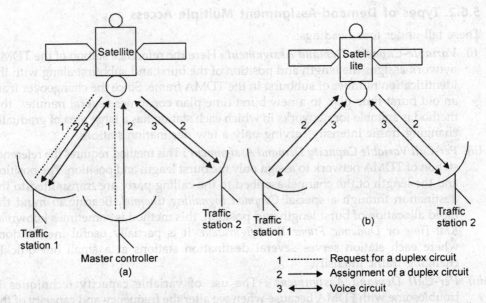

Fig. 5.15. Demand Assignment: (*a*) Centralized control, and (*b*) Distributed control using idle-busy table for satellite channel pool

Each scheme has its own advantages and shortcomings. In the centralized control system, individual traffic stations do not bear the responsibility of channel assignment. Thus the processing capability and cost of traffic stations decrease. Further, the fact that the control data are compact and status data for the whole network are not transmitted, reduces the overhead charges. Another advantage of this type of system is that it can adapt to traffic intensity varying the capacity of each station. The principal drawback of the system is that the function of the network completely relies on the master controller degrading the reliability. If the master controller breaks down, the whole system collapses. Hence, a standby controller must be kept as spare. Moreover, a large *Capacity Request Channel*, connecting all traffic stations to the master controller, together with a large *Capacity Assignment Channel* for the master controller to link with the traffic stations, and the enormous processing capability requirements of the master controller make its use prohibitive for a high traffic system.

On the contrary, in a distributed control system, as the traffic themselves do the assignment work through a *Common Signalling Channel*, failure of a station does not affect the system performance leading to a higher reliability. Its main demerit is the need of complex equipment for maintaining the network database, specially where the satellite channel pool idle-busy table is kept. Further, any lack of co-ordination between the stations may lead to poor utilization of satellite capability. Hybrid stations are sometimes used to solicit advantages of both types.

5.6.4. Frame and Burst Structures for DA-TDMA

It will be logical to study the DA-TDMA frame structure shown in Fig. 5.16 apropos to the TDMA frame structure illustrated in Fig. 5.7. A closer examination of the two diagrams reveals that the DA-TDMA frame contains a superframe which consists of N frames if there are N transmitting stations in the frame. The reference burst includes a *Capacity Assignment Channel* for transmission of capacity assignment messages to the traffic stations. Each traffic station is addressed once per frame or once per superframe.

It is further noticed that each traffic station sends a *Superframe Short Burst* (SSB) once in every superframe. These short bursts belong to the particular station whose frame is under consideration, e.g., SSB in frame 1 is concerned with station 1 and similarly for other SSB's. Regarding the structure of the SSB itself, it has a *Capacity Request Channel* through which the traffic station links with the reference station requesting for more capacity to deal with any additional traffic load. Besides, SSB also carries a *Common Signalling Channel*. This is used between traffic stations for the purpose of distributed call processing and call assignment. *Call Signalling Messages* between source and destination stations are conveyed on this channel.

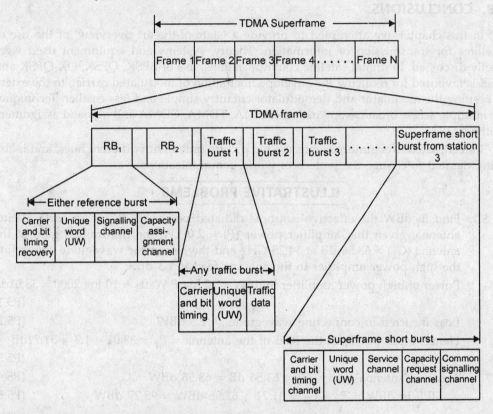

Fig. 5.16. Frame structure of DA-TDMA

5.7. DIGITAL SPEECH INTERPOLATION (DSI)

We have studied in the previous section how an improvement in satellite capacity and hence an increase in system efficiency is brought about with the aid of demand assignment. Another efficiency-increasing technique, useful for voice traffic, is digital speech interpolation. To "interpolate" means to insert or change by insertions.

If we examine voice communication such as telephonic conversation between two persons, we find that, on the average, for one-half the time, one person talks while the other listens to him. Thus on a one-link path, less than 50 per cent of the dialogue time is occupied by speech signals. Combined with the pauses for thinking before answering a question, or pauses separating syllables, words and sentences, the occupied time is even less than ~40 per cent. Because two channels are used for a conversation, 60 per cent of the time of a channel is not utilized. The percentage time lost in this way can be reduced by assigning a transmission channel to the telephone channel only during periods of speech spurts. The operating mechanism of digital speech interpolation is to assign a satellite channel for communication only when a speech spurt takes place. By doing this, n conversations can be transported on m channels, where $m < n$. *Speech Interpolation Gain* is measured by the ratio n/m.

DSI becomes increasingly effective with the proliferation of terrestrial channels. It is used with TDMA as a data compression process to squeeze the number of satellite channels necessary to transmit a number of terrestrial channels.

5.8. CONCLUSIONS

In this chapter, we attempted to provide a 'state-of-the-art overview' of the use of satellites for transmission of information. Theory, systems and equipment used were briefly discussed. In digital satellite communications, use of BPSK, QPSK, OK-QPSK and MSK is favoured for reducing the envelope fluctuation of modulated carrier, to the extent of keeping the modulator and demodulator circuitry simple and less costlier. Techniques for multiple access broadcasting include FDMA, TDMA, CDMA and demand assignment methods.

Indeed, satellite communications is a big picture tinted with different hues, and is still being painted to change the pattern of world communications.

(ILLUSTRATIVE PROBLEMS)

5.1. Find in dBW the effective isotropic radiated power (EIRP) of an earth station antenna, given that amplifier power (P) = 2.0 kW, the transmitted gain of the antenna (G_T) = 63.56 dB at 14.25 GHz and the loss in the waveguide connecting the high power amplifier to the antenna feed is 1.3 dB.

Power of high power amplifier in dBW = 10 log P Watts = 10 log 2000 = 33.01dB

(P5.1)

Loss incurred in connecting waveguide = 1.3 dBW (P5.2)

Hence, input power at the feed of the antenna = P_T = 33.01 – 1.3 = 31.71dB

(P5.3)

Transmit antenna gain = G_T = 63.56 dB = 63.56 dBW (P5.4)

∴ EIPR in dBW = $P_T + G_T$ = 31.71 + 63.56 dBW = 95.27 dBW (P5.5)

5.2. Calculate the uplink and downlink carrier-to-noise ratios $\left(\dfrac{C}{N}\right)_u$ and $\left(\dfrac{C}{N}\right)_d$ and

also the total carrier-to-noise ratio $\dfrac{C}{N}$ for a TDMA-based Ku-band (14.25/11.95 GHz) digital satellite-communication link operating in single carrier per transponder mode whose main parameters are listed below: (*i*) *Satellite parameters:* Satellite saturation $EIRP = EIRP_{s,\,sat}$ = 283.57 dBW, satellite antenna gain-to-noise temperature = $\dfrac{G_u}{T_u} = 1$ dB/K, TWTA input back-off = BO_i = 5 dB, TWTA output back-off = BO_0 = 2 dB, (*ii*) *Earth Station Parameters:* Antenna gain-to-noise temperature ratio $\left(\dfrac{G}{T}\right)$ = 20 dB/K, Maximum uplink slant range d_u = Maximum downlink slant range d_d = 37,506 km, Uplink tracking loss = 1.1 dB, Downlink tracking loss = 0.7 dB; (iii) *Carrier Modulation and Other Parameters:* Type QPSK, Noise Bandwidth (B) = 30 MHz, saturation power flux density at satellite transponder = Ω_{sat} = – 80 dBW/m^2, Attenuation due to atmosphere = 200 dB for both uplink and downlink.

From your calculations, comment on whether the satellite is uplink or downlink limited?

We note that uplink carrier frequency = f_u = 14.25 GHz, downlink carrier frequency = f_d = 11.95 GHz, velocity of light = c = 3 × 10^8 m/sec, Boltzmann's constant = k = 1.38 × 10^{-23} J/K. We have,

$$\text{EIRP}_{sat}(\text{dBW}) = \Omega_{sat} \text{ (dBW)} + 10 \log (4\pi d_u^2) + L(\text{dB}) \tag{P 5.6}$$

$$= -80 \text{ dBW} + 10 \log \{4 \times 3.14 \times 37{,}506 \times 10^3)^2\}$$
$$+ 1.1 \text{ dB} + 200 \text{ dB} \tag{P 5.7}$$

$$= -80 + 162.47 + 201.1 = 283.57 \text{ dBW} \tag{P 5.8}$$

Also, $$\left(\frac{C}{N}\right)_u = \text{EIRP}_{sat}(\text{dBW}) - 20 \log \left(\frac{4\pi f_u d_u}{c}\right) + \frac{G_u}{T_u} (\text{dB/K})$$

$$- 10 \log k - 10 \log B - BO_i \text{ (dB)} - L(\text{dB}) \tag{P5.9}$$

$$= 283.57 dBW - 20\log\left(\frac{4 \times 3.14 \times 14.25 \times 10^9 \times 37{,}506 \times 10^3}{3 \times 10^8}\right)$$

$$+ 1 \text{ (dB/K)} - 10 \log (1.38 \times 10^{-23}) - 10 \log (30 \times 10^6)$$
$$- 5 \text{ dB} - 1.1 \text{ dB} - 200 \text{ dB} \tag{P5.10}$$

$$= 283.57 - 206.996 + 1 + 228.6 - 74.77 - 5 - 1.1 - 200 \text{ dB} \tag{P5.11}$$

$$= 25.3 \tag{P5.12}$$

and $$\left(\frac{C}{N}\right)_d = \text{EIRP}_{s,sat}(\text{dBW}) - 20\log\left(\frac{4\pi f d_d}{c}\right) + \frac{G}{T}(\text{dB/K}) - 10 \log k$$

$$- 10 \log B - BO_0 \text{ (dB)} - L'(\text{dB}) \tag{P5.13}$$

$$= 283.57 dBW - 20\log\left(\frac{4 \times 3.14 \times 11.95 \times 10^9 \times 37{,}506 \times 10^3}{3 \times 10^8}\right)$$

$$+ 20 \text{ (dB/K)} - 10 \log (1.38 \times 10^{-23}) - 10 \log (30 \times 10^6)$$
$$- 2 \text{ dB} - 0.7 \text{ dB} - 200 \text{ dB} \tag{P5.14}$$

$$= 283.57 - 205.467 + 20 + 228.6 - 74.77 - 2 - 0.7 - 200 \tag{P5.15}$$

$$= 49.23 \tag{P5.16}$$

Obviously, the carrier-to-noise ratio for the downlink is higher than that for the uplink. Therefore, the function of the communication satellite is limited by the uplink.

To total carrier-to-noise ratio is given by

$$\frac{C}{N} = \left(\frac{C}{N}\right)_u^{-1} + \left(\frac{C}{N}\right)_d^{-1} = \left\{\frac{1}{25.3} + \frac{1}{49.23}\right\}^{-1} \tag{P5.17}$$

$$= (3.95 \times 10^{-2} + 2.03 \times 10^{-2}) = 16.72. \tag{P5.18}$$

5.3. (*a*) Determine the frame efficiency of a TDMA system whose principal parameters are given below: TDMA frame length = 8 ms, TDMA Burst Bit Rate = 90 Mbps, two reference bursts plus thirty traffic bursts, Carrier and clock recovery sequence = 256 bits, Unique word length = 20 bits, Order wire channel length = 128 bits, Management channel length = 256 bits, Transmit timing channel = 320 bits, Service channel = 64 bits, and Guard time = 48 bits.

(*b*) The above TDMA system carries PCM encoded voice channels at a bit rate of 64 kbps and data signals at a bit rate of 16 kbps. If half of the capacity is allocated to voice channels and other half to data channels, how many voice and data channels can the frame accommodate?

(*a*) Number of bits in the reference burst = Number of bits in carrier and clock recovery sequence + Number of bits in unique word + Order wire channel bits + Management channel bits + Transmit timing channel bits = 256 + 20 + 128 + 256 + 320 = 980 bits. (P5.19)

Number of bits in the preamble of traffic burst = Number of bits in carrier and clock recovery + Those in unique word + Order wire channel bits + Service channel bits = 256 + 20 + 128 + 64 = 468. (P5.20)

Total number of bits in the overhead portion of the frame = 2 × Number of bits in reference burst + 2 × Guard time + 30 × Number of bits in the preamble of traffic burst + 30 × Guard time = 2 × 980 + 2 × 48 + 30 × 468 + 30 × 48 = 1960 + 96 + 14040 + 1440 = 17536. (P5.21)

Total number of bits in a TDMA frame = $8 \times 10^{-3} \times 90 \times 10^6 = 7.2 \times 10^5$.
(P5.22)

TDMA frame efficiency

$$\eta = \left(1 - \frac{17536}{7.2 \times 10^5}\right) \times 100\% = 98.96\%$$ (P5.23)

(*b*) Number of bits in an 8-ms TDMA frame for a voice subburst
$$= 64 \times 10^3 \times 8 \times 10^{-3} = 512 \text{ bits}$$ (P5. 24)

Similarly, number of bits in an 8-ms TDMA frame for a data subburst $= 16 \times 10^3 \times 8 \times 10^{-3} = 128$ bits. (P5.25)

If x denotes the total number of channels, then the total number of voice bits

in $\frac{x}{2}$ voice channels $= \frac{x}{2} \times 512 = 256x$ and likewise, total number of data bits

in $\frac{x}{2}$ data channels $= \frac{x}{2} \times 128 = 64x$.

∴ Total number of bits in a frame $= 256x + 64x = 320x$ (P5.26)

Since the total number of bits in a frame $= 8 \times 10^{-3} \times 90 \times 10^6 = 7.2 \times 10^5$

∴ $320x = 7.2 \times 10^5$ or $x = \dfrac{7.2 \times 10^5 \times 0.9896}{320} = 2226.6$ (P5.27)

∴ $\dfrac{x}{2} = 1113.3 = 1114$. Thus, Number of voice channels = Number of data channels = 1114. (P5.28)

REVIEW QUESTIONS

5.1. Comment, in the light of satellite communications, on the remark, "Digital technology is a flexible technology which can be diecast to perform variegated functions."

5.2. What portions of the electromagnetic spectrum are used for satellite communications? What are the frequency limits of the Ku-band, K-band and Ka-band. Define the frequency range of millimetre wave portion.

5.3. How many seconds correspond to the period of rotation of a geosynchronous satellite? What is meant by a geostationary orbit? Give the distance between a geostationary satellite and the subsatellite point.

5.4. Give three reasons explaining why most commercial satellites are geostationary? Which regions of earth are not covered by an arrangement of three geostationary satellites?

5.5. With the help of a diagram, define the azimuth and elevation angles of the earth station antenna. Mention the maximum slant range and longest roundtrip delay experienced for a geostationary satellite with 5° elevation angle.

5.6. Point out the stages involved in launching and fixing a satellite in a geostationary orbit.

5.7. Briefly describe the principal subsystems constituting the satellite segment and the earth station segment in a typical satellite link.

5.8. What is the need for attitude control of a satellite? What is the meaning of spin-stabilization and three-body axis stabilization of a satellite?

5.9. Write down the equation for the gain of an antenna. Define effective isotropic radiated power of a satellite or earth station.

5.10. Give the equations for the uplink and downlink carrier-to-noise ratio (in dB) of a satellite link. Explain the meanings of the symbols used.

5.11. What is meant by Multiple Access of a Satellite? Indicate the four common multiple access techniques. Provide a brief description of their operating mechanisms.

5.12. What do you mean by intermodulation product? How does intermodulation product generation hamper the working of an FDMA satellite transponder? What is the influence on its performance if the number of carriers is increased?

5.13. Highlight the advantages of Time-Division Multiple Access over Frequency-Division Multiple Access. In what respects does FDMA override TDMA?

5.14. How is jamming protection integrated into an access method? How does the receiver separate the different signals in Code-Division Multiple Access? What is Spread Spectrum Multiple Access?

5.15. How is a satellite communication link represented in terms of multiplexing, modulation and multiple access techniques? What are the main multiplexing and modulation schemes used with FDMA?

5.16. Show on a diagram the architecture of a TDMA frame. Indicate the subcomponents of the reference as well as traffic bursts. Elucidate the role of these subcomponents.

5.17. How is the unique word in the reference burst of TDMA detected at the demodulator? Mention the three subbursts which comprise the signalling channel of the reference burst.

5.18. What are the revenue-earning and overhead components in a TDMA frame? Explain. Define Frame Efficiency.

5.19. Explain the statement, "TDMA system design is based on a compromise between system efficiency and system complexity". How is this trade-off worked out?

5.20. Define Frame Acquisition in TDMA. What are the two frame acquisition methods? Explain their principles.

5.21. What is Frame Synchronization in TDMA? Describe the Open-Loop and Closed-Loop methods for synchronizing frames in TDMA.

5.22. Name the digital modulation techniques which are of primary interest for use with TDMA. What are the reference carrier and symbol timing requirements of power efficient systems with coherent demodulation?

5.23. For the M-ray PSK digital modulation scheme, explain using suitable block diagrams, the operations of carrier and symbol timing recovery circuits.

5.24. What is the elementary principle of CDMA operation? Describe the principal steps involved in the Direct Spreading method for CDMA.

5.25. Draw and explain the block diagrams of the transmitter and receiver stations for frequency hopping CDMA.

5.26. Define Processing Gain and Jamming Margin with reference to CDMA. Write the formulae giving the maximum number of customers who can share a given bandwidth in CDMA. On what assumptions is it based?

5.27. Indicate the drawback of fixed demand assignment. How does demand-based assignment of earth station and satellite transponder capacities, improve the system efficiency? Name the two principal subcategories of demand-assignment multiple access.

5.28. Write down the Erlang B formula for the probability that a call will be stopped. Explain the symbols.

5.29. List the four types of demand assignment methods for multiple access, giving their specific features and application areas.

5.30. What are the two types of demand assignment control? Explain using suitable diagrams, how do they function? Give their relative merits and demerits.

5.31. Draw the frame structure of demand-assignment TDMA. In what ways does it differ from an F-TDMA frame? Elaborate the role of the portions which are different?

5.32. What do you understand by Digital Speech Interpolation? How does it improve the satellite channel capacity?

5.33. Explain the following:

(a) Only a restricted set of digital modulation techniques is appropriate for satellite communications.

(b) In TDMA, the RF amplifier at satellite transponder output can operate near saturation without introducing any crosstalk between individual transmissions.

(c) A TDMA system requires increased complexity of ground station equipment, as compared with an FDMA system.

(d) Centralized control demand assignment TDMA offers low reliability but the traffic station cost is also low.

(e) Digital speech interpolation provides efficient utilization of satellite transponder capacity.

(REFERENCES AND FURTHER READING)

5.1. T.T. Ha, *Digital Satellite Communications*, Macmillan Publishing Company, New York, 1986.

5.2. G. Maral and M. Bousquet, *Satellite Communications Systems*, John Wiley & Sons, Chichester, 1986.

5.3. T. Pratt and C.W. Bostian, *Satellite Communications*, Wiley, New York, 1986.

5.4. T.P. Harrington and B. Cooper, Jr, *Hidden Signals on Satellite TV*, Howard W. Sams & Co., Indianapolis, 1986.

5.5. E. Fthenakis, *Manual of Satellite Communications*, McGraw Hill Book Co., New York, 1984.

5.6. V.K. Bhargava, D. Haccoun, R. Matyas and P.P. Nuspl, *Digital Communications by Satellite*, John Wiley & Sons, New York, 1981.

5.7. J. Martin, *Communications Satellite Systems*, Prentice Hall, Inc., Englewood Cliffs, 1978.

5.8. J.J. Spilker, Jr., *Digital Communications by Satellite*, Prentice Hall, Inc., Englewood Cliffs, 1977.

ᔕᔕᔕ

6 High-Definition Television (HDTV)

Television has gradually evolved since its inception and standardization of the now primitive-looking "monochrome or black-and-white TV" through colour TV, stereo sound, multichannel sound, closed captioning, ghost cancellation, etc., to the current proposals termed as Advanced Television (ATV) by the Federal Communications Commission (FCC), USA. High-Definition Television, acronym HDTV, also called Improved-Definition Television (IDTV) or Enhanced-Definition Television (EDTV), comes under such proposals.

HDTV is defined by the International Radio Consultative Committee (CCIR) as a wide aspect ratio television system possessing twice the number of scanning lines and horizontal resolution as compared to traditional TV. It is a form of telecommunication for conveying transient images of stationary or moving objects, effected by spreading the picture in a 16:9 wide screen format to provide a feeling of reality, naturalness and spontaneity. It is also contrived for offering superior picture quality than conventional television. Information content of HDTV picture is about five times that of the conventional TV picture.

6.1. THE NEED FOR HDTV

Upon retrospection of the history of TV growth, we find that at the time of advent of analog TV services, television was meant mainly for over-the-air terrestrial broadcasting of news, entertainment and sports material. Ever since there is a phenomenal widening of the scope of television. As the TV technology has matured, in the present scenario, television is finding applications in videoconferencing, desktop computing, telemedicine and distance learning. These proliferating applications have placed additional demands on TV services. The prevailing practice is inadequate to cope up with the challenge. The marriage of TV with PC will make broadcast TV a strong multimedia tool and the adoption of HDTV will make multimedia broadcasting possible. HDTV is the solution providing both high-resolution images and multimedia capability.

Apart from the penetration of TV into areas not visualized at the time of its introduction, over fifty years ago, the distribution means for TV programmes have also multiplied. These are now disseminated through video tapes, discs, optical fibres, co-axial cables and satellite broadcasting. Moreover, previous TV was primarily analog in nature. Signal processing by digital techniques has already started and still continues to augment the capability of audio and video parts in both programme recording and broadcasting. HDTV will greatly benefit from these ongoing developments. Another conspicuous feature is that the average size of the TV receiver has been increasing over the years. At the same time, the viewer-to-display distance has shrunk, resulting in a change in viewing habits which must be taken care of.

In this chapter, the shortcomings of the present analog TV will be first understood. Goals and characteristics of HDTV will be outlined. Since appreciation of HDTV concepts calls for a reconaissance of the controlling factors for resolution of a TV picture, we shall investigate picture resolution—both vertical and horizontal—and try to follow the operation of a future HDTV system, in the light of these discussions. Issues related to coding, recording and production of HDTV programmes as well as emission systems for HDTV will be addressed. The Grand-Alliance TV system, a transmission standard for delivery of HDTV, chartered by FCC, will be briefly reviewed. 3-D TV and interactive TV (ITV) will also be described

6.2. DRAWBACKS OF PRESENT ANALOG TV SERVICE

One approach of progressing towards HDTV, is to eradicate the difficulties faced with current analog TV. Notable problems are mentioned below:

(*i*) *Interline Flickering, Line Crawling and Vertical Aliasing :* These defects become more pronounced when we are considering textual matter with sharply defined edges or slowly moving graphics of high resolution. Such maladies have been removed in computers by using *progressive scanning* in place of interlaced scanning. Employing 60 Hz progressive scanning for TV pictures will help us in reducing these flaws. However, it must be pointed out that movie, sports or other similar pictures do not contain high resolution graphics or text in motion. So these disturbances are not noticed in such situations.

(*ii*) *Flickering Over Larger Regions :* This is particularly observed when we take a closeup view of the TV screen and also for bigger screens. The reason is that our eyes can distinguish the variations of brightness with time even at frequencies ≥ 60 Hz in the peripheral areas of human vision. The obvious remedy is to raise the frame rate upto 72 Hz in tune with the practice for computer displays. But in case of television, this measure undesirably increases the bandwidth and is therefore not favoured.

(*iii*) *Visibility of the Stationary Raster :* In larger displays, the eye can separately detect the scanning lines constituting the picture giving an unpleasant look much to the annoyance of the audience. The effect is minimized by making provision for more spatial resolution.

(*iv*) *Cross-Spectral and Cross-luminance Effects :* These are produced in the analog TV during the cross-modulation process used for generating the composite signal. By compressing individual colour components and time-division multiplexing the compressed bits, both these defects can be mitigated.

(*v*) *Occurrence of Ghost Phenomena :* Multiple receptions of the same signal shifted in the time scale relative to each other, give rise to the appearance of the so-called *Ghosts* in analog TV. Digital TV has a plausible solution to the ghost problem in the form of *Adaptive Equalization* which effects ghost cancellation without influencing the conveyed bit stream.

(*vi*) *Co-channel and Neighbouring Channel Interferences :* The NTSC signal containing high energy and sharp-transition synchronizing pulses is extremely wasteful in spectrum allocation because of the intruding effects of the co-channels and adjacent channels. Co-channels are two signal emissions from different locations in the same frequency band. To avoid co-channel interference, the two stations concerned must be spaced sufficiently far apart so that they are unable to exert any significant influence on each other. By neighbouring channel interference, we understand the disturbing effect which occurs when spectrally similar channels are distant enough so that signals of different strengths reach the receivers. To minimize this, such channels called *Adjacent Channels*, have to be located geographically close together because then their spectral characteristics do not intermingle with each other.

Because the above solutions to interference effects are frequently impracticable, currently the problem is overcome by keeping adjacent channels to the one being broadcasted, empty at a given place. These channels can however be used at a different place. The channels thus left vacant are called *Taboo Channels*; "taboo" means a ban or prohibition on something. The HDTV signal is planned to be assigned these taboo channels, for presently these channels represent a wastage of bandwidth.

6.3. PICTURE RESOLUTION CONSIDERATIONS

As we find, picture resolution plays a paramount role in high-definition television. A tutorial survey of the principal factors determining resolution is therefore called for. *Resolution* (Δ) of a picture in a given direction, vertical or horizontal, designated as Δv, Δh, is measured by the maximum number of alternate black-and-white lines which are distinctly discernible to the human eye, in the concerned direction.

6.3.1. Picture Resolution in the Vertical Direction

It is intuitively evident that the chief governing parameter of vertical resolution (Δv) is the total number N of raster scan lines per frame less the number of lines N_{vr} per field that are lost during vertical flyback of the scanning spot from the termination of field I to the beginning of field II in *interlaced raster scanning, i.e.*, the difference $(N - N_{vr})$. Another major constraint on Δv stems from the understanding that the scanning process employed for converting the optical image into a video signal in a TV camera at the transmitter, as well as the reverse transformation for image reconstruction by a picture tube at the receiver, are essentially sampling operations, subject to the conditions laid down in the Sampling Theorem. If the information signal is not strictly bandlimited, distortion will take place due to the aliasing effect. Combining the influence of both vertical retrace and aliasing, the vertical resolution Δv per unit raster height (a) is given by

$$\frac{\Delta v}{a} = \frac{k}{a}(N - 2N_{vr}) \qquad \qquad ...(6.1)$$

lines per unit distance, where k is a constant $\sim$ 0.6 to 0.7 called the *Kell Factor*. The phenomenon of aforesaid dependence of vertical resolution, *viz.*, its expressibility as a fraction of $(N - 2 N_{vr})$ is known as the *Kell Effect*. Clearly, Δv is augmented by increasing the Kell factor to make it closer to the maximum value of unity. The critical parameter of interest is the number of raster scan lines.

6.3.2. Picture Resolution in the Horizontal Direction

Like vertical resolution, it is irresistible to speculate that the horizontal resolution Δh is a function of the maximum number of lines that can be distinguished horizontally in a TV picture by a human observer. Assuming that the picture elements termed *Pixels* are alternate black-and-white spots arranged on a scanning line, the resulting video signal is a square wave having a fundamental frequency equal to the video bandwidth B. Then, noting that each cycle of the square wave represents two pixels, the horizontal resolution per unit raster width b is expressed as

$$\frac{\Delta h}{b} = \frac{2B}{b}(T - T_{hr}) \qquad \qquad ...(6.2)$$

lines per unit distance, where T is the time during which one scanning line is completed and T_{hr} is the time lost during the flyback stroke for horizontal retrace. Obviously, Δh improvement demands more signal bandwidth.

6.4. FEATURES OF HDTV PROPOSALS

Based on a systematic study of limitations of current analog TV and the factors determining picture resolution, several schemes have been proposed for HDTV realization. While complete concurrence among these proposals is lacking, they share some common features which are summarized below:

(*i*) *Enhanced Spatial Resolution* : The primary motivation for HDTV has been a better picture quality. This is accomplished by using twice the spatial resolution in both horizontal and vertical directions than the current TV called *Standard TV* (STV). Consequently, the number of scanning lines increases to >1000 with over 1000 pixels per scan line.

(*ii*) *Increased Temporal Resolution* : For improved reception of quick-action athletics, acrobatics, other sports and similar programmes, an idea which has gained wide acceptance, is the use of *Progressive Scanning* at the rate of 60 frames/sec. While this considerably weakens the artifacts caused by interlaced scanning, it also makes the system compatible with computers which are already following this practice. An unwanted side effect is the multiplication of active pixels in the HDTV signal by a factor of 5 thereby enlarging its bandwidth.

(*iii*) *Higher Image Aspect Ratio* : Subjective tests, psychological and psychophysical experiments have revealed that a horizontal viewing angle of at least 30° and hence a large screen size, is necessary for obtaining a sensation of reality. It is further found that a higher aspect ratio is required for a larger screen.

In fact, it has been unequivocally shown that viewer appreciation of image quality is increased on raising the aspect ratio of image from 4:3 to 5:3 or 16:9, resulting in a wider screen TV. This happens because most natural scenes benefit more from an increase in width than in height. Consumer's experience in 35-mm cinematographic film watching bears eloquent testimony to this observation. Thus HDTV will be a television system with a wide screen of 16:9 aspect ratio.

(*iv*) *Improved Audio Quality* : Steps (*i*)–(*iii*) are meant for picture quality amelioration. But audio quality is no less significant. HDTV will be furnished with 4–6 channel high-fidelity surround sound of CD-grade. In this multichannel audio signal, each channel will be individually compressed. This audio compression will be followed by time-division multiplexing of audio bits with compressed video bits along with the bits for captioning, teletext, encryption, etc.

(*v*) *Use of Digital Signal Processing Methodologies* : The HDTV signal will employ digital methods for coding and compression of bit streams to save the valuable bandwidth of broadcast spectrum. Pursuance of DSP approach will bring in its wake all the accompanying advantages of digital techniques.

(*vi*) *Harmonious Operation and Adaptability with the Evolving Telecommunications and Computer Infrastructure* : Introduction of features like progressive scanning, square pixels and digital representation greatly help in signal processing for editing, creating special effects, storage and down-conversion to analog TV requirements. MPEG compression algorithms reduce the HDTV signal bits to computer instructions and data which are easily amenable to processing and manipulation for desired picture and sound generation. Encapsulation of audio and video bit streams into fixed-length packets using transmission error correction methods, and synchronization through packet identifiers, headers and descriptors allows their conversion into packets for Asynchronous Transfer Mode (ATM).

(*vii*) *Simulcasting of HDTV Signal with NTSC Analog TV Signal* : Higher spatial and temporal resolution together with multichannel surround sound systems are the chief contributing factors which are responsible for drastically increasing the HDTV signal bandwidth ~ 30–140 MHz. In analog form, the signal cannot be accommodated in any of the existing analog channels. The prime necessity for popularization of HDTV is that the bandwidth stock of the terrestrial spectrum should be judiciously exploited without any surplus burden. For efficient spectrum utilization, one has to take recourse to digital compression for reducing the bit rate from 1 Gbit/sec to 20 Mbit/sec which can be cramped into the standard 6-MHz bandwidth.

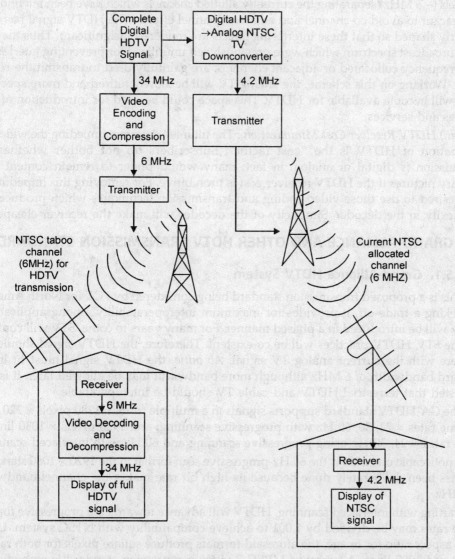

Fig. 6.1. Methodology of sending the same programme on HDTV and NTSC channels at the same time for reception by HDTV and conventional TV receivers

Furthermore, the HDTV system should allow for co-existence of the prevailing NTSC system. Hence, interference from adjacent channels including the analog TV channels, must be minimized. In digital HDTV scheme, besides squeezing the video and audio bits into a bandwidth equal to that of current analog TV signal, the signal is produced at a lower power and has also no high power carrier components. The low-power full-strength complete HDTV signal is broadcasted simultaneously with the current analog TV signal

(Fig. 6.1) with the latter obtained by downconverting the HDTV signal to STV level. By this strategy, consumers having ordinary receiver sets can still watch their programmes while others buying newer HDTV sets can get the benefit of superior quality viewing. The analog signal sent in one of the existing channels, is detected by ordinary receivers producing normal pictures and sound as we are used to watching. The low power digital HDTV signal is allocated a taboo channel in the broadcast spectrum. *Taboo Channels* are those channels (~ 6 MHz) separating the currently allotted channels which have been intentionally kept vacant to avoid co-channel and adjacent channel effects. The HDTV signal has to be properly shaped so that these interfering effects are rendered insignificant. Thus the slots of the broadcast spectrum which were previously left unutilized for preventing interference with frequency collocated or adjacent channels, are gainfully used to transmit the HDTV signal. Working on this scheme, the analog TV will be slowly retired and more spectrum space will become available for HDTV. This space could be used for introduction of new features and services.

(*viii*) *HDTV Receiver Cost Minimization :* The ultimate deterrent impeding the widescale permeation of HDTV is the "cost factor". Subscribers do not bother whether the transmission is digital or analog; in fact, many would prefer to remain content with ordinary pictures if the HDTV receiver cost is prohibitive. For removing this impediment, it is desired to use those video coding and transmission techniques which produce less complexity in the decoder. Simplicity of the decoder will make the receiver cheaper.

6.5. GRAND-ALLIANCE AND OTHER HDTV TRANSMISSION STANDARDS

6.5.1. Grand-Alliance HDTV System

This is a proposed transmission standard being considered by FCC for North America. By seeking a trade-off, it provides for maximum interoperatability among applications. HDTV will be introduced in a phased manner. For many years to come, STV will continue and the STV, HDTV practices will be co-existent. Therefore, the HDTV signal should not interfere with the current analog TV signal. *Ab initio*, the HDTV signal must fit in the standard bandwidth of 6 MHz although more bandwidth may be allowed later. It is also suggested that terrestrial HDTV and cable TV should be interoperatable.

The GA-HDTV standard supports signals in a multiple format: 1280 pixels × 720 lines at frame rates = 24, 30, 60 Hz with progressive scanning; and 1920 pixels × 1080 lines at frame rates = 24, 30 Hz using progressive scanning and 60 Hz with interlaced scanning.

A noticeable omission is the 60 Hz-progressive scan format in the 1920 × 1080 standard. This has been deliberately done because its high bit rate makes the channel bandwidth > 6 MHz.

Starting with interlaced scanning, HDTV will advance towards the progressive format. Frame rates may be divided by 1.001 to achieve compatibility with NTSC system. Using a 16:9 aspect ratio for image, the aforesaid formats produce square pixels for both rasters of 720 and 1080 lines. A subset of MPEG-2 video compression standard is embodied in the GA-HDTV system. The important compression method used is the Direct Cosine Transform (DCT) of motion-compensated signals. Compression efficiency is increased by prefiltering/subsampling for handling various types of signals.

Regarding the audio signal, a 5-channel audio with surround sound system is employed. The audio signal is compressed into a 384 kbits/sec bit stream. The audio and video data together with auxiliary data are packaged into fixed-length packets for easy interoperation with ATM.

The modulation scheme selected for over-the-air terrestrial transmission is analog 8-Vestigial Side Band (8-VSB) giving 32.38 Mbits/sec of raw data in the 6-MHz bandwidth. For high rate cable transmission of data, 16-VSB scheme will be used. Coaxial cables can transport a higher bit rate in the 6-MHz channel because of the absence of co-channel interference and negligibly small adjacent channel disturbance.

The GA-HDTV system provides a flexible video compression solution applicable to several industries such as broadcasting, computer/multimedia, graphics and imaging. This becomes evident when we note that 1280 × 720 is a subset of 1280 × 1024 graphics monitor. Lower film rate permits the compression of 1920 × 1080 for entertainment use and MPEG-2 syntax makes the system compatible with other standards. Since GA decoders will accept a variety of formats, the transition of the system to higher quality with improved coding methods, will be considerably smooth.

6.5.2. Other Transmission Standards

The Japanese system of HDTV, entitled as "Multiple Sub-Nyquist Encoding" (MUSE in short), uses Frequency Modulation (FM) and occupies 27 MHz of bandwidth for a single channel. Since the bandwidth far exceeds the 6-MHz NTSC limit, the system has not proved to be attractive for terrestrial broadcasting. However, satellite transponders can accommodate a minimum of 36 MHz of bandwidth and optical fibre transmission upto 50 MHz.

The International Radio Consultative Committee (CCIR) has given the following recommendation: 1125 lines/frame with 1035 active lines per frame and 33.750 kHz line frequency. An aspect ratio of 16:9 is used along with 2:1 interlaced scanning and a field rate of 60 frames/sec. Many European countries have urged the CCIR to recommend for progressive scanning at 50-Hz field rate.

After this perfunctory treatment of the principles of HDTV, from the next section we shall start looking into the coding, compression, recording and emission systems for HDTV signal.

6.6. HDTV SIGNAL CODING AND COMPRESSION

6.6.1. Major Considerations

HDTV signal coding is easier than conventional TV signal coding because the HDTV signal has a small frequency component in the high-frequency region. But it is difficult than conventional TV in the sense that tolerance limits on picture quality are more scrupulous. Due to the extremely high sampling rates used in HDTV, the parameters of noise reduction and compression, and hardware implementation are crucial to coder construction. HDTV cameras and lenses provide low energy in high-frequency component. With advancements in image pickup methods, the statistical characteristics of HDTV cameras will be comparable to STV level. Since high-definition cameras give a larger thermal noise, signal prefiltering is indispensable. Adaptive spatial filters reduce random noise and increase coding efficiency.

Video compression as a pivotal technology in HDTV development, has been implemented in video servers, digital cameras, video tape recorders (VTRs) and other devices, and is extensively being used in program production, distribution and storage.

6.6.2. Subsampling Technique

The studio signal produced by PCM at typically 1.18 Gbits/sec, has to be coded at 135 Mbits/sec for transmission. Multisubnyquist sampling like *Quincunx Sampling* decreases the data rate to a quarter of the initial value. However, it is only effective in static portions of the image and moving picture quality is poor. This method is replaced by Interframe DPCM.

6.6.3. Intrafield/Interframe DPCM

Quincunx subsampling is followed by extrapolation of the missing pixels from existing intrafield pixels. Prediction errors are quantised and coded by a variable-length code; vector quantisation is used. If the motion between contiguous frames is small, interframe correlation is large and more effective than intrafield prediction. Interframe DPCM has evolved towards interframe direct cosine transform (DCT) method.

6.6.4. DCT Coding

This method reduces the image spatial redundancy. For natural images, there is a concentration of power of transformed coefficients towards the low-frequency region. A real-time programmable encoder for motion compensation and DCT coding employs exhaustive parallel architecture and elaborate hardware.

6.6.5. Motion-Compensated (MC) Hybrid DCT Coding Method

The MC hybrid DCT coding technique under the Motion Picture Expert Group-2 (MPEG-2) compression standard, holds a great potential as a future HDTV coding method, both for broadcasting and products. Systems employing digital modulation will rely on MPEG-2 coding. Receiver price will fall by using MPEG-2 decoder IC. MPEG standard will also provide a common platform suitable for consistent working of different equipment.

As indicated earlier, the MPEG-2 video algorithm utilizes traditional motion (MC) and DCT methods. Interframe prediction with MC decreases temporal redundancy of video sequences. MC prediction is carried out on a frame basis and selectively on a field basis. DCT is switched between a frame- or field-image basis. Both interlacing and progressive scanning formats can be treated.

6.7. HDTV SIGNAL RECORDING TECHNOLOGY

6.7.1. HDTV Cameras and Charge-Control Devices (CCDs)

Cameras are now available which can work in both 4 : 3 and 16 : 9 aspect ratios to facilitate operation in an NTSC/HDTV simulcasting environment. At present, 1″ (diagonal size 16 mm) CCD having 2×10^6 pixels and 2/3″ CCD with 1.3×10^6 pixels, are practically used. A CCD with an image area of 2/3″ and pixel count = 2×10^6 is aimed at. When the CCD chip size is decreased and the pixel count increased, the pixel size is proportionately smaller. But a small pixel has a low sensitivity. This problem of degradation of sensitivity with pixel size has to be solved. Further refinements in CCDs have set the goal at raising the pixel count to 6×10^6 (3×10^3 by 2×10^3) and introduction of progressive scanning.

6.7.2. Digital Video Tape Recorders (VTRs)

Digital VTRs make it possible to store HDTV programmes without any deterioration in quality. Typically a VTR uses a 1/2″ cassette for 1 hour recording at 140 Mbits/sec. A low-cost data or bitstream recorder can be used to store and playback the 19 Mbits/sec compressed signal. MPEG-2 is useful for VTRs except for fast forward and reverse playback functions. The target of future VTR research is to store several hours of programmes on 8 mm tape.

6.7.3. Digital Disc Recording

Laser disc recording technology is beginning to compete with traditional tape-based equipment. For constant angular velocity, optical discs can playback 8 minutes per side; for uniform linear speed, they can playback 15 minutes of programme per side without any compression. A *Digital Video Disc* (DVD) is fast emerging. A 2-hour programme at 20 Mbits/sec can be stored in an 18 Gbyte disc. *Disc arrays* provide a large storage capacity and random access. In future recording systems, various recording media will coexist and will be used, depending on the application.

6.7.4. Super High-Definition (SHD) Still/Moving Image Recording

Super high-definition TV integrates the concepts of TV using interlaced scanning with progressive-scanning based computer displays and high-resolution movie films. A programmable real-time image processing system using MPEG-2 coding algorithm gives adequate image quality. The input device is an image scanning system for 70 mm film. Frame storage having a high capacity is used, and the processing system is configured in a massively parallel architecture.

Motion pictures are recorded on a 70-mm film and afterwards scanned and stored in the computer hard disc. The hard disc serves as the source of SHD moving pictures.

Table 6.1 compares the merits and demerits of optical film and HDTV as video post production media.

Table 6.1. Comparative Assessment of Optical Film and HDTV as Imaging Medium for Video Post Production System

Pros. and Cons of Optical Film	Advantages and Limitations of HDTV
Film is the extremely high band Red-Green-Blue (RGB) medium for image recording and reproduction with worldwide compatibility. Unique features of the film like sharpness, colour gamut, tone scale and dynamic range make it a sturdy post production system. Film masters presently represent the highest quality imaging medium for telecine transference.	Graphic supercomputers along with powerful video composing hardware are finding their way into video post production centres. This is being done to exploit their production and creative flexibilities and the ability to perform operations on digitized film images. The video composing suite is evolving into a resolution-independent digital film suite.
Reasons for popularity of film include: (*i*) the high degree of creativity provided to cinematographers for slow-motion and fast photography. (*ii*) Availability in different formats like 16 mm, 35 mm and 65 mm which gives the producers economic choice according to their needs.	However, insofar as spatial resolution is concerned, the 1000 scanning lines of HDTV are inadequate for applications with extensive minute details. The capability must be augmented to thrice as much (using 3000 lines) in situations where the high-frequency image content is preponderant and has to be intercut with the original camera negative film.
(*iii*) Ability of using various film stocks to suit the lighting conditions. Also, the broad dynamic range of film images allows artistic manipulations to be made at the time of telecine transfer to video. (*iv*) Proven credibility of film as an archival	Further, the 8-bit video representation of HDTV does not fit well with > 2.0 logarithmic-shaped density range of optical film. Scenes in which the brightness spans over a wider ratio, are not satisfactorily

image storage medium. Optical basis of film production eliminates the need for archiving complicated electronic playback equipment for reproducing the stored images.

On the contrary, the slow optical printing processes cannot compete with the rapid pace offered by the video composing suite. Video tape formats and disc-based video-composing hardware, have edged away optical printing for TV commercials. But when a film master is necessary, video recorders are insufficient to digitize and store the information content of film originals.

produced by HDTV. Film images subjected to multiple image processing, are prone to aliasing on smooth tone areas like human flesh. Higher quantisation such as 10-bit logarithmic, is required for reaching upto the expectations of wide density range of film.

Over and above, the Y/R-Y/B-Y subsampled colour space representations of HDTV constitutes a major inhibiting factor. Due to the subsampling and storing of the blue channel at half resolution, the quality of extracting blue-screen mattes and preserving finer details in scene objects with colourful beauty, is obviously restricted. Digital film systems storing fullband RGB images do not face such a problem.

6.8. HDTV PROGRAMME STATION AND STUDIO EQUIPMENT

6.8.1. Signal Format Converters

In analog NTSC, the signal is acquired, stored and distributed in essentially a single format from its origination to the consumers. But digital TV will allow operation in several formats. So signal format conversion will be necessary many times and at several locations. While operational simplicity in working with a single format will be lost, the flexibility of moving from one format to the other will be available depending on the particular application. Modes of operation will include serial, parallel, uncompressed and compressed formats.

A *Downconverter* changes from HDTV to NTSC format. When NTSC programmes are obtained from a 60.00 Hz source, frame rate conversion is also necessary. An *Upconverter* alters from NTSC to HDTV standard and allows us to access the vast library of programmes in NTSC. Since both interlaced and progressive formats are permitted for HDTV, the format converters allow deinterlacing along with spatial and temporal up/down conversions.

6.8.2. Networking

The use of MPEG-2 compression and introduction of multimedia services will call for replacement of hard-wired networking with virtually connected, flexible and efficient systems. Asynchronous Transfer Mode (ATM), Fibre Distributed Data Interface (FDDI), etc., are some of the promising candidate technologies.

6.8.3. Interfacing and Concatenation

Concomittant operation of various media will warrant the need for appropriate interfacial equipment. Also, signal multiplexing and formatting will have to be done for terrestrial broadcasting, satellite distribution, on-line services and archival purposes (Fig. 6.2). Artifacts produced by linking of different compression schemes and signal processing methods, will have to be eliminated. The effects of concatenation will have to be accounted for in the design and layout of the distribution chain to avoid any loss of video quality.

Suitable compression ratios must be chosen to allow for production, mixing and editing together with storage and switching costs for distributing signals between the network and its branches. A new MPEG-2 profile known as 4:2:2 profile gives better video quality and chromatic resolution and also allows for a higher bit rate. It will be widely used in broadcasting for applications involving multiple generations of encoding and decoding and picture manipulation operations.

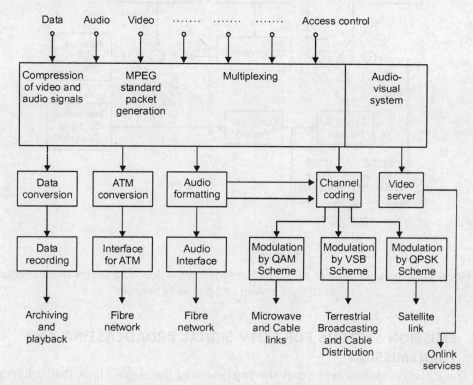

Fig. 6.2. Block diagram representation of studio interfaces for multiplexing and formatting of data, audio, video, etc., signals for archival, fibre, microwave and satellite distribution and other services

Distribution of programmes among the members of a network can be done either by terrestrial emission at 19 Mbits/sec or at higher bit rates. The first approach saves transmission bandwidth and cuts down conversion expenditure at local stations. But there is insufficient quality headroom in the signal for downstream processing. The second distribution mode permits enough headroom for downstream processing but overburdens the bandwidth. The choice between the two modes is dictated by bandwidth, interfacing and subjective quality requirements.

6.8.4. Simulcasting Configuration

During the transitional phase, both 59.94 Hz and 60.00 Hz NTSC programmes will exist. HDTV programmes will be prepared at 60.00 Hz and will have to be frame rate converted for downconversion to NTSC. Figure 6.3 depicts the block diagram of the simulcasting configuration in a studio environment.

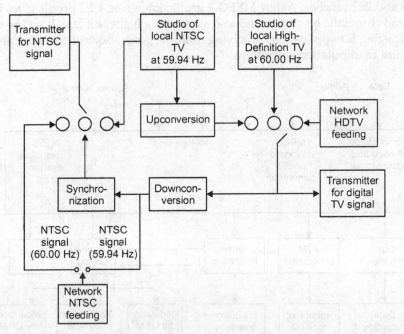

Fig. 6.3. Studio-environment configuration showing the flow diagram for simultaneous telecasting of analog and digital TV services

6.9. EMISSION SYSTEMS FOR HDTV SIGNAL BROADCASTING AND TRANSMISSION

The emission system represents the final stage of the signal chain that delivers the signal from the station to the subscribers.

6.9.1. Satellite Transmission

Intraframe DCT coding is used along with QPSK modulation. The video coding rate is 60 Mbits/sec and the bandwidth after QPSK modulation is 140 MHz.

6.9.2. Terrestrial Broadcasting

There are three main types of modulation for HDTV: Frequency Modulation (FM), Vestigial Sideband Amplitude Modulation (VSB-AM) and Orthogonal Frequency-Division Multiplexing (OFDM). FM is the best choice for easy changeover from the existing system to HDTV practice.

Orthogonal Frequency-Division Multiplexing (OFDM) is a multi-carrier digital modulation technique providing a signal which is more robust to the disturbing effects of echoes. It employs either 1705 carriers (2 K Mode) or 6817 carriers (8 K Mode). The former is used for single-frequency small-area transmission and the latter for single-frequency large-area broadcasting.

The data carriers in OFDM use QPSK or different levels of QAM. Coded OFDM (COFDM) is a combination of OFDM with coded modulation. It gives a larger transmission capacity with a comparatively narrow bandwidth.

Digital modulation methods are advantageous when the received error rate is less than a prescribed limit. Also, they require a lower transmitter power. However, digital modulation exhibits a sharp cutoff in weak reception conditions. Comparing OFDM with VSB-AM technique, we note that OFDM combats multipath degradation effects. But it suffers from hardware complexity because it is based on FFT computation and requires a broader dynamic range for transmitter and receiver. Exactly opposite is the case for VSB modulation with a smaller dynamic range requirement; a conventional TV transmitter can be used by incorporating a transmission equalizer in the receiver.

An important consideration in favour of OFDM is the saving in frequency bandwidth because of possibility of construction of a single frequency network using OFDM. However, it must be remembered that such a network can hold only under the condition of same programme content of every transmitter in the network. Also, the limitations of OFDM should not be overlooked. For instance, the period of guard interval decides the tolerance of multipath disturbance. A ghost of length greater than period of guard interval cannot be removed. A longer period is easily obtainable in audio transmission because of slow data rate. The same is not true for video transmission because a long period is given by a longer FFT.

6.10. HDTV REALIZATION BY RECEIVER HARDWARE REDESIGN FOR REAL-TIME IMAGE ENHANCEMENT

To circumvent the problems encountered in alteration of transmission standards and making allowance for *downward compatibility* with the existing receiver sets, an alternative solution has been proposed. In this proposal, the number of scanning lines is doubled at the *receiver only*, keeping the transmission standards untouched. This is made possible with the help of special circuit design techniques for digital signal processing to improve the resolution of the received picture. The principle of this method is *real-time two-dimensional filtering*. We begin by understanding the approach for non real-time applications, i.e., for processing one image at a time instead of a stream of images at the rate of 30 frames/sec.

9.10.1. Non Real-Time Image Enlargement

The block diagram of the system is illustrated in Fig. 6.4. The system consists of a *Read/Write (R/W) Memory Array* followed by an *Interpolation Array* (realized as an FIR filter using the *Pipeline Systolic Structure*), for doubling the image resolution, and a High-Pass Filter (HPF), either FIR or IIR type using *Sample and Hold Architecture*, for image deblurring purpose; the blurring effect is caused during interpolation. The image is first elongated by storage in a $2N \times 2N$ array with assignment of zero value to every other row and column. Then convolution of the stretched image is performed with an interpolation operator. The resultant image is slightly blurry and of lower quality than the one obtained by applying the Sampling Theorem. It is deblurred by spatial techniques through high-pass filtering.

The steps involved in image magnification are as follows: First, the digitized image (suppose 256×256 pixels) is written on the Read/Write Memory. During writing, care is taken to ensure that pixels are written on alternative sites on any given row (as indicated by the hatched squares) and also on alternate rows; unfilled squares stand for empty positions. The second step is the passage of the image through the interpolation array, producing a 512×512 pixel image. From here, the image is fed to HPF for enhancement. Finally, after conversion into analog form, the image is displayed on a 512×512 pixel screen.

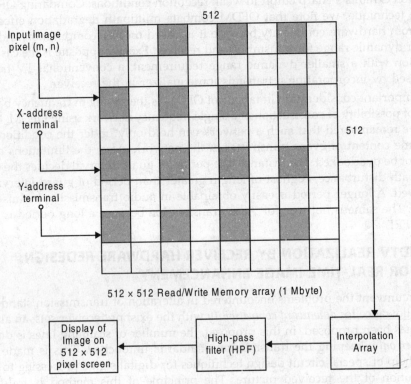

Input image
pixel (m, n)

512

X-address
terminal

512

Y-address
terminal

512 × 512 Read/Write Memory array (1 Mbyte)

Display of
Image on
512 × 512
pixel screen   ←   High-pass
                      filter (HPF)   ←   Interpolation
                                          Array

Fig. 6.4. Concept of doubling the number of raster lines in
non-real time image magnification

6.10.2 Relation Between the Frequency (f_2) of Reading the Image from Memory and the Sampling Frequency (f_1) of Incoming Signal

It is obvious that the reading rate of image to memory must be four times its writing rate out of memory to ensure that the read time of image is equal to its write time. It may be noted that

$$\text{Write Time of Image} = \frac{1}{60} + \frac{1}{60} = \frac{1}{30} \text{ sec} \qquad \qquad ...(6.3)$$

Let f_1 be the sampling frequency of received signal. Then $f_1 = \dfrac{256}{H}$ where H denotes the line delay. Clearly,

$$\text{Image Write Time} = \frac{1}{f_1} \times 256 \times 256 \qquad \qquad ...(6.4)$$

Since an NTSC image is composed of two fields with each field written into memory in $\dfrac{1}{60}$ sec.,

$$\text{Image Read Time} = \frac{1}{f_2} \times 512 \times 512 = \frac{4}{f_2} \times 256 \times 256 \text{ in terms of frequency } f_2 \text{ of reading}$$

the image out of memory. Thus we obtain

$$f_2 = 4f_1 \qquad \qquad ...(6.5)$$

9.10.3. Real-Time Image Size Doubling

The apparent limitation of the preceding method is due to the fact that one cannot simultaneously read from and write into memory. So, during the time of reading from memory and processing the present image, the subsequent image cannot be processed. For overcoming this problem, two memory arrays are used, as shown in Fig. 6.5. The function of the *Write Mode Address Registers* is to handle interlaced scanning. They write at suitable positions in the R/W memory. The role of *Read Mode Address Registers* is to read the 1 MB memory with a reading rate = 4 × Writing Rate. The operational frequency of interpolation and HP filters is equal to 4 × Horizontal sampling frequency (f_1). When reading of one image is performed from one memory array, writing of the succeeding images is done to the other memory array, and loss of images is prevented.

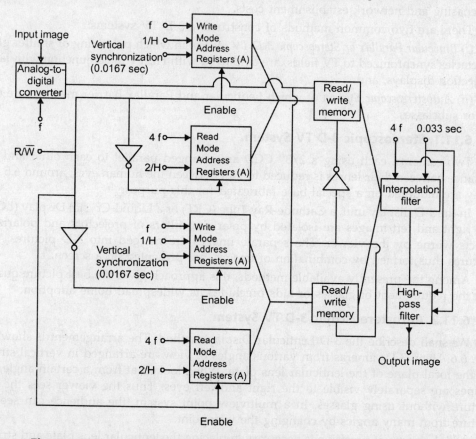

Fig. 6.5. Real-time image size doubling (f denotes the horizontal sampling frequency and H the period of a horizontal line)

For image display, two memory buffers of size 512 × 512 pixels, are used. The incoming image is written in one memory buffer while the previous image is read off from the second buffer.

Repeating the above procedure, we can achieve a resolution of 1024 × 1024, 2048 × 2048, ... The limits are imposed by the Sampling Theorem and technological constraints. The method uses fast DRAMs (Dynamic Random Access Memories). Using presently available DRAMs with speeds upto 250 MHz, one can increase the resolution by four times.

6.11.   THREE-DIMENSIONAL TELEVISION (3-D TV) AS A POST HDTV SYSTEM

With the maturing and burgeoning of the HDTV network supplying pictures of quality matching 35-mm cinema films at our homes, the next stride will be to launch 3-D TV which will provide high-resolution, real-time, stereoscopic pictures. It will be another quantum leap ahead of 2-D HDTV giving a perception of depth and naturalness because the real-world phenomena are experienced by us in three dimensions. The field of 3-D TV is still in its infancy and riddled with problems which must be successfully overcome. These include: (*i*) Development of displays which neither require any special glasses to be worne by viewer nor cause any viewer fatigue and also can be watched by a group of people. (*ii*) Ability to produce 2-D pictures on ordinary receivers necessitating little modifications, if any. (*iii*) Bandwidth reduction for 3-D TV signal. (*iv*) Lower receiver purchasing and network establishment costs.

There are two common methods of constructing 3-D TV systems:

(*i*) *Binocular Parallax or Stereoscopic 3-D TV System* in which polarizing or shutter glass spectacles synchronized to TV fields, are employed with HDTV in conjunction with large projection displays, and

(*ii*) *Autostereoscopic System* of which Lenticular and Parallax Barrier methods are two major subclasses.

6.11.1. Stereoscopic 3-D TV System

Two cameras, each using a 2/3″ CCD are arranged parallel to each other and the distance between their lenses is reduced to that between the human eyes, around 6.5 cm. They are mounted on a special base fabricated for this purpose.

In the 3-D display unit, a Cathode-Ray Tube (CRT) or a Liquid-Crystal Display (LCD), the right and left images are isolated by polarizing filters of projectors and polarizing spects worne by the viewer. The separate images are merged into 3-D pictures. The pictures thus formed by combination of images, are presented on a screen.

Among the presently available methods, this approach gives the best picture quality but the requirement of glasses or aids precludes its widespread home adoption.

6.11.2. Autostereoscopic 3-D TV System

We shall describe the 3-D Lenticular Display method. The arrangement is shown in Fig. 6.6. Here, 3-D cameras from various angles of view are arranged in vertical stripes on the focal plane of the lenticular lens plate. When looked at from a certain angle, the stripes are separately visible to the right and left eyes. Thus the viewer sees the 3-D picture without using glasses. In a multiview point system, the audience can see the picture from many angles by changing the viewpoint.

A high degree of precision is necessary in placing the lenticular lens plate and striped image relative to each other; otherwise moire patterns result or the 3-D picture disappears altogether. As LCDs with 1×10^6 pixels are being produced to build HDTV displays, accurate positioning of the pixels with respect to the lenticular lens has beocme possible.

Note: A *Lenticular Lens* consists of a transparent plate having a large number of narrow cylindrical lenses arranged on its surface in close proximity.

6.11.3. 3-D TV Signal Processing

Compression of 3-D information using picture redundancy is adequate for single viewpoint stereoscopic TV but does not meet the needs of autostereoscopic displays characterized by multiviewpoints. To compress pictures taken by several cameras, one method is to construct a *3-D Object Model* inside a computer from pictures taken with parallax from a number of angles with the help of intelligent information processing technology. Then an intermediate picture of the view is formed. From a foreknowledge of physiology and psychology, and using neutral networks, the disparity of edge in a given direction is determined. The picture is reconstructed on the basis of reproduced intermediate viewpoints. As an alternative to the object model method, another useful method works on making "Interpolation Pictures".

6.12. INTERACTIVE TELEVISION (ITV)

Of late, an area which has been the focal point of attention, is the infusion of "interactive capability" into TV services, changing the "Dumb Box" of the living room into an "Intelligent Box". These interactive features will largely be the result of assimilating digital signal processing into TV hardware, and HDTV will partake of these benefits. Interactive TV is a residential service to consumers wherein they can exercise both minute and rough control over the contents of the programme being viewed; they can also avail of services like video telephony, video films on demand, home shopping and computer games, through their TV sets. This will dawn an era of "individual programmes for each viewer".

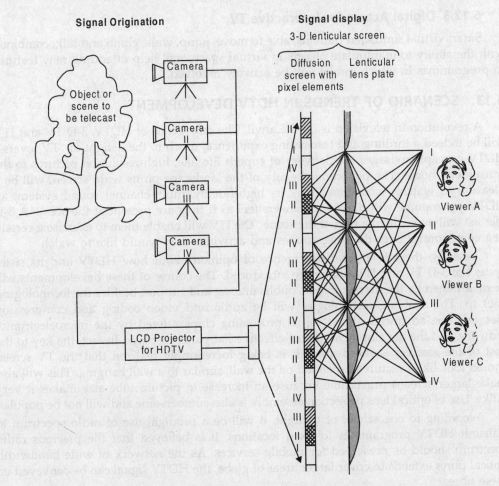

Fig. 6.6. Three-dimensional HDTV setup for multiviewpoint autostereoscopic display with a single LCD video projector and 3-D lenticular screen

6.12.1. "Viewer" and "User" Roles of Audience

The status of the TV audience will switch between "viewer" and "user" roles. While watching regular TV programmes like news, sports commentary, conversations, telecasts of events, etc., he/she is a viewer in the traditional sense of watching TV. When a person benefits from facilities/services provided by TV as in case of computer, he/she becomes a user.

6.12.2. Modes of Interaction with TV

A menu of programmes will be displayed on the TV screen. The person can select the programme of interest, download it and enjoy it at leisure. In another interaction mode, he/she enters a programme on the keyboard when similar types of programmes being offered by several channels appear. Then the person chooses from among these programmes, downloads the desired programme and views it at will.

The person can also participate in games on TV. Teaching of specialized subjects such as Mathematics and Science will be made easy by assigning problems and asking questions, and removing difficulties faced by students. For activities like dancing, singing, etc., one can seek guidance and clarifications from the teleteacher.

6.12.3. Digital Actors for Interactive TV

Smart virtual simulated humans, able to move, jump, walk, climb and talk, combined with the ability to manipulate objects in virtual space, will help in adding new features to programmes in which public will be actively involved.

6.13. SCENARIO OF TRENDS IN HDTV DEVELOPMENT

A revolution in television is on the anvil. The emergence of HDTV, 3-D TV and ITV will be indeed a thrilling and fascinating experience, much to the delight of "TV lovers". HDTV concept envisages the delivery of superb life-like, high-resolution pictures to the consumer's home. The panoramic beauty of the landscape on its wide screen, will be a pleasure to watch. Accompanied by its high-fidelity, multi-channel sound system, an HDTV programme will make the viewers feel as if they are present at the scene. A 3-D tele ast will make them a part of the scene. The ITV will enable them to exercise a certain deg ee of control over the programmes and activities they would like to watch.

resently, there is a great divergence of opinion about how HDTV and its sister syste 1 of 3-D TV and ITV, should be introduced. The course of these developments will be de ermined by the market trends, public interest and support besides the technological back .p. The enabling technologies will be audio and video coding and compression met ods, the advanced digital signal processing chips offered by the microelectronics indu try, and the development of cost-effective flat panel displays. In fact, the key to the cost of the receiver is the display. It is being increasingly realized that the TV screen should look like a picture suspended on the wall, similar to a wall hanging. This will also make larger screens practicable because an increase in picture tube size makes it very bulky. Use of optical lens projection assembly is also cumbersome and will not be popular.

According to one school of thought, it will be a prodigal use of radio spectrum to transmit HDTV programmes to fixed locations. It is believed that the precious radio spectrum should be preserved for mobile services. As the network of wide bandwidth optical fibres extends to cover larger areas of globe, the HDTV signal can be conveyed on these fibres.

A different school of thought advocates that using *Hierarchical Coding*, a *Hierarchical HDTV Service* can be provided showing higher quality pictures on HDTV receivers and tolerable quality pictures on ordinary or mobile receivers.

Another line of thinking is that the resolution of current analog TV is adequate for many applications. Instead of directly introducing HDTV, first the TV services should be made entirely digital and interactive, and then HDTV should be ushered in, followed by 3-D TV.

HDTV may also evolve along an altogether different route as the *picture gallery* of the information superhighway. As more and more information services become digital, applications of HDTV in medicine, education, entertainment, etc., to name a few, may act as a catalytic agent, accelerating the rate of its widespread deployment. Essentially, digital networking and broadcasting with HDTV as its core picture component, will provide flexible, multifunctional multimedia services. HDTV receiver will be the viewer's window to multimedia. The interesting subject of multimedia will form the content of the next chapter.

(ILLUSTRATIVE PROBLEMS)

6.1. Given that the number of samples per active line for standard television (STV) is 720, calculate the same for HDTV.

Number of samples per active line in HDTV

$$= \text{Number of samples per active line in STV} \times 2 \times \frac{\text{Aspect Ratio of HDTV}}{\text{Aspect Ratio of STV}}$$

...(P6.1)

The factor 2 in this equation accounts for the use of *progressive scanning* in HDTV instead of *interlaced scanning* in STV.

Hence, the required number of samples per active line in HDTV

$$= 720 \times 2 \times \frac{\frac{16}{9}}{\frac{4}{3}} = 1920. \qquad \text{...(P6.2)}$$

6.2. For an HDTV system employing a 1080-line raster, the Kell factor is 0.73. Estimate the vertical resolution of its picture.

Vertical Resolution of the picture (Δv) = Kell Factor (k) × Number of lines in the raster (N) (expressed in TV lines per picture height, *i.e.*, TVL/PH) ...(P6.3)

Since HDTV uses progressive scanning, the number of lines lost during vertical flyback (N_{vr}) = 0. Substituting the given values, we obtain

$$\Delta v = 0.73 \times 1080 = 788.4 \text{ TVL/PH} = 789 \text{ TVL/PH}. \qquad \text{...(P6.4)}$$

6.3. For an 1125 lines/60-Hz field rate HDTV system, the standards are: Active Line Time = 25.86 μ sec, Nominal Bandwidth = 30 MHz. Calculate the analog horizontal resolution capability.

The Analog Horizontal Picture Resolution $(\Delta h)_A$ of a TV system is related to the bandwidth requirement by the formula

$$(\Delta h)_A = \frac{\text{Horizontal Active Line Duration} \times 2 \times \text{Bandwidth (MHz)}}{\text{Aspect Ratio}} \text{ TVL/PH}$$

...(P6.5)

$$= \frac{25.86 \times 10^{-6} \times 2 \times 30 \times 10^{6}}{16/9} = 872.78 \text{ TVL/PH} \qquad \dots(P6.6)$$

$$= 873 \text{ TVL/PH}. \qquad \dots(P6.7)$$

6.4. The sampling frequency for the 1125 line HDTV system production is 74.25 MHz. Find the digital horizontal resolution of the picture.

$$\text{Digital Horizontal Resolution } (\Delta h)_D = \frac{25.86 \text{ } \mu\text{sec} \times 2 \times 74.25 \text{ } MHz/2}{16/9} \qquad \dots(P6.8)$$

$$= 1080.06 \text{ TVL/PH} = 1080 \text{ TVL/PH}. \qquad \dots(P6.9)$$

Division by 2 is done because the highest video frequency that may be reproduced is one-half of the sample frequency.

REVIEW QUESTIONS

6.1. Give some examples of the expansion of TV applications, introduction of newer delivery media and other factors responsible for exposing the limitations of analog television standards established over 50 years ago.

6.2. What is a Backward-Compatible Television System? Was the introduction of Colour TV a backward-compatible change? Will the proposed HDTV system be a backward compatible one?

6.3. Briefly describe the main problems of current analog TV, suggesting possible remedies for each.

6.4. What artifacts are associated with interlaced scanning? Why has the computer industry forsaken interlaced scanning? What do you mean by progressive scanning?

6.5. What are Ghosts? Is Ghost Cancellation easier for digital TV?

6.6. Write short notes on: (a) Cross-colour and Cross-luminance Effects, and (b) Co-channel and Adjacent Channel Interference.

6.7. Explain how the STV signal packaged for terrestrial transmission is extremely wasteful of the broadcast spectrum? What are Taboo Channels in the TV spectrum? Why are these channels so called?

6.8. What is meant by Resolution of a TV picture? Write down the expressions for: (i) Vertical Picture Resolution per unit raster height and (ii) Horizontal Picture Resolution per unit raster width.

6.9. What is Kell Effect? Define Kell Factor. What are the typical values of Kell Factor for TV practice?

6.10. How does aliasing reduce the vertical resolution of a TV picture?

6.11. Enumerate the main features of the current HDTV proposals. Mention the approximate bitrate and bandwidth necessary for an HDTV signal. By what factor must this bitrate be decreased to accomodate it in a 6-MHz channel?

6.12. Highlight the characteristics of HDTV which make it interoperatable with the evolving telecommunications and computing infrastructure.

6.13. Discuss how the simulcasting of digital HDTV will be done with the NTSC analog TV? Show the simulcasting operation diagrammatically.

6.14. What measures are adopted to ameliorate the audio quality in HDTV?

6.15. Give the values of the following parameters for HDTV: (i) Aspect Ratio, (ii) Number of scanning lines, (iii) Number of samples per active line, and (iv) Typical source information rate and sampling frequency.

6.16. What are the multiple signal formats supported by the Grand-Alliance HDTV (GA-HDTV) transmission standard? How does GA-HDTV system provide a flexible video compression solution applicable to several industries?

6.17. What is the modulation scheme chosen for over-the-air terrestrial transmission in GA-HDTV system? Why does GA-HDTV system not include a 1920 × 1080 progressive scan format at 60 Hz?

6.18. What does GA-HDTV system propose for the audio part of HDTV signal?

6.19. What compressed bitrate and bandwidth are prescribed for the HDTV signal?

6.20. Name the principal coding and compression methods for HDTV signal. Point out the main features of each method.

6.21. In what respects is HDTV coding easier than conventional TV coding? In what ways is it difficult?

6.22. On what schemes is the MPEG-2 video coding based? Why is this method very promising for future HDTV coding?

6.23. How many pixels does a 1" CCD for an HDTV camera contain? How many pixels are present in a 2/3" CCD? What type of problem occurs when the CCD chip size is decreased and the pixel count increased?

6.24. Mention some developments in digital tape and disc recording for HDTV. How does Super High-Definition (SHD) TV propose to integrate the different display environments like TV, computer, cinema films, etc.?

6.25. What types of Format Converters are needed for changing between NTSC and HDTV formats and among progressive and interlaced HDTV formats?

6.26. How is the future studio networking expected to change from the present dedicated hard-wired facilities? What networking technologies will play an important role in digital studios?

6.27. Sketch the block diagram of studio interfaces for signal multiplexing and formatting. Include different input signals and show the distribution services.

6.28. Why must concatenation of different compression schemes in HDTV signal processing be carefully considered? What could result from ignoring suitable concatenation?

6.29. Show with a diagrammatic illustration the Simulcasting Configuration in a studio environment for co-existence of 59.94 and 60.00 Hz NTSC programs with 60.00 Hz HDTV programs.

6.30. Name the modulation schemes for HDTV transmission via satellite and terrestrial means.

6.31. Explain the terms: (a) Orthogonal Frequency-Division Multiplexing (OFDM) and (b) Coded OFDM. Make a comparison between OFDM and VSB-AM techniques.

6.32. Name an analog modulation scheme for HDTV. Which requires a smaller transmitter power: analog or digital modulation?

6.33. Explain the basic idea of HDTV realization by receiver redesigning. Does this method require any changes in the transmission standard?

6.34. Demonstrate the concept of magnification of a non real-time image using a R/W memory, interpolation array and high-pass filter. Why is this method unsuitable for real-time applications? Draw and explain the operation of a system using two memory arrays for doubling the size of an image in real time.

6.35. What major problems must be solved for achieving success in three-dimensional television?

6.36. What are the two common methods of construction of 3-D television systems? Which of these methods requires that the viewer wears special glasses? Which method presently gives the best picture quality?

6.37. Explain, with the help of a diagram, the principle of production and display of three-dimensional television pictures based on the autostereoscopic approach.

6.38. What is the meaning of interactive TV? How will interactivity enhance the usefulness of TV?

6.39. When will the audience be a viewer of TV? When will it be a user? Give some examples of the types of interaction with TV. What is a Digital Actor?

6.40. Throw some light on the likely pathways along which the evolution of HDTV will take place?

6.41. How will the progress in the area of flat-panel displays aid in promoting HDTV?

6.42. Many industrialized nations are laying down optical fibre cables to far-off locations. Comment on the use of fibre optic and fixed-wire connections for HDTV transmission.

6.43. Project on the growth of HDTV as a component of the interconnected web of information superhighway.

REFERENCES AND FURTHER READING

6.1. T. Izumi, *Strategy for Promotion of HDTV Service and for Implementation of Digital Broadcasting in Japan*, SMPTE Journal, Vol. 107, No. 3, March 1998, pp. 178–182.

6.2. B.G. Haskell, A. Puri and A.N. Netravali, *Digital Video: An Introduction to MPEG-2*, Chapman & Hall, New York, 1997.

6.3. W.Y. Zou and J.A. Kutzner, *Practical Implementation of Digital Television: Update 1996*, SMPTE Journal, Vol. 106, No. 4, April 1997, pp. 233–242.

6.4. H. Watanabe and H. Yasuda, *Obtaining Higher Resolution in Asia: Advances in Digital Signal Processing for HDTV*, IEEE Signal Processing Magazine, July 1997, pp. 52–62.

6.5. S. Ono, N. Ohta and T. Aoyama, *Super High-Definition Images Beyond HDTV*, Artech House, Boston, 1995.

6.6. A.N. Netravali and B.G. Haskell, *Digital Pictures: Representation, Compression and Standards*, Plenum Press, New York, 1995.

6.7. Proceedings of the IEEE, Vol. 83, No. 7, July 1995, *Special Issue on Digital Television: Hardware and Applications*.

6.8. Y. Ninomiya and L. Chiarigliona (Eds.), *Signal Processing of HDTV, VI*, (Proceedings of the International Workshop on HDTV '94, Turin, Italy, Oct. 26–28, 1994), Elsevier, Amsterdam, 1995.

6.9. M.A. Sid-Ahmed, *Image Processing: Theory, Algorithms and Architectures*, McGraw Hill, New York, 1995.

□□□

Multimedia Communications

7.1. WHAT IS MULTIMEDIA?

Human anatomy supports five senses namely sight, hearing, smell, taste and touch with brain as the sixth co-ordinating and interpreting sense to react intelligently to any situation. A similar situation exists in the realm of signal processing. Looking back, we find that digital audio, video, computer graphics and word processing have evolved as separate disciplines. Recent developments in digital signal processing, hardware and software have enabled us to integrate these different data streams on a common platform. Although the above fields are not exactly analogous to human senses, their combination opens up an unlimited vista and makes the world understandable not only to children but also to adults engaged in industry, business and science. This is, broadly speaking, what multimedia is about.

The term "Multimedia" is variously and often ambiguously defined. Hearing this word immediately conjures up in our minds the picture of a computer employing a video disc and producing high-quality images, graphics and animation along with a sound blasting card for playing music and lots of fun making. Here, the focus is entirely on technology and multimedia seems to be defined by the hardware requirement. To some extent, the user's experience is also involved. In fact, the scope of multimedia is much wider. It means the use of computers to communicate, inform and educate. Multimedia involves the integration and interaction among text, handwriting, data files, imagery, graphics, speech, audio, video and animation (Figs. 7.1 and 7.2) to create new systems and to store, access, disseminate and distribute information through end-user co-operative applications.

But multimedia is not the sole province of computers. It is a technology pervading through the traditional giants of communication, computing and information processing. Presently, multimedia technologies span over entertainment, telecommunications, computer software and hardware industries.

A "multimedia experience" ranges from the simple newspaper reading or TV watching, listening to a piece of music on the computer or playing computer games, to the exotic experiences of *Distance Learning* in which we acquire skills and knowledge from a remote instructor; *Virtual Library Access* involving instant access to any required publication, browsing, selectively printing and even modifying the contents thereof; and the concept of *"Living Books"* providing animation and demonstrations.

"Multimedia Utilities" include adding sound to files; creating animation; video and 3-D effects for educational use, as in medical teaching, specially for surgery; in developing a "Children's Dictionary" incorporating sights and sounds; for inclusion of special audio-visual effects in business and advertising presentations, and so forth.

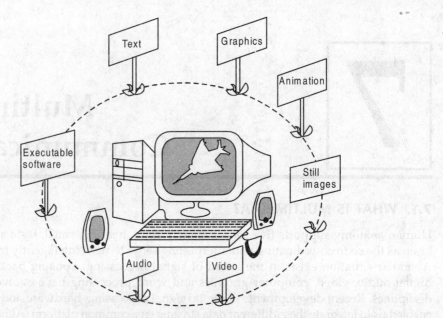

Fig. 7.1. The multimedia elements

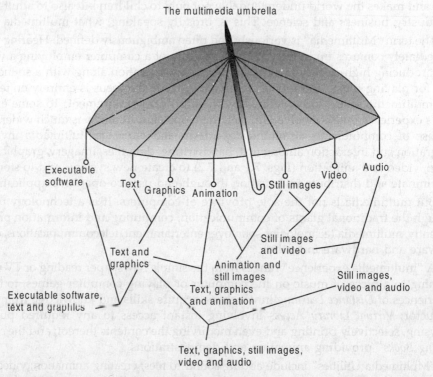

Fig. 7.2. Matrix of "Mixes" of multimedia elements. Several other combinations are also possible involving mixtures of data streams of different signals in varying proportions

It is anticipated that in not too distant future, an era of "Hypercommunication" will be born, merging humans in the Cyberspace involving millions of computers connected through the Internet with emotional human-like *Virtual Agents* generated by computers. Today, people shop and transact business on the Internet; they go for "Net Surfing" on an information sea. Video Games allow us to enjoy good stories as heroes in the cyberspace and virtual worlds. Metamorphosis technologies will enable us to recognize and produce facial expressions. Articulated animation with emotion-recognition functionalities will be possible. This will be the age of "Multimedia, Network and Information Society".

Table 7.1 summarizes the technological boosting factors which have spurred multimedia growth. Figure 7.3 presents the properties of three main delivery methods of multimedia signals in the industry today.

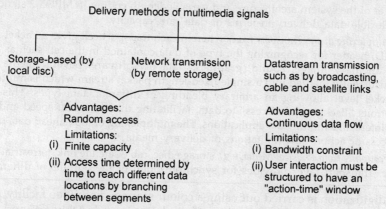

Fig. 7.3. Characteristics of multimedia signal delivery methods

7.2. MULTIMEDIA BASICS

7.2.1. Multimedia Capable Equipment

Minimum requirements of such an equipment include a personal computer (25 MHz, 486 SX µP, as per Multimedia Marketing Council's level 2 specification) equipped with sufficient hard disc capacity (160 Mbytes), enough memory (4 M bytes), a CD-ROM drive with a transfer rate > 150 kbits/sec, 16-bit sound, two-button mouse, a super VGA graphics adapter, colour monitor with 640 × 480 resolution and 65, 536 colours, serial port, parallel port, MIDI I/O port, joystick prot, etc. A specimen *Multimedia Hardware System* consists of a Pentium processor with 32-MB CPU memory, a CD-ROM drive, 2 GB of hard disc, SVGA colour monitor, 32-bit sound card, speaker, microphone, mouse, fast LAN connections, video camera, video-cassette recorder and player, audio tape player, scanner and colour printer. The *Multimedia Software* includes: Windows Operating System, word processing programs, image processing tools, spread sheet, audio recording and playback tools, database software for text, still pictures and graphics, task-oriented tools, e.g., educational programs, e-mail facility, etc. The hardware and software lists are representative only, and need to be constantly updated due to the relentless growth in multimedia PCs (MPCs) and the promise of broadband access from home and from the wireless connections.

The user can prepare the list of multimedia items according to individual needs. For those who wish to record sound, a studio-quality microphone and a high-end sound board are necessary. To compose music, the required MIDI keyboard is added. Plugging in the stereo system into the back of the sound card, one can feed music from CDs, LPs, cassettes or directly from radio, into the computer.

Table 7.1. Triggering Factors for Multimedia Proliferation

The popularization of multimedia is encouraged by the overall progress in the digital arena and by the provision of a flexible working environment, as follows:

- *Versatility of Digital Representation* of various signals in layered form such as the picture layer, video and audio compression layer, transport layer (of MPEG-2 packets), and transmission layer (of 8-VSB modulation with 6-MHz bandwidth) in HDTV system.

- *System Flexibility and Multifunctionality*, e.g., multiple picture formats like 1920 H × 1080 V and 1280 H × 720 V active pixels and frame rates of 60, 30 and 24 Hz in HDTV. These multiple formats and frame rates together with header/descriptor data structures at each layer of the system architecture and variable-length coding in MPEG-2 standard, provide a flexible data delivery in terms of data rate/capacity.

- *Multiplexing at the Transport Layer* wherein each transport cell gives a Packet Identification (PID) header for recognizing the type of data contained in the cell such as video, audio, or ancillary image, sound, graphics, data or software. Several media streams are concurrently merged into a single fixed-length packet stream which is multiplexed at the packet level allowing an arbitrary blending of different data types. This multiplexing permits "Background Access" to data, facilitating the appparent speed and responsivity of interactive multimedia applications. The multiplexing of look-ahead data diminishes the access or action time limitations of delivery media.

- *Decoupling from Physical Media*, e.g., storage disc, cable satellite link, terrestrial broadcasting, etc. Transport layer provides for synchronization of the outputs of different media.

Photodigitization is carried out using a colour scanner. For video facility, a camcorder, VCR and a video capture card, are to be procured. Readymade "chip art" and photographs can be purchased from multimedia and desktop publishing vendors.

Animation is the process of generating, usually graphically, a series of frames, and then displaying them in rapid succession to obtain a feeling of motion. A video file can be created by animated means instead of a video camera. A wide range of software packages is available with amazing capabilities to sketch and animate objects.

The multimedia interested hobbyist keeps a track of the new product announcements and advertisements to upgrade the hardware of the equipment and also to update the system software.

For testing whether an equipment is multimedia capable, a sound should be heard on pressing the relevant icon or at the appropriate place in the program. Further, a multimedia program should not stop on the way before completion, due to a shortage of memory space. Also, sound and images should not jump out at anyone.

7.2.2. Multimedia Material Classification

The reader must distinguish "multimedia material" from "multiple media material". For example, e-mail, voice mail, image mail, video mail and handwritten documents sent by facsimile exchange, all essentially fall under the head "message" transmitted through different media. The common items in multimedia can be placed under the following categories:

Games, Fun and Entertainment Material including video games, animation sequences, music, realistic sound mimicry, etc.

Powerful Reading and Library Material consisting of audio-visual books, magazines and journals, encyclopaedias, reference literature, etc. and documents recorded on CD-ROMs.

Creative Material helping one to write new multimedia programs or produce new types of systems, presentations and tools.

7.2.3. Multimedia Generations

At the genesis of this development lie simple text-based monomedia computers constituting one extremity of the multimedia continuum. They are followed by computers containing video cards capable of performing simple graphic operations. The next place is occupied by computers having 8-bit resolution sound cards with the capability to produce low-fidelity sounds. At the ensuing milestones reside computers with 16-bit resolution and 32-bit resolution sound cards providing life-like synthesis of sound and digital sound recording facility. Large and voluminous databases can be stored in computers with CD-ROM. Still ahead on the ladder, one can place computers incorporating NTSC video for digital video recording. This is a process of on-going improvement leading to increasing functionality.

After this introductory review of the structural aspects of multimedia, from here onwards we try to gain an insight into multimedia signal processing. A huge body of signal-processing theories, algorithms and implementation techniques, have been developed for monomedia and these are being applied to multimedia. Multimedia signal processing, still in its infancy, is defined, in principle, as the combined processing of multiple media streams, e.g., the concomitant use of audio, video and closed-caption data for searching and browsing of multimedia databases on a content basis.

7.3 MULTIMEDIA SIGNAL PROCESSING (MMSP)

As we understand, the enormous edifice of multimedia is erected on the infrastructure of digital signal processing techniques and algorithms operating on digital devices like sound capture and playback devices, cameras, video capture and display devices, handwriting terminals, etc. The field of Multimedia Signal Processing, with acronym MMSP, is both multidisciplinary and interdisciplinary in scope, deriving from the cross-fertilization of novel ideas and methods from multiple signal sources. It seeks to provide services which seamlessly intergate text, speech, audio, images and video media, in a manner that maintains the ease of use and interactivity of the conventional Plan Old Telephone Service (POTS), irrespective of the bandwidth and the method of access to the service. Key technologies for achieving this goal are:

Representation (Coding) and Compression of Multimedia Signals : This entails algorithms of signal processing, associated standards and transmission considerations. For speech coding, it is necessary to define the attributes of a speech coder, classify the currently available types of speech coders and establish the criteria for selection of a speech coder for a specific multimedia application. CD-quality audio coding for multimedia utilizes perceptual audio coding. Audio Coding Standards for multimedia include the original MPEG Coder, MPEG-2 Coder, MPEG-AAC Coder, Dolby AC-3 Coder, etc.

In Image Coding, the coding of Bilevel FAX images and that of continuous-tone images, both grey scale and colour images, is important. For compression of still images, the standard algorithm is the JPEG algorithm. Main video coding standards are MPEG-1, MPEG-2 and MPEG-4.

Organization, Storage and Retrieval of Multimedia Signals : Here we are concerned with the delivery method and speed of the material. The signal transference may be implemented either by streaming or full downloading in accordance with the different resolutions of the multimedia material and the receiver capabilities. One can perform layering and embedding of images and video so that the low-resolution versions are first received and subjected to processing, while the high-resolution versions are displayed if the customer waits longer before initiating action or sends a request for them. The performance of a multimedia system is evaluated in terms of the *Quality of Service* (QoS) provided by it. For example, the packet network guarantees the delivery of data using the standard TCP/IP data protocol but does not assure of QoS for real-time signals like voice traffic in packet telephony.

Access Methods to the Multimedia Signal : This involves the matching of the user with the machine. Over the years, the most popular access method to a multimedia system has been the *Graphical User Interface* (GUI) via a standard personal computer. A more natural method is the *Spoken Language Interface* (SLI). These SLIs are based on Speech Synthesis or Text-to-Speech (TTS) systems, evaluated from the intelligibility and naturalness of synthesized speech. They are also devised on the principle of *Speech Recognition* in which the spoken message is transcribed into individual words, and *Spoken Language Understanding* to extract the meaning of the recognized message. *Agent Interfaces* are required for monitoring the multimedia sessions and assisting in accessing the system.

Searching of Multimedia Documents : With the storage of large volumes of information in multimedia repositories, the need for intelligent information retrieval arose. The searching methods, working on machine intelligence, utilize text-based indexing, speech indexing, image indexing and video indexing. Searching is done via text requests, image matching and speech queries. Heterogeneity of multimedia information calls for application of two or more methods acting in collaboration.

Browsing of Multimedia Documents : Frequently, large document collections are withdrawn from the library. Most of this matter is not of any interest to the user necessitating the filtering of the collection to obtain the desired information, by a process called *Browsing*. The Browsing method makes use of human intelligence to find the relevant material through image-based browsing, scene-based browsing, video-skimming browsing and audio-skimming browsing.

Each of the above areas has engaged the attention of researchers worldwide. Significant issues in these areas will be dealt with in the sequel. Many of these topics have been discussed at length in preceding chapters but the perspective here is tilted towards multimedia.

7.4   ISSUES IN NETWORKED MULTIMEDIA

For any multimedia link, three essential prerequisites are networking, multiplexing and control. Networking refers to the type of network used for transferring multimedia information, e.g., POTS or PSTN (with both analog and digital links like ISDN) and networks with data transmission protocols such as TCP/IP, frame relay and ATM. With the help of *Multiplexing Protocols*, the different multimedia data streams are mixed together to form a single stream for the purposes of storage or transmission. *Control Protocols* help in setting up, altering and breaking multimedia connections.

Two major problems associated with data transmission over packet neworks are: (*i*) Adaptation of signal processing techniques to specific needs of packet networks like accommodating for packet losses, delays, jitter, etc., and coping with network heterogeneity. (*ii*) Enforcement of Intellectual Property Rights (IPRs) for protection of transmitted data, which has become difficult with the relative ease of illegal duplication with the availability of broad-bandwidth networking.

7.4.1. Compression Algorithms for Variable Bandwidth Multimedia Multicast

In a typical multimedia network, it may so happen that the larger number of receivers connected to the network have a range of bandwidths. In such a situation, a compression rate satisfying the high-bandwidth receivers will cut off those having a low bandwidth and vice versa. The alternative approach of simulcasting a signal having several data rates will double the bandwidth of the network and is therefore not a plausible solution. For applications of this nature, the compression algorithm should allow easy extraction of data streams of different rates from a single composite incoming data stream.

The obvious difficulty is that an efficient compression algorithm removes all the redundancy in the compresssed data, making it necessary that this data be delivered absolutely free from errors. Any single error left over in a picture may lead to loss of the full picture. Inclusion of error concealment capability in the receiver aids in minimizing the visual unpleasantness due to errors. Robustness can be built into the system by inserting "pointers" into data which help in using the partially received data. Furthermore, loss of different portions of data, e.g., a header or a small data segment, has varying impacts. The loss of a header has a devastating effect because it contains the quantisation information but the loss of a short segment of data could possibly be hidden by error concealment in the receiver. Keeping this in view and noting that shorter data segments are less prone to errors, vital portions of data are concentrated into shorter separately recognizable segments.

7.4.2. Data-Embedding and Watermarking Algorithms for Copyright Protection and Adding Special Features

Apart from system-level security including encryption, data-embedding and watermarking technologies employ special alogrithms to embed text, binary streams, audio, image or video in a host multimedia signal for providing passive and active copyright protection. The embedded data are perceptually inaudible or invisible and statistically undetectable maintaining the quality of the source data.

Watermarks are used to identify the original owner or distributor of a piece of digital data such as an image or music producer as well as the authorized recipient in case a single copy is to be delivered to a particular person. Upon subsequent detection of the watermark in an illegal copy, the piracy can be traced. A watermark can also be used to decipher when an image modification was done, e.g., to authenticate a video clip for broadcasting news. While watermarks for ownership should be highly resistant to modifications, those for identifying modifications should be easily erasable by the alterations. It may be pointed out that the above class of problems can be tackled not only by signal processing but by overall system design considerations.

Data embedding is used for embellishment to insert special effects in the host multimedia signal such as embodying multilingual soundtracks in a cine film. New services can be delivered, e.g., watching a movie in a certain rating from a single multicast stream. Here, extra scenes are hidden in a given version of the movie. In this way, concealing of data aids in multimedia personalization. Also, no additional bandwidth or storage space is demanded. Superimposition of important reference, descriptive or control data on a given signal is often used for tracking the use of a particular clip such as for payment per use applications like billing for commercials.

7.4.3. Mechanisms of Data Concealment and Other Subtleties

The immediate questions striking the minds of most readers are: Why and how is data concealing possible? Why does not the embedded data disturb the host signal? And if it disturbs the host, why is the perturbation not observed. The answers to these queries become evident when we note that the various data-hiding schemes exploit the finite resolution ability of the human auditory and visual systems and a phenomenon called *Masking*. By limited resolving power we mean that an audio or visual signal cannot be detected by a human observer unless its intensity or contrast level lies above a threshold value. The masking phenomenon implies that an audio or visual signal becomes imperceptible in the presence of a certain signal termed the *Masker Signal*.

The operational procedures of these data-hiding schemes rely on alteration of selected samples of the signal or its transform-domain coefficients, either absolutely or with respect to the samples. The modifications can be effected in amplitude or phase, or jointly in amplitude and phase. Some schemes change the least significant bit of the host signal, or its transform-domain representation, others function by addition of a small, constant amplitude, pseudo-noise sequence to the signal concerned or its transform-domain coefficients; still others substitute the signal spatial or temporal frequencies or frequency bands by the data to be cached.

It goes without saying that the data hiding process must be reversible, enabling us to reclaim the hidden data at will. In many instances, data retrieval is necessary even after the signal is subjected to compression, editing, interformat translations, interdomain conversions from digital to analog and *vice versa*. For recovery of the embedded data, one requires prior knowledge of the signal changes applied for concealing, secret keys such as data location and statistical characteristics of the hiding process.

In many applications, the hidden data must be statistically undetectable. For this purpose, some data hiding schemes employ random insertion and modification patterns derived from pseudo-noise sequences. These patterns cannot be resolved or conjectured in a realistic time frame. Safety of a data hiding procedure is confirmed if one is unsuccessful in recovering the hidden data even after knowing the full and exact data hiding algorithm, unless one input to the algorithm, termed its *Key*, is given.

Watermarking algorithms must give a definitive verdict about the original owner of a digital signal. Subsequent users may insert their own watermarks in a given signal, and if the watermarking scheme is unable to infer the order of insertion of watermarks, a deadlock takes place. The genuine owner generally keeps a copy of the original signal for watermark detection. Schemes which do not employ the original data for watermark detection are highly susceptible to deadlock. Dual watermarking schemes use a pair of watermarks, one of which is detected with the help of original data set and the other without referring to it.

7.5. INTELLIGENT MULTIMEDIA THROUGH NEURAL NETWORKS

To keep pace with the growth of multimedia technology, intelligent handling of information for automated identification and interpretation of multimodal signals has become almost indispensable. Due to the adaptive learning capability of neural networks, they can be trained to interpret the possible changes in a given object or pattern. With the incorporation of statistical signal processing and optimization methods in neural models, and with the advent of hierarchical models, the neural networks have become promising candidates for multirate, multiresolution MMSP.

7.5.1. Common Attributes of Neural Processing and Intelligent Multimedia Processing (IMP)

For intelligent processing of signals, multimedia processing will function in much the same way as the human brain, sharing its properties such as:

Data Processing Engine for Multimodal Signals : Human beings handle data inputs received through optic, auditory and sensory nerves based on adaptive learning and retrieving algorithms of the neural networks.

Multimodality : Data from various sources like speech, lip motion, gestures, body language and other human reactions to situations, are jointly and simultaneously processed to ellicit the response.

Unsupervised Grouping and/or Supervised Learning Mechanisms : Clustering and modelling of data are powerful capabilities of adaptive neural processing, making neural networks a core technology for muitimedia functionalities.

Neural networks are highly useful *Pattern Classifiers*, specially appealing when explicit *a priori* knowledge of the probability distribution is not available. By virtue of their property of *Training by Example*, these networks are taught to give outputs approximating *aposteriori* class probabilities. Their ability to approximate unknown systems sufficiently accurately from scanty sets of noisy data, speaks of their *universal approximation capability*.

7.5.2. Application Areas of Neural Networks in Multimedia

The deployment of neural networks in multimedia is particularly attractive in the following applications:

Human Perception such as facial expression and emotion studies, colour judgement, etc.

Machine-Human Communication, for example, face recognition, analysis of lip reading and so on.

Multimodal Representation and Information Recovery like linking of multimedia objects, information search, motion tracking, animation, etc.

To give a few examples of the above applications, we may mention the location of a desired picture in a big archive, searching for a certain video clip in a video archival storage, providing audio-visual teaching courses to customers consisting of varied categories such as students, professionals and laymen, creating and maintenance of multimedia data bases supplying information in different forms, e.g., audio, video, textual, etc. Thus neural networks (NNs) offer a panacea to a broad spectrum of multimedia problems such as efficient representation, detection and classification of information, fusion of multimodal signals, multimodal transformations and synchronization. NNs constitute a niche technology for visualization, tracking and segmentation of images and video signals, detection and recognition of faces and objects, image, video and audio content indexing and browsing, personal authentification and recognition, and so forth.

7.6. ACCESSING, SEARCHING AND BROWSING OF MULTIMEDIA DOCUMENTS

Proper utilization of a multimedia system hinges upon the accessing method. The access is done through the *User Interface,* which forms the link between the man and the machine.

7.6.1. User Interfaces

So far, the most widely applied user interface has been the *Graphical User Interface* (GUI) featuring several interactive capabilities such as: (*i*) *Continuous Representation of the Graphical Objects on the Monitor Screen and the Actions which can be Performed Thereupon* : The user executes one operation after another and easily learns after a little experience how can these steps be carried out to obtain a desired result. (*ii*) *Quick, Incremental and Reversible Actions:* The idea is that the user immediately sees the result of his/her action and with the help of "undo" command reverts back to the original state in the event of a mistake.

(iii) Labelled Icon Pressing and Pull-Down Menus: These eliminate the need of memorizing and recalling text commands, which makes the use of systems unnecessarily complicated and inefficient, frequently leading to confusion.

Basically, the success of GUIs lies in their ability to take care, cope and cooperate with the limits of human cognitive processing. We tend to forget the types of actions that can be executed and their commands unless they are continuously displayed. It is also important that the result of each action should be instantly visible.

However, in the human world, everyday man-to-man interaction is through speech which one starts using from childhood even without any formal education. *Spoken Language Interfaces* therefore represent the simplest and easiest modes of access to multimedia. But still much is desired to be done for making speech an effective interfacing medium in man-computer communication at par with the use of speech in man-man interaction.

7.6.2. Indexing Methods

Retrieval of information from large multimedia libraries and data bases calls for efficient indexing methods. Among the various media comprising the multimedia, indexing techniques for textual information are in the most advanced state of development. *Text Repositories* are classified as: *(i) Structured Repository* whose organization consists of predefined fields like *data bases*, amenable to conventional database queries; and *(ii) Unstructured Repository*, also called *Natural Language*, which exists in publications, either in printed hard copies or in electronic storage. Unstructured text can be selectively covered with the help of *Full-Text Search* based on constructing an *Inverted Index* which functions like an index in the opposite sense recording for each word the document in which it can be found. Multiple words are engaged for carrying out full-text searches. *Boolean Logical Operators* are employed for imposing additional limits; *Special Characters* are used for partial matching; *Morphological Normalizations* are used for locating possible variations of a particular chosen word; *Semantic Normalizations* are applied for searching categories of words having analogous meanings; *Proximity Constraints* are helpful in retrieving those protions of text in which certain words occur close together; and *Approximate Matching Methods* aid in detecting similarity between words which do not match precisely (to circumvent errors due to spelling mistakes resulting from manual entry of words or from speech recognition systems).

A different class of problems involves *Information Extraction* from a large storage. Here, the selected documents are first retrieved, pertinent fragments from these documents are withdrawn, the information of interest is derived from the fragments followed by joining together the derived information portions to form a continuous whole.

Two interesting emerging areas are *Text Segmentation* which entails the recognition of internally consistent text portions that can be easily demarcated from surrounding text segments; and *Text Theme Decomposition* involving the resolution of text in accordance with its semantic content.

Now regarding *Speech Indexing*, the task may vary from complete speech material identification to discernment of a specific event therein. By converting from speech to text, a *Transcription* of the spoken material is produced. This transcription is subjected to the usual text indexing methods. The alternative technique of detecting particular words and phrases in the speech, known as *Word Spotting* employs labelled speech data for determining the parameters of a set of Hidden Markov Models (HMMs). The HMMs are statistical representations of speech events including the background and general models of speech besides those for the words and phrases being considered.

A similar method of speech indexing called *Acoustic Indexing* uses *Phone Lattices* or *Strings* comprising an assigned word and a set of HMMs to produce several probable phone sequences. This method relying on acoustic models in lieu of language models has been used for video-mail retrieval.

Other methods of speech indexing include *Detection of Speech Events* such as speech-to-silence and speaker-to-speaker transitions. Speaker identification systems will be helpful for such indexing.

Audio Indexing works on lines similar to speech indexing. A textual representation of the audio signal is produced so that text-based indexing can be done. Otherwise, an audio stream is employed to detect significant events in the signal, e.g., the presence of music or dialogues.

Automatic *Image Indexing* techniques are still in a preliminary stage. These techniques classify images in accordance with colour and brightness characteristics, texture variations, extracted shapes, figure captions and legends. To find a photograph or a video clip from millions of pictures or video tapes, indexing methods like "Metadata" and "Domain Taxonomies" are used. "Metadata" means external data used to index and summarize the content of the visual material. It includes bibliographical information, the conditions of image capture, encoding parameters or subjective interpretations. Taxonomy is a hierarchy of classes or groups organized at various levels such as semantic (politics, humour), or visual (scenery, buildings). Suitable metadata elements and taxonomies are selected to build an image data base. Metadata and taxonomies have inherent limitations due to manual annotation and finite extent of the knowledge of indexing person. Standardization of image and video metadata as well as taxonomies will improve the interoperatability between various image data bases.

Video Indexing is accomplished by detection of scene fading and breaking, by perceiving camera movements, by scanning the accompanying text meterial, and by converting the speech of the associated audio into text.

7.6.3. Browsing Aids

To circumvent the limited capabilities of linear audio and video media, speed changing methods such as pitch preserving replay of audio are used, both in fast and slow motion. Similar speeding up and slowing down is done for video replay. The chief browsing methods are: (*i*) *Audio Skimming* by playing audio at a faster rate than real time and carefully listening to locate the section of interest. (*ii*) *Video Skimming* by faster playing as in audio. The number of frames/sec is maintained constant. (*iii*) *Image-Based Browsing* where a stream of images is displayed for the viewer to select the desired one. (*iv*) *Scene-Based Browsing:* Similar to image process in which a stream of video breaks is shown.

7.7. MULTIMEDIA SIGNAL PROCESSOR AND MEMORY MICRO-ELECTRONIC CHIPS

A striking difference between ordinary signal processing and MMSP is that the latter is a real-time signal processing involving real-time compression of audio and video signals as well as generation of 2-D, 3-D and 4-D computer graphics while the former deals mainly with texts, tabulations, diagrams and photographs. Signal processors for multimedia

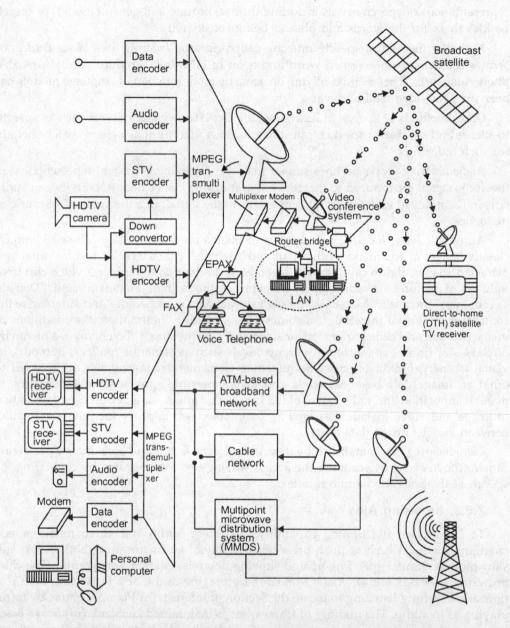

Fig. 7.3. Satellite-based telecommunication infrastructure for multimedia

applications must possess ten times the processing capability of currently available processors. Further, the required operational speeds are enormously higher than achieved with these processors. The presently used general-purpose microprocessors for personal computers and workstations use built-in hardware for MMSP. Special characteristics like intensive computation, high input/ouput or memory access and complexity of control, and frequent occurrence of small integer operands desired from multimedia processors, render many common processors incapable of performing the task. Novel architectural strategies can be combined with programmable approaches to produce function-oriented ASICs for MMSP subtasks.

On the basis of architecture, multimedia signal processors are subdivided into five classes: *Reduced Instruction Set Computer (RISC) Chips* for workstations and servers; *Complex Instruction Set Computer (CISC) Chips* for personal computer: *Embedded RISC Microprocessors* for applications originally using DSP chips, and also for Internet terminals, car navigation, etc.; *Low-Power Digital Signal Processors (DSPs)* for mobile communication services; and *Media Processors* which play the supporting role in PCs for accelerating multimedia. These five classes of processors can be clubbed together into two generic groups, namely, *Microprocessors Incorporating a Multimedia Instruction Set* and *Microprocessors Based on Highly Parallel DSPs*.

MMSP is acting as a booster for new generation μPs and DSPs. Current developments in multimedia processors aim at MPEG-2 decoding in software. So the high performance levels and functionality desired for MPEG-2 video decoding are of central importance in the design of suitable processor architectures. These architectures must, of necessity, include the bit manipulation function, arithmetic operations, access to a large memory, stream data input/output and real-time task switching. Various microchips are being enhanced in terms of these controlling functions.

For realization of a portable *Video-Communication Terminal*, MMSP functions like video and audio codes have to be integrated on a single chip of Si along with μP functions for the user interface and ASIC functions, e.g., a wireless modem. In this way, several monolithic Si multimedia systems are expected to be commonplace.

Developments in the fields of processor and memory ICs ove the last two decades have taken place in conformance with *Moore's Law* which states that: The computation and storage costs are halved after a period of $1\frac{1}{2}$ years. Looking at these trends, it can be surmised that within a span of another two years, single memory chips with 1 Gbyte of memory sufficient to accommodate the contents of an encyclopedia (or for buffering the audio and video frames of an MMSP system), will be available, tremendously expediting indexing, searching and browsing capabilities for multimedia. It may be noted that 16 Mytes of memory is necessary for storing the contents of a complete book.

7.8. ENABLING TELECOMMUNICATION TECHNOLOGIES FOR MULTIMEDIA

There is a unanimity of opinion on developing an "Information Superhighway" providing a variety of multimedia services including still pictures, HDTV, interactive shopping, financial transactions like video banking, real estate listing, air travel/hotel reservations; telecomputing, telecommuting; distance learning through books, magazines, museum and picture galleries on TV and PC, and culminating in a *Virtual University* through the deployment of courseware on the global computer network. To build the multimedia infrastructure to meet these goals, a large number of communication technologies will work in unison at full potency (Fig. 7.3). Notable among these technologies are summarized below.

7.8.1. POTS (or PSTN) and ISDN

For over a century, the Plain Old Telephone Service (POTS) network, also referred to as the Public Switched Telephone Network (PSTN) has been the workhorse of voice-band communications, carrying real-time moderate fidelity speech signals. Two major modifications since its inception include the provision of an independent digital signalling system for faster call set up and network digitization into 64 kbits/sec channels for upgradation of fidelity and improved reliability (See Fig. 7.4)

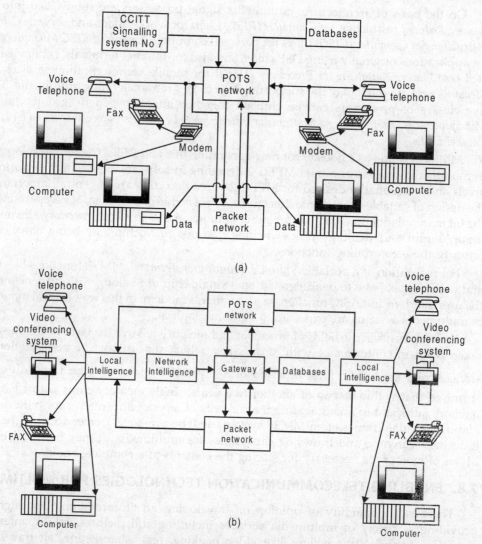

Fig. 7.4. Multimedia telecommunication networks: (a) Present network, and (b) Future ATM-based network with optical fibre backbone

Wideband signals such as speech, audio, images, video, FAX, etc., cannot be transported over POTS. Using Integrated Services Digital Network (ISDN), to access two or more 64 kbits/sec channels, higher data rate connections to POTS are obtainable. The term "ISDN" is sometimes confused to imply a separate discrete network. This is only partially true because in many countries ISDN will use the same switches and transmission facilities as the POTS network. Nonetheless, several vital standards and concepts have emerged under ISDN, dramatically influencing network design. ISDN standards define two different access interfaces to the network—Basic Rate Interface (BRI) and Primary Rate Interface (PRI). The bit rate at BRI is 192 kbits/sec comprising three independent channels—two Bearer or B-channels, each at 64 kbits/sec and one Data or D-channel at 64 kbits/sec, and another 64 kbits/sec for framing, octet timing, activation and deactivation of link between the terminals and network termination. Frame length = 48 bits and frame duration = 250 μsec. PRI is a higher level network interface providing up to 30 B-channels and two further 64 kbits/

sec channels, one for network and frame synchronization and the other for the D signalling channel, so that the total primary transmission rate = 32 × 64 kbits/sec = 2.048 Mbits/sec. The 256 Mbits/sec stream is subdivided into frames of 256 bits each and the frame duration is 125 μsec. In some countries, the existing communicaions infrastructure operates at a primary rate of 1.544 Mbits/sec, using 24 PCM channels. This 1.544 Mbits/sec facility offers upto 23 B-channels along with a D-channel at 64 kbits/sec and 8 kbits/sec for synchronization.

Devices assigned specific functions and responsibilities under ISDN are called *Functional Devices.* These include: (*i*) *Network Termination Type 1 (NT1)* which represents the termination of physical connection between the customer and exchange. (*ii*) *Terminal Equipment (TE)* which denotes any user equipment like phone, FAX, PC, TV, etc. (*iii*) *Terminal Adapter (TA)* for allowing communication between any non-ISDN terminal and the network following ISDN protocols.

To access ISDN, one needs the services of a digital exchange along with 2B + D channel, equipment like NT1, TE and TA, and *Signalling System Number 7 (SS7)*, the high speed digital common channel signalling system for use with stored program control exchanges.

ISDN can be applied to multifarious tasks including publishing and advertising, LAN to LAN videoconferencing, telecommuting, telemedicine, telemarketing, legal and security jobs, Internet, infrastructural and tariffing activities, etc.

The original ISDN is often referred to as *Narrowband-ISDN* or *N-ISDN. Broadband-ISDN* or *B-ISDN* is an enhancement over N-ISDN which will use optical fibre links to deliver larger bandwidths with more information carrying capacity at higher transmission speeds ~Gigabits/sec (10^9 bits/sec). Extension of B-ISDN to domestic users will make digital video services such as Cable TV (CATV) and video telephone available to the public at large.

7.8.2. Packet Network for Data Transmission

The conventional "circuit-switched operation" of telephony network suffers from gross underutilization of the available transmission capability specially for transmitting data. This is because in this network a circuit is engaged for a user throughout a conversational session oblivious of the fact that the user is not transmitting any information during the pauses or when he/she is listening to the person talking from the opposite side. This operational mode of reserving the circuit for the subscribers works satisfactorily for speech conversation but becomes inefficient for data traffic which is frequently *bursty* in nature with long spells of no signal intervening short information outbreak periods. Further, data transmission is not so sensitive to delays as speech transmission. It is also not necessary that data reaches the receiver in the same sequence as sent from the transmitter, thus permitting the sharing of network among a large number of customers.

Packet-Switched Network (Fig. 7.5), developed primarily for data routing, is employed for transferring contiguous or bursty non-real time data with the help of address information in the data stream. Here, the network circuits are used for interconnecting the nodes and the information is conveyed from one node to another in a *Store-and-Forward* manner, until it reaches the node for the destination terminal. A packet network is particularly useful for sending data, FAX and still images but is inappropriate for real-time signals like speech, audio and video.

The packet network is accessed through programs stored in PC and is thus PC-oriented. Data for Internet is transmitted over packet networks through Transmission Control Protocol (TCP)/Internet Protocol (IP).

The long signal delays incurred in the packet networks can be overcome to a certain degree, by suitable coding and compression techniques. The sound can be reconstructed using a sound card in a multimedia PC. But still problems due to low bit rate compression, acoustic echo cancellation, packet buffering, modem delays, routing, queing and network congestion delays and delay occurring in PC sound card sum up to degrade the perceived quality of the connection.

7.8.3. ATM Network

Asynchronous Transfer Mode (ATM) network was designed to fulfil the needs of both real-time high speed voice, image and video signals as well as the bursty data traffic. These requirements are posed by interactive multimedia, office environment, video conferencing, etc. ATM can be supported by all physical media including the twisted pair coaxial cables, optical fibres and wireless links.

To distinguish between synchronous and asynchronous transmission, we note that *Synchronous Transmission* is a communication mode in which a clock signal accompanies the data so that the bit location can be determined at both transmitting and receiving ends. In *Asynchronous Transmission*, no timing or synchronization information is sent. ATM network is a network in which data are encapsulated within a fixed-length (53 byte) *packet* or *cell* consisting of a 48-byte user information field plus a 5-byte header incorporating the routing information about the destination address, priority and service type.

The ATM concept differs vastly from the traditional store-and-forward networks. The fundamental structural unit of ATM is the cell which is small in length as well as fixed in size. A small cell size gives low latency (delay) and a small header size yields a higher efficiency. In contrast to the ATM, the TCP/IP protocol of the Internet uses very large packets ~1-2 kbytes for high-efficiency data movement. Another advantage of ATM results from avoiding variable-length packets. This increases the routing speed because fixed-length cells need less overhead for transmission on data communication networks. In addition, the waiting period is minimized for a high priority cell which arrives immediately after the entry of a low priority cell to the resource.

ATM offers a great flexibility in capacity by allocating as much capacity as necessary for a particular service. The demand for capacity is met by providing the requisite number of cells. The capacity is varied according to the expansion of customer's business and to allow for selection of quality of service, even during a call or for addition of new services. Choice of service quality and allowance for additional services are very useful for multimedia.

7.8.4. Bandwidth-on-Demand Concept

We have indicated in the foregoing that reasonable quality multimedia signals require high data transmission rates. This has led to adoption of measures for increasing the bandwidth according to the multimedia application. For instance, an important inhibiting factor setting the limitations of access to POTS network upto 64 kbits/sec, is the voice modem. Access to consumers can be provided at data rates from 1.5 Mbits/sec to 155 Mbits/sec by introducing a series of technological changes such as: (*i*) *Special Modems* at the end of each connection from the telephone office along with line conditioning by the local exchange carrier. These are the *Digital Subscriber Line (DSL)* modems comprising the popular types such as Asymmetric-DSL (ADSL), Hybrid-DSL (HDSL), Symmetric-DSL (SDSL) and Self-Adaptive-DSL (SADSL) classes. Two-way delivery over CATV network using cable modems will uplift CATV service. (*ii*) *Fibre-to-the-Home (FTTH) and Hybrid Fibre-Coax:* In the FTTH approach, the copper cable is straightway replaced by optical fibre. In the Hybrid Fibre-Coax method (Fig. 7.5) the fibre connection is made up to central location in each neighbourhood followed by optical-to-electrical signal transformation and the delivery of electrical signals via standard coaxial cables. The prohibitive cost factor involved in the former approach is partially reduced in the latter. However, a compromise is struck between the data rates and the price payed for service. (*iii*) *Fixed Wireless Loops* wherein a local wireless station is erected in the consumer's home. This small station is pointed directly at the network wireless station. Several problems of mobile wireless stations like fading, multipath interference, etc., are thus obviated. This also yields more efficient bandwidth utilization.

7.8.5. Intelligent Networks (IN) and Smart Terminals

"Intelligence" means the ability to access and process stored information so that an intelligent network is one that can work on stored information. To explain more clearly, the IN concept refers to a telecommunications network architecture in which intelligence is

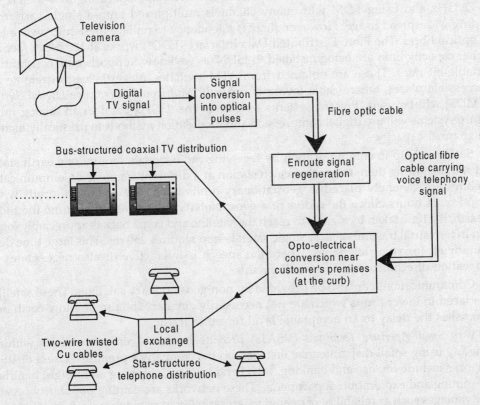

Fig. 7.5. Architecture of the hybrid Fibre-Coax configuration as an alternative to direct fibre-to-the-home system

added to the network making it more *user friendly* whereby network operators can introduce additional services with greater ease and effectiveness than admissible under the current network architecture. The idea of IN derives immense benefits from *Computer Power* providing a framework with the capability of centralized programming, activation and flexible connectivity for construction of new services for the whole network. Two simple IN examples are the networks providing premium, freecall and similar services, and the cellular radio networks.

An In comprises the "Basic Network" consisting of switches and terminals for handling the main traffic, and the parts imparting intelligence to the network namely, the additional processing devices for initiation, reception and transference of messages; the information resources like databases and message recorders; and service control facilities for monitoring the provision of special features on the network.

In retrospect, we find that every significant breakthrough in networking has been preceded by a major advancement in the user interface, e.g., the telephone was first invented and then the switch networks grew. Likewise, the invention of TV was followed by the spread of TV network and the invention of PC created th LAN/WAN networks. Looking at this pattern of growth, it can be conjectured that the multimedia will prosper through innovative ideas to produce *Smart Terminals* for creating, displaying, indexing, searching and browsing of multimedia contents easily, conveniently and rapidly.

7.8.6. Terrestrial and Satellite Communication Links

For fixed point-to-point transmission, microwave links operating at 4-6 GHz and 10-12 GHz and using FDM with many channels multiplexed onto a single carrier, are finding widespread usage. However, there is a tendency to replace these microwave links by optical fibres. The Fibre Distributed Data Interface (FDDI) works at 100 Mbits/sec and higher capacity links are being installed. B-ISDN, as we know, supports both constant and variable bit rates. These are obtained from ATM switches. Nevertheless, in remote and inaccessible places, where cable laying is difficult, *Multipoint Microwave Digital Systems* (MMDS) will be used. Present systems operate in the 2 GHz band in an analog mode. Future systems will use digital compression and modulation methods to drastically increase the channel capacity.

Satellites help in communication by receiving radio signals sent by one earth station and retransmitting them to another earth station at a different frequency. Communication satellites are generally placed in geostationary orbits which are equatorial orbits with a period of 24 hours. Since the radius of a geostationary orbit is about six time the radius of earth, the time taken by signals to reach the satellite and come back is appreciably longer than in terrestrial transmission. A single satellite hop requires 250 ms. This large time delay is annoying for voice telephony where the speech is interactive. It also necessitates the application of echo control to speech circuits.

Communications can also be provided by non-geostationary satellites. These satellites are placed in lower orbits which are not necessarily circular. The use of a low-earth orbit diminishes the delay to an acceptable level for voice traffic.

Very Small-Aperture Terminals (VSATs) provide business communications within a company using small dish antennae installed on the company's premises. Users of VSAT networks include finance and banking, travel and tourism, shipping and freight handling, and mining and exploration departments. These networks are gaining popularity because of advantages such as reliability of operation, accessibility to remote places, high bandwidth capability, fast deployment and flexible network configurations.

The VSAT networks carrying compressed multimedia information at large data rates will function in Ku and Ka bands supporting data rates from 1.6 to 160 Mbits/sec. They will operate in *Mesh Configuration*.

The life span of a satellite is governed by the time of failure of its main systems and subsystems, the exhaustion of fuel for attitude control, the efficiency degradation of solar cell panels and the degeneration of rechargeable batteries. Satellites are generally designed for a lifetime of 7-10 years which may be increased to 10-15 years.

Satellites will play a major role for providing services which exploit their fundamental characteristics such as broadcasting and wide-area mobile communications. They will also continue to be used for international and intercontinental fixed services, specially to avoid the hardships of cable laying in hostile and unapproachable regions.

7.8.7. Direct-To-Home (DTH) Receive System and Interactive Video-on-Demand (VoD) Service

The DTH receive system is intended for straightforward reception of a large number of TV programme channels without any dependence on cable operators. These systems function in the Ku-band (~12 GHz) using 30-45 cm diameter dish antennae. A small-size antenna suffices here because of the strong satellite signal in this frequency range. Usually, a bandwidth equal to 27 MHz is allocated to one transponder of the satellite. This bandwidth is adequate for transmission of one channel in the analog mode.

Compression of the signal to MPEG-2 format yields bit rates from 2-8 Mbits/sec. Then multiplexing many TV signals onto a single bit stream at 45 Mbits/sec, and using QPSK modulation with a bandwidth efficiency of 2 bits per Hz, a set of four channels can be transmitted in the 27-MHz slot. This can be augmented to 15 channels after accepting a lower data rate with some sacrifice in picture quality. Employing 24 transponders in the satellite, the home dish antenna can capture programmes from $24 \times 15 = 360$ channels. An intense competition with CATV is in the offing.

Further, to combat the drudgery of watching routine TV programmes or rather be dictated by the whims of service providers, viewers in future will make use of VoD facilities. Such a service will permit direct access to the viewers to a video library, a picture archive, a music album or a news programme, sitting at home. The service will also put in the user's hand, the interaction ability such as starting, stopping, rewinding or even editing the contents of a programme.

Interactive services of this nature require a substantial digital storage space, and will be made possible via efficient compression algorithms.

7.8.8. Digital Cable TV

In the face of competition from DTH receive system, cable TV companies will have to upgrade their plants and convert their systems to digital domain to promote their business.

Here also the restriction on the number of channels is imposed by bandwidth at our disposal. The present analog system allows for as many as 70 channels in 550 MHz bandwidth. For better bandwidth utilization, the signal is compressed in accordance with MPEG-2 standard. After multiplexing, the signals are modulated in 128 QAM mode (efficiency = 7 bits/Hz). Following this approach, the number of channels can be increased to 500 for digital cable TV.

The major obstacles to digital conversion are that the cable operators need special cable modems and the consumers require set-top converter for demodulating the digital signal. One-way cable service uses a single 6-MHz cable channel for delivering signals at 1-10 Mbits/sec. Two-way cable service employs two 6-MHz cable channels, one for downstream delivery and the other for upstream delivery. Special amplifiers and isolation techniques are ncessary for building such two-way systems since the CATV network was originally designed for one-way traffic. Multimedia applications mandate two-way data flow.

7.8.9. Digital Video Broadcasting (DVB)/Digital Terrestrial Television (DTT)

Traditional TV broadcast programmes are available, free of cost, on domestic receivers and mobile systems. Their dominance will continue for the next two decades or so, after which they are likely to relinquish the scene in favour of digital video broadcasting.

In DVB system, MPEG-2 compression is used to accommodate four digital channels in a 7-MHz TV channel (in the present norms). The signals for the four channels are multiplexed and the multiplexed signals are subjected to a special digital modulation technique known as *Coded Orthogonal Frequency-Division Multiplexing (COFDM)*. This system has been devised for minimization of multipath propagation problems encountered in digital modulation. In the COFDM system, a single carrier does not undergo modulation, as is done in common practice. Instead, a large number of carriers, e.g., 2048 carriers, are taken and each carrier is QPSK-modulated by a segment of the input stream of data. The system is based on a *Spread Spectrum Method* in which each constituent carrier bears a small data stream.

The COFDM technique can provide multichannel television broadcasting from a single transmitter with the attendant saving in transmitter construction and maintenance costs for multichannel transmission. Inclusion of more audio or data channels is also possible for provision of additional services like teletext, facsimile, multilingual subtitling, etc. Moreover, the lower power threshold demanded of digital systems, enables a wider coverage at a given power, much beyond the limits of its analog counterpart. A further advantage is that the system functions reliably for mobile communications also. A DVB transmitter can be used for a single HDTV channel.

7.8.10. Multimedia Products

With the flourishing of multimedia industry, manufacturers will be encouraged to launch a veritable spate of new products geared towards multimedia use. Already available list of common multimedia items includes the audio and video cards and the CD-ROMs for recording and replaying music. The storage capacity of a CD-ROM is ~500 Mbytes. A new type of CD known as *Digital Versatile Disc (DVD)* can distribute from 4.7×10^{12} to 1.7×10^{13} bytes of data on a 120 mm disc. The DVD family comprises DVD-Video, DVD-Audio, DVD-ROM, DVD-R (Recordable) and DVD-RAM, covering home entertainment, computers and business applications in a single digital format. The much higher capacity of DVD as compared to CD-ROM is because of a smaller track pitch and pit size in the former (engraved using a shorter wavelength laser beam), and the recording of data in as many as upto four layers.

A plethora of innovatively designed multimedia items and products are anticipated to flood the market, promising a quantum elevation in the level of business and entertainment in tomorrow's world. The recent explosion of interest in multimedia and the convergence on the Internet as a vehicle for information, provides a glimpse of the advanced information society of the not-too-distant future. The curtain to these changing lifestyles will be raised in the following section.

7.9. PROJECTIONS ON THE FUTURE WORLD OF INFORMATION TECHNOLOGY

Tracing the history of technological advancement of mankind, we find that this saga is marked by several phases and milestones: Stone Age → Copper Age → Bronze Age → Iron Age → Industrial Revolution → Electrical Age → Electronic Age → Information Age. We see that we are now delicately poised on the brink of an information revolution. The information society offers new opportunities and goals in the fields of multimedia signal processing, broadband and intelligent communication networks and DSP microelectronic chips. Living in the "Cyberspace" of millions of computers linked through the Internet, we can envision dramatic societal changes, as exemplified by the below-mentioned multimedia applications (Fig. 7.6)

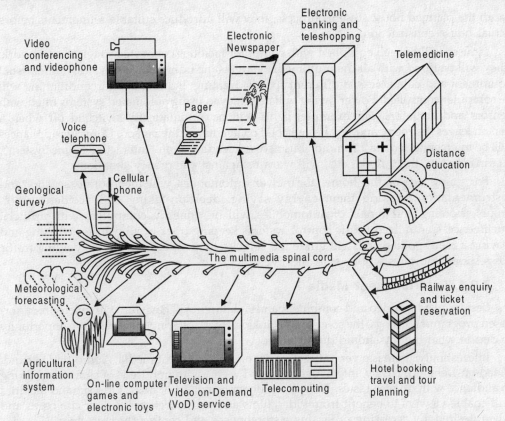

Fig. 7.6. Some of the services emanating from the multimedia spinal cord

7.9.1. Telecommuting

This means doing one's regular job while sitting at home. The idea of telecommuting will be made possible by the progress in interactive multimedia services apart from FAX, e-mail, videophone, Internet and World Wide Web. There will be less need for people to physically travel to the work place and the concept of "residential business" will gain acceptance. The number of people working at home will increase.

7.9.2. The Office Environment

There is a distinct move towards "paperless offices". Offices will be full of PCs, word processors and computer terminals. Modems will be connected to some PCs for data communications. By inter-office and intra-office networking, it will be possible to transfer files and access records and databases. The clumsy looking pileup of files on the clerk's desk will no longer be seen. FAX will be replaced by computer graphics. Cordless pocket phones will be used for voice communication. PBXs will keep track of staff in the premises. There will be quite a lot of car phones, personal mobile phones and pagers.

7.9.3. Intelligent Homes and Conveyance

This will be an era of computer-adied design of homes including garden design, furniture layout in the drawing room and other rooms, kitchen design and so on. After the design work is over, people will use graphics, 3-D simulations and virtual reality software to visualize how they will live in the proposed house. They may like to walk, sleep and eat in the planned house. By this process, they will introduce suitable refinements before actual house construction.

Houses will be well equipped with computer facilities connected to telecom network. They will be fitted with all the multimedia gadgets including voice services, audio-visual equipment and data access at different speeds. Heating, lighting and airconditioning will be computer controlled. Power saving will be achieved using automated systems fitted with sensors and actuators. For example, lights will be automatically switched off when a person leaves the room, and will be switched on at entry of the person. Domestic appliances will be interconnected via a common bus network leading to an "Interactive Home System". Alarms for fire, theft, flood, etc., will warn us against emergency situations.

For going out of the home, the newer automobiles will incorporate sensors and instrumentation, making them energy saving, decision-taking and accident proof. Troubleshooting and repair of automobiles will be done by computers with artificial intelligence. Centralized traffic control systems keeping track of all vehicles entering and leaving a metropolitan city, will guide the vehicles to an optimised route avoiding traffic congestions. Journeys will be safe and lively.

7.9.4. Entertainment Media

Besides playing video and computer games, children will have fun with microprocessor-based programmable toys, the so-called "Thinking Toys", offering them with the opportunity to decide what the toy should do for them.

Interestingly, there is a very attractive list of entertainment media: Audio-on-Demand, Video-on-Demand, HDTV, interactive TV, 3-D TV, etc., with hundreds of channels catering to audience with diverse tastes. TV will no longer be an "Idiot Box". On-Demand facilities will enable viewers to benefit from video films and audio sections of their choice, as and when desired, by accessing programme storehouses and centres through their PC.

Using graphics and simulations software, film and TV personnel will be able to produce movies in a short time span with limited resources, imitating the acting of their superstar.

7.9.5. Healthcare and Telemedicine

Automatic diagnostic tools and therapeutic instruments will keep surveillance of the critically ill. Delicate operations will be performed by robots. Medical reports will be sent through the network.

Telemedicine or Teledoctoring is a kind of teleworking defined as medical practice performed from a distance, enabling a doctor at one location to examine and treat a patient at another remote location. Also, doctors or students in the classroom can closely view a complicated surgery in process at a major hospital. Expert surgeons can guide difficult operations being carried out elsewhere by watching their video display.

Telemedicine facility will be realized through a meshing of multimedia, computers, imaging, information and telecommunication services with medical expertise and knowledge base. Components of a distributed telemedical network will include: (*i*) *Computer* for patient data storage and management; (*ii*) *Communication Link* such as ISDN; (*iii*) *Videophone* for face-to-face dialogue between doctors at the two ends; (*iv*) *Telepresence* which means a hospital consultant supervising a paramedic from remote; (*v*) *Teleradiology* used to transmit X-ray images; and (*vi*) *Vital Signs Monitor* for sharing pulse rate, blood pressure, ECG, etc., between practitioners.

Telemedicine will offer the benefits of: *Remote Consultation*, also called *Teleconsultation*; Transference and exchange of clinical information between doctors for their knowledge upgradation; Improvement in medical care in rural and distant inaccessible regions. Table

7.2 presents a glimpse of the important application areas of telemedicine along with their multimedia requirements.

Table 7.2. Multimedia and Remote Control Requirements of the Different Applications of Telemedicine

Sl. No.	Application	Description	Multimedia Requirement	Remote Control Requirement
1	2	3	4	5
1.	Teleradiology	Medical practice using images transmitted by radiological modalities including X-ray, MRI, CT scan, Nuclear Medicine, Ultrasound, etc., which play a crucial role in diagnosis.	Large images	Nil
2.	Telecardiology	Based on transmission of images of heart and other relevant data.	High-quality video	Nil
3.	Telepathology	Examination of tissues resected from a patient by a microscope under remote control.	Still image	Microscope, Camera
4.	Teledermatology	Similar to telephathology except that the skin of the patient is examined.	High-quality video/Still image	Camera, Microsocpe
5.	Tele-endoscopy	A doctor guides the endoscope to the region of interest while a remote specialist views the video sequence in real time.	High-quality video	Nil
6.	Telepsychiatry	Remote psychiatric practice and advice.	Video teleconferencing	Camera

7.9.6. Distance Learning

It is a kind of training, orientational study or collection of information, through electronic communication system in which the teacher and the student are allowed to be separated by space or time or both space and time. The allied term "Asynchronous Learning" refers to learning at a different time. Another related term is " Flex Learning" which refers to the flexible nature of distance learning wherein the tutor and the pupil need not be synchronized in space or time.

Multimedia computers, videoconferencing, interactive learning through compact discs and professional educational programmes from broadcast media and Internet, are all different manifestations of distance learning. The ultimate goal of distance education will be to supplement the educatoin of a child all throughout, starting from infant classes to the doctoral level, with the aid of multimedia. He or she will be able to read books and journals at the home video terminal after downloading the portions of interest from a computerized database library into the home computer. Printouts of desired pages can be taken for reference and record.

Revolutionay changes are in store for the printing and publishing industries. For printing of books, periodicals and newspapers, each person will access the database and choose the concerned topics for printing according to individual requirements. Paper

Newspapers will make room for Electronic Newspapers, read by browsing through the pages of the database library, and printing as and when needed. Newsprint will be a relic of the past and the society will progress towards a "Paperless Society".

7.9.7. Electronic Banking and Shopping

Money transfers will be conducted through computers. Dependence on currency notes will decrease.

There will be an increasing tendency to shop from home. The sale items of a show-room at a far-off station will be demonstrated through video. Consumers will choose the desired commodities, prepare the order list and make payments electronically via the telecommunications network. Retail outlets will keep *Electronic Point-of-Sale Terminals* for automatic stock recording and reordering.

7.9.8. Agricultural Information Systems

Computers will control the cultivation of crops right from the selection and sowing of seeds, application of fertilizers and pesticides, through watering and irrigation, depending on the weather forecasts, to harvesting and marketing. Exchange of information among farmers will increase crop yield and minimize wastage. Farm machinery such as tractors will be equipped with mobile voice communications.

7.9.9. Network Infrastructure

In the multimedia age, every individual will carry an electronic card of the size of a credit card. The electronic card will contain the bio-data and other useful information about the person, encoded in a digital format. Address translation and personal numbering facilities will be used to locate an individual automatically wherever he or she may be. Using miniaturized communication devices, a person away from home, for example on a journey, can contact and keep in touch with family members, as desired. Credit or debit card readers will be available on telephones and work stations for call accounting purposes.

Videotelephony for interactive discussions on documents placed in front of the camera, will be a major breakthrough. Voice input to machines, based on speech recognition equipment, will enable us to control machinery through the network from remote.

7.9.10. Virtual Reality

Innovations in the software and hardware for virtual reality will bestow upon us the ability to produce and watch events simulated through computers, thus creating a "Virtual World" containing virtual factories for testing automobiles before putting them on roads, virtual playgrounds for learning skills and tricks and so on. This concept is gaining popularity in medical teaching where trainee surgeons can actually perform a "mock operation" to acquire useful practice before applying the knife on the patient. This will also lessen the risk factor in critical operations.

7.10. COMMENTARY

Like a mutating virus, the multimedia technology is rampaging ahead almost unstoppably. Just as the construction of roads, railways and irrigation canals led to the industrial revolution, in the same way, telecommunication is the vehicle of multimedia revolution. It appears that in future people will work more at home than outside. They will fully avail of the multimedia services, spending more time with their family members. The relatively less need to travel will ease the pressure on urban transport.

This metamorphosis of multimedia and information technologies is taking place so rapidly as to defy comprehension. For instance, it is difficult to predict which device : PC or TV, will be the future dominant multimedia viewing screen. However, it may be surmised that the existing TV paradigm will shift from the passive TV reception towards consumers accessing and interacting with both the TV contents and services.

A significant issue on the agenda is that human communication involves several media including, above all, body language and also music, text, audio and video. Therefore, success in multimedia depends on a strong intermixing of engineering with humanistic aspects, rather than concentrating on barren technology.

The motto of multimedia age is a "free society" with free-flowing information. This means that any person should be able to seek any desired information from any place at any time. It is equally important for the telecommunications network to have the capability to track any person anywhere on the globe.

The challenges of multimedia age are very exciting. Our indicators of success in this age will be how knowledge is stored, how it is processed to enhance its innovativeness and how it is accessed. We look forward to the "multimedia age" with great hopes and aspirations.

(ILLUSTRATIVE PROBLEMS)

7.1. In a multimedia transmission system, the bandwidth of the video signal is 4 MHz. Uisng a 512-line raster with 30 frames per second, find the approximate number of pixels per line in the image.

If this signal is ascribed 8 bits per sample, what will be the bandwidth required for transmitting the signal by PSK scheme which needs 1 Hz per two bits?

From the Sampling Theorem, the required minimum sampling rate for preserving the useful information in the image = $2 \times 4 = 8$ MHz. This sampling rate represents the number of pixels per unit area in the image. So, the number of pixels per unit area in the video signal = 8 MHz = 8×10^6 per second. Since 30 frames are transmitted every second, the number of pixels in 30 frames = 8×10^6 giving the

$$\text{number of pixels in one frame} = \frac{8 \times 10^6}{30} = 2.67 \times 10^5. \qquad \text{(P 7.1)}$$

We are given that the raster contains 512 lines. Therefore, the number of pixels in 512 lines = 2.67×10^5 from which the Number of pixels per raster line =

$\dfrac{2.67 \times 10^5}{512} = 520.83 \approx 521$ pixels. Thus each image frame comprises 512×521 pixels

= 266752 pixels. (P 7.2)

When the assignment of bits to the samples is done at the rate of 8 bits per sample, the total number of bits required for 266752 samples or pixels is = 266752×8 = 2134016 bits. Thus the video signal containing 30 frames per second carries $2134016 \times 30 = 64020480$ bits/sec. But 2 bits correspond to a frequency of 1 Hz in PSK. Hence the bandwidth requirement for the PSK modulated signal = $64020480/2 = 32010240 = 32 \times 10^6$ Hz = 32 MHz. (P 7.3)

7.2. In a multimedia system, newspaper and documentary pages containing text and half-tone images, are sent by facsimile transmission. How much time will it take to send a standard A-4 page (8.5" × 11") over a 4.8 kbits/sec telephone line at a resolution of 7.7 lines per millimetre in the vertical direction and 100 lines per inch horizontally?

The vertical resolution in points per inch (ppi) is calculated as follows: 7.7 lines

per mm $= \dfrac{7.7 \text{ lines}}{1 \text{ mm}} = \dfrac{7.7 \text{ lines}}{0.1/2.54 \text{ inch}} = 195.58$ lines per inch. 195.58 lines per inch

translate into 196 points per inch. This means that vertically, 1" of the A-4 page contains 196 points. Therefore, page length of 11" will consist of 11 × 196 = 2156 points. In the horizontal direction, in 1" of the page, there are 100 lines. So, in 8.5" of the breadth of A-4 page, we have 8.5 × 100 lines = 850 lines. Thus the total number of bits required for 196 ppi × 100 lpi sampling density = 2156 × 850 = 1832600 bits = 1.83 × 10^6 bits.   (P 7.4)

Now, since 4800 bits are transmitted in 1 sec, therefore 1.83 × 10^6 bits will be

transmitted in $\dfrac{1.83 \times 10^6}{4800 \times 60} = 6.35 \min.$ (P 7.5)

7.3. (a) Digital audio and video require a stupendous amount of information bandwidth unless compression techniques are applied. The high-definition television (HDTV) signal (1920 × 1080 pixels with 12 bits per pixel at 30 frames/sec) is compressed to 20 Mbits/sec. Calculate the compression ratio. (b) The video-phone terminal (128 × 96 pixels with 7.5 frames/sec) is expected to be compressed to 10-20 kbits/sec. Determine the compression ratio, assuming 8 bits per pixel and a final bit rate of 15 kbits/sec.

(a) The bit rate of the uncompressed HDTV signal

$= 1920 \times 1080 \times 12 \times 30 = 7.46496 \times 10^8$ bits/sec.   (P 7.6)

Sincel the bit rate of the compressed signal is 20 Mbits/sec = 2 × 10^7 bits/sec,   the required compression ratio is

$$r = \dfrac{7.46496 \times 10^8}{2 \times 10^7} = 37.32$$ (P 7.7)

(b) Uncompressed video phone signal bit rate = 128 × 96 × 12 × 7.5

$= 1105920$ bits/sec   (P 7.8)

and Compressed video-phone signal bit rate = 15 × 10^3 bits/sec (P 7.9)

∴ Ratio $r = \dfrac{1105920}{15 \times 10^3} = 73.73$ (P 7.10)

7.4. The audio output of the microphone of a multimedia kit takes values between 0 and 2.0 units. If the samples are uniformly quantised to 256 levels, write down the expressions for transition and reconstruction levels. What is the quantisation interval?

If the microphone is used for voice or music, bandlimited to between 50 Hz and 8000 Hz, calculate the binary data rate for the audio signal.

Transition levels are given by

$$t_k = \dfrac{2}{256}(k-1) = \dfrac{1}{128}(k-1), \quad k = 1, 2, 3, ..., 256$$ (P 7.11)

Reconstruction levels are represented by

$$r_k = t_k + \dfrac{1}{256}, \quad k = 1, 2, 3, ..., 256$$ (P 7.12)

The quantisation interval

$$q_k = t_k - t_{k-1} = r_k - r_{k-1} = \frac{1}{128}(k-1) - \frac{1}{128}(k-2) \qquad \text{(P 7.13)}$$

$$= \frac{1}{128} = 7.8 \times 10^{-3} \text{ sec.} \qquad \text{(P 7.14)}$$

Since the given audio signal is quantised to 256 amplitude levels, the number of binary digits per sample = $\log_2 256$ = 8 bits per sample. Also, the Nyquist sampling frequency is 2 × 8000 Hz = 16000 Hz = 16 k samples/sec from which the required binary data rate (bit rate) = 16 k samples/sec × 8 bits/sample = 128 kbits/sec.

$$\text{(P 7.15)}$$

7.5. Calculate the uncompressed signal-bit rates or bit count rates for the following multimedia services: (*i*) CD-Audio (Sampling frequency = 44.1 kHz, 16 bits per sample, 2 channels); (*ii*) FAX (1700 × 2200 pixels per frame with 1 bit per pixel); (*iii*) NTSC television (480 × 483 pixels per frame with 16 bits per pixel and 29.97 frames per sec); (*iv*) HDTV (1280 × 720 pixels with 12 bits per pixel at 59.94 frames per sec); and (*v*) Video-conferencing system with Common Intermediate Format (CIF) having 352 × 288 pixels per frame, 12 bits per pixel and 14.98 frames per second. Under the assumption that modern compression technology gives compression rates of 20-30: 1 for audio signals and 100 : 1 for video signals without any significant loss of quality, find the compressed signal bit rates for the above services. (You may take compression ratio = 22 : 1 for CD-audio).

(*i*) Uncompressed CD-Audio Signal Bit Rate = 44.1×10^3 samples per sec × 16 bits per sample × 2 channels = 1.41×10^6 bits/sec = 1.41 Mbits/sec. (P 7.16)

After 22:1 compression, the bit rate for 2-channel CD-audio signal = $\frac{1.41 \times 10^6}{22}$

$$= 64.09 \times 10^3 \text{ bits/sec} \approx 64 \text{ kbits/sec.} \qquad \text{(P 7.17)}$$

(*ii*) Uncompressed bit count of the FAX signal = 1700 × 2200 pixels per frame × 1 bit per pixel = 3740000 bits per frame = 3.74×10^6 = 3.74 Mbits per frame. By compression in the 100 : 1 ratio, the bit count becomes = 37.4 kbits per frame.

$$\text{(P 7.18)}$$

(*iii*) Before compression, bit rate of NTSC TV signal = 480 × 483 pixels per frame × 16 bits per pixel × 29.97 frames per sec = 1.1117×10^8 bits/sec = 111.17 Mbits/sec, which after compression by a factor of 100, reduces to 1.11 Mbits/sec.

(*iv*) In the uncompressed state, bit rate of HDTV signal = 1280 × 720 pixels per frame × 12 bits per pixel × 59.94 frames per second = 6.62888×10^8 bits/sec = 662.89×10^6 = 662.9 Mbits/sec. By compressing this signal 100-fold, the bit rate falls to 6.63 Mbits/sec.

(*v*) Bit rate of CIF video-conferencing signal = 352 × 288 pixels per frame × 12 bits per pixel × 14.98 frames per sec = 1.822×10^7 bits/sec = 18.22 Mbits/sec. When compressed, the signal bit rate reduces to 182.23 kbits/sec.

REVIEW QUESTIONS

7.1. Explain the meaning of the term "Multimedia". Enlist some common signals under the multimedia umbrella.

7.2. Define multimedia from the point of view of: (i) its physical content, and (ii) its performance about what it does for us. Name four major industries spanned by multimedia technology.

7.3. What preliminary requirements must be met by a computer system in order to qualify as a multimedia capable equipment?

7.4. Classify the various kinds of multimedia materials.

7.5. Highlight the different generations of multimedia development.

7.6. Name the ingredients of a commercial multimedia hardware kit. Mention some software components also.

7.7. Outline the scope of Multimedia Signal Processing (MMSP). What type of signal processing problems have to be considered for seamless integration and ease of use of different media?

7.8. Give the bit rates of the uncompressed signal for: (a) Narrow-band speech, (b) Wide-band speech and (c) Two-channel stereoquality CD audio.

7.9. Name the main attributes of a speech coder. What are your expectations about the attributes of an ideal speech coder?

7.10. Which one gives a smaller delay: Telephone Bandwidth PCM Coder or Wide-band ADPCM Speech coder? Which one is suitable for teleconferencing?

7.11. Differentiate between Linear Prediction Analysis-by-Synthesis (LPAS) Coder and Parametric Speech Coder.

7.12. Which of the following multimedia applications involves live conversation: (a) Distance Learning, (b) Video Telephony/Conferencing and (c) Multimedia Messaging? Give your views about the properties of speech coders required for each application.

7.13. Write notes on: (a) Acoustic Echo Control and (b) Network Echo Cancellation.

7.14. What is meant by Perceptual Audio Coding? Name some audio coding standards for multimedia. Why was it felt necessary to create MPEG-AAC (MPEG-Advanced Audio Coder)? Name one important application for which the Dolby AC-3 Coder has been selected.

7.15. Give three examples of multimedia applications which depend upon image coding.

7.16. Indicate the main difference in the approaches towards speech coding and the coding of image and video signals. Give some examples of spatial and temporal redundancies in images and video sequences.

7. 7. Briefly describe the JPEG method for compression of continuous-tone still images.

7 18. State the main differences between video and image signals from the standpoint of coding.

.19. What are the main features of MPEG-1 and MPEG-2 video coding standards? What is Object-based Coding used in MPEG-4 standard?

7.20. Explain the bimodality of human speech and hence argue as to way a proper consideration of interaction among various media is vital for multimedia.

7.21. Draw and explain the model of human communication mechanism. Give an explanation, in the light of human lip reading, how the study of deeper interaction layer concerning emotions, will improve multimedia presentations?

7.22. Discuss some of the problems arising from the non-addressal of the requirements of networked transmission by compression algorithms.

7.23. How do we protect the intellectual property rights (IPRs) associated with multimedia? What is a Watermark? What different functions are performed by a watermark?

7.24. Why is it possible to hide data in audio, image and video files in a way that it is perceptually inaudible or invisible? Mention some multimedia services which can be delivered by data embedding.

7.25. When does a "deadlock" occur in the insertion of digital watermarks by multiple users? How is the deadlock resolved? Which type of watermarking algorithms are most susceptible to deadlocks?

7.26. Discuss the commonality of characteristics between neural processing and intelligent multimedia processing. Give some application examples of multimedia signal processing which are most suited to the use of neural networks.

7.27. Explain how the Graphical User Interface (GUI) takes into account the limitations of human cognitive processing to become an effective interfacial tool for a wide range of multimedia applications.

7.28. What technologies form the basis of the Spoken Language Interfaces (SLIs) for natural and intelligent man-machine interaction?

7.29. By approximately what factor must the processing capability of microprocessors be increased to handle real-time audio and video signals for multimedia? Classify the multimedia processors according to their basic architecture.

7.30. Point out the special characteristic features demanded of multimedia processors. Suggest the approaches which are necessary to obtain these features.

7.31. Shed light on the developments necessary to realize portable multimedia systems like a Video-communication terminal on Silicon.

7.32. Justify the statement, "The POTS network is well designed and engineered for handling the switching and transmission of 3-kHz voice calls." Mention two significant architectural modifications that have been made to the POTS network since the conception of its initial design.

7.33. For what type of applications, the POTS network is not well suited? How are these services delivered over the POTS network?

7.34. What networks are suitable for moving bursty, non real-time data traffic among computers? Can these networks be used for sending live telephonic talks? Indicate the major delay factors degrading the perceived quality of connection in a multimedia PC-based packet telephony network.

7.35. Comment on the statements: (*i*) ISDN is not a separate discrete network. (*ii*) ATM offers a packet protocol suitable for both real-time audio and video signals as well as for data transmission.

7.36. Describe the two forms of user access and the various interfaces in ISDN. What do you understand by Broadband ISDN?

7.37. What is the size of the ATM cells. How many octets are present in an ATM header and how many in the information field? What is the purpose of the header? What user requirement is reflected by the number of ATM cells per unit time?

7.38. Write the expanded form of TCP/IP. What is it used for?

7.39. Outline approaches like the use of special modems, fibre-to-the-home, hybrid fibre-coax and similar innovative ideas to increase the bandwidth on demand for broadband multimedia services.

7.40. What is Video-on-Demand (VoD) service? What special communication techniques are needed for this service?

7.41. Why a small dish antenna suffices for DTH receiver? Explain how the number of channels per satellite transponder is increased in the DTH system to compete with the existing cable TV?

7.42. What is the present channel capacity in the 550 MHz bandwidth for the present analog cable TV? What is the likely channel capacity for the 550 MHz bandwidth using digital compression methods? For conversion to digital technology, what special equipment will the cable TV operators and consumers need?

7.43. What does the acronym MMDS stand for? In what situations is the wireless delivery of multiple TV channels mandatory?

7.44. What special features of Digital Video Broadcasting (DVB) cannot be matched by cable or satellite systems? Describe Orthogonal Frequency Division-Multiplexing (OFDM). What type of problem encountered in digital modulation, is overcome by OFDM?

7.45. Write notes on: (*a*) Intelligent Network, (*b*) Smart Terminal, (*c*) Metadata and Taxonomy.

7.46. Distinguish between Structured and Unstructured Text. How are unstructured text documents selectively retrieved?

7.47. Present a résumé of the methods of speech indexing.

7.48. Describe in brief, how are image and video indexing performed?

7.49. Why are powerful browsing capabilities indispensable for multimedia information retrieval? Outline the methods for browsing multimedia documents.

7.50. We are the witnesses to revolutionary changes in the telecommunications scene which are changing our lives and work styles in a most fundamental way. Look around yourselves, carry out an extensive literature survey, gather information from various sources, think and contemplate to paint your own picture of the "Future Dreamworld of Multimedia and Information Technologies". You may touch upon the infrastructural support, electronic facilities, the anticipated society transformations and other topics of interest.

REFERENCES AND FURTHER READING

7.1. Proceeding of the IEEE, Vol. 86, Nos 5 & 6, *Special Issues on Multimedia Signal Processing*, May and June, 1998.

7.2. L. Hanzo, *Bandwidth-Efficient Wireless Multimedia Communications*, Proc. of the IEEE, Vol. 86, No. 7, July 1998, pp. 1342-1382.

7.3. G.Davenport, *Defining Multimedia*, IEEE Multimedia, Jan-March 1998, Vol. 5, No. 1, pp. 8–15.

7.4. M.J. Riezenman, *Communications Technology 1998, Analysis and Forecast*, IEEE Spectrum, Jan. 1998, Vol. 35, No. 1, pp. 29–36.

7.5. T. Chen (Ed.), *The Past Present and Future of Multimedia Signal Processing*, IEEE Signal Processing Magazine, July 1997, pp. 28-51.

7.6. *Workshop on Multimedia Communication Technology* (MCT-97), CEERI, Pilani, September 21-22, 1997.

7.7. T.S. Chua, H.K. Pung and T.L Kunii (Eds.), *Multimedia Modelling: Towards Information Superhighway*, World Scientific, Singapore, 1995.

7.8. J. Keyes, *The McGraw-Hill Multimedia Handbook*, Mc-Graw-Hill, Inc., New York, 1994.

□□□

Appendix A

COMMON ACRONYMS AND ABBREVIATIONS

AAC	Advanced Audio Coding
AAL	ATM Adaptation Layer
ACSE	Association Control Service Element
A-D (or A/D)	Analog-to-Digital (Converter)
ADM	Adaptive Delta Modulation
ADPCM	Adaptive Differential Pulse-Code Modulation
AGC	Automatic Gain Control
AM	Amplitude Modulation
ANN	Artificial Neural Network
APC	Adaptive Predictive Coding
APCM	Adaptive Pulse-Code Modulation
ARP	Address Resolution Protocol
ASE	Application Service Element
ASIC	Application-Specific Integrated Circuit
ASK	Amplitude-Shift Keying
ATC	Adaptive Transform Coding
ATD	Asynchronous Time Division (Multiplexing)
ATM	Asynchronous Transfer Mode
ATV	Advanced Television
AVI	Audio Visual Inferface
AVO	Audio Visual Object
AWGN	Additive White Gaussian Noise
BBC	Baseband Coding
BER	Bit Error Rate
BIBO	Bounded Input, Bounded Output
B-ISDN	Broadband Integrated Services Digital Network
BP	Band-pass (Filter)
bps	Bits per second (Unit of bit rate)
BPSK	Binary Phase-Shift Kying
BRI	Basic Rate Interface in ISDN

BS	Band-Stop (Filter)
CCD	Charge Control Device
CCIR	International Radio Consultative Committee
CCITT	International Telegraph and Telephone Consultative Committee
CCR	Carrier and Clock Recovery (Sequence)
CCR(SE)	Commitment, Concurrency and Recovery (Service Element)
CD	Compact Disc, Call Deflection
CDDI	Cable Distributed Data Interface
CDM	Code-Division Multiplexing
CDMA	Code-Division Multiple Access
CFB	Call Forwarding Busy
CFNR	Call Forwarding No Reply
CFU	Call Forwarding Unconditional
CIF	Common Intermediate Format
CISC	Complex Instruction Set Computer
CLI	Calling Line Identification
CLIP	Calling Line Identification Presentation
CLIR	Calling Line Identification Restriction
C/N	Carrier-to-Noise (Ratio)
COFDM	Coded Orthogonal Frequency-Division Multiplexing
CPFSK	Continuous Phase Frequency-Shift Keying
CRC	Cyclic Redundancy Check
CRT	Cathode Ray Tube
CT	Cordless Telephone
CTV/CATV	Cable Television
CVSDM	Continuously Variable Slope Delta Modulation
CW	Call Waiting
D-A (or D/A)	Digital-to-Analog (Converter)
DAMA	Demand-Assignment Multiple Access
dB	deciBel
DBS	Direct Broadcasting By Satellite
DC	Downconverter (in Satellite Communication)
DCPSK	Differentially Encoded Phase-Shift Keying
DCT	Discrete Cosine Transform
DDI	Direct Dialling In
DM	Delta Modulation
DPCM	Differential Pulse-Code Modulation
DPSK	Differential Phase-Shift Keying
DRAM	Dynamic Random Access Memory
DSBSC	Double Sideband Suppressed Carrier
DSI	Digital Speech Interpolation
DSL	Digital Subscriber Line

DSP	Digital Signal Processing
DTH	Direct-to-Home (Receiver)
DTT	Digital Terrestrial Transmission
DTW	Dynamic Time Warping
DVB	Digital Video Broadcasting
DVD	Digital Video Disc
EDTV	Extended (Enhanced) Definition Television
EHF	Extremely High Frequency
EM	Expectation-Maximization (Algorithm)
E-mail	Electronic Mail
ERP	Effective Radiated Power (e.g., of an antenna)
Fax	Facsimile
FCC	Federal Communications Commission
FCS	Frame Check Sequence
FDDI	Fibre Distributed Data Interface
FEC	Forward Error Correcting (Code)
FDM	Frequency-Division Multiplexing
FDMA	Frequency-Division Multiple Access
FM	Frequency Modulation
FSK	Frequency-Shift Keying
FTP	File Transfer Protocol
FTTC	Fibre to the Curb
FTTH	Fibre to the Home
GA-HDTV	Grand Alliance High-Definition Television (System)
GEO	Geosynchronous Earth Orbit
GLP	Generalized Linear Phase
GSM	Groupe Special Mobile
GUI	Graphical User Interface
HDLC	High-Level Data Link Control
HDTV	High-Definition Television
HTML	Hyper Text Markup Language
IDTV	Improved Definition Television
IF	Intermediate Frequency
IMP	Intelligent Multimedia Processing
IN	Intelligent Network
IPR	Intellectual Property Right
IRC	Internet Relay Chat
IRP	Impulse Response Truncation
ISDN	Integrated Services Digital Network
ISO	International Standards Organization
ISP	Internet Service Provider
IT	Information Technology

ITV	Interactive Television
JPEG	Joint Photographers Expert Group
LAN	Local Area Network
LAP-B	Link Access Protocol-Balanced
LAR	Log-Area Ratio
LCD	Liquid Crystal Display
LCN	Logical Channel Number
LEO	Low-Earth Orbit (Satellite)
LO	Local Oscillator
LPAS	Linear Prediction Analysis-by-Synthesis (Coder)
LPC	Linear Predictive Coding
LSB	Least Significant Bit
MA	Moving Average (Signal or Model)
MAN	Metropolitan Area Network
MC	Motion Compensation
MCI	Malicious Call Identification
MEO	Medium-Earth Orbit (Satellite)
MHS	Message Handling System
ML	Maximum Likelihood (Estimation)
MMDS	Multipoint Microwave Digital System
MMSE	Minimum Mean Square Error
MMSP	Multimedia Signal Processing
MOS	Mean Opinion Score
MPEG	Moving Pictures Experts Group
MRF	Markov Random Field
MRI	Magnetic Resonance Imaging
MSB	Most Significant Bit
MSK	Minimum Shift Keying
MSN	Multiple Subscriber Number
MTSO	Mobile Telephone Switching Office
MUD	Multiple User Dimension
MUSE	Multiple Sub-Nyquist Encoding
Mux	Multiplex/Multiplexer
NIC	Network Interface Card
N-ISDN	Narrowband Integrated Services Digital Network
NMR	Nuclear Magnetic Resonance
NMS	Network Management Software
NOS	Network Operating Software
NRZ	Non-Return to Zero
NSAP	Network Service Access Point
NTSC	National Television System Committee
OFDM	Orthogonal Frequency-Division Multiplexing

OK-QPSK	Offset Keyed Quaternary Phase-Shift Keying
OLA	Overlap-Add (Convolution)
OQPSK	Offset Quaternary Phase Shift-Keying
OSI	Open Systems Interconnection
OSQ	Optimal Scalar Quantisation
PAL	Phase Alternation Line
PAM	Pulse Amplitude Modulation
PBX	Private Branch Exchange
PC	Personal Computer
PCM	Pulse-Code Modulation
PDM	Pulse Duration Modulation
Pel	Picture Element (Pixel)
PFM	Pulse Frequency Modulation
PID	Packet Identification (Header)
PLL	Phase Locked Loop
PLP	Packet Level Protocol
PM	Phase Modulation
PN	Pseudo-Noise (random sequence)
POTS	Plain Ordinary Telephone Service
ppi	Points per inch
PPM	Pulse Position Modulation
PRI	Primary Rate Interface
PS	Packet Switching
ps	Picosecond
PSF	Point Spread Function
PSK	Phase-Shift Keying
PSTN	Public Switched Telephone Network
PWM	Pulse Width Modulation
QAM	Quadrature Amplitude Modulation
QoS	Quality of Service
QPSK	Quaternary Phase-Shift Keying
RAM	Random Access Memory
RCSR	Real, Causal, Stable, Rational (Filter)
RISC	Reduced Instruction Set Computer
RMS	Root Mean Square
ROM	Read-Only-Memory
ROSE	Remote Operations Service
RTSE	Remote Transfer Service Element
R/W	Read/Write (Memory)
Rx	Receiver
SAR	Synthetic Aperture Radar
SBC	Subband Coding

SCPC	Single Channel per Carrier (Transmission)
SDH	Synchronous Digital Hierarchy
SECAM	Sequence de Couleurs Avec Memoire
S/H	Sample and Hold
SHD	Super-High Definition (Image/TV)
SHF	Super High Frequency
SI	Speech Interpolation
SISD	Single Instruction Single Data
SISO	Single Input, Single Output (System)
SLI	Spoken Language Interface
SLL	Side Lobe Level
SMTP	Simple Mail Transfer Protocol
S/N	Signal-to-Noise (Ratio)
SNACF	Sub-Network Access Control Function
SNDCF	Sub-Network Dependent Convergent Function
SNHC	Synthetic/Natural Hybrid Coding
SNICF	Sub-Network Independent Convergence Function
SNR	Signal-to-Noise Ratio
SPC	Stored Program Control
SQ	Segment Quantisation
SS7	Signalling System Number 7
SSB	Single Sideband (Modulation)
SSBSC	Single Sideband Suppressed Carrier
SSMA	Spread Spectrum Multiple Access
STM	Synchronous Transfer Mode
STS	Space-Time-Space (Switching)
STV	Standard Television
SVGA	Super Video Graphic Adapter
TA	Terminal Adapter
TC	Transform Coding
TCP/IP	Transmission Control Protocol/Internet Protocol
TDM	Time-Division Multiplexing
TDMA	Time-Division Multiple Access
TE	Terminal Equipment
TP	Terminal Portability
TRMA	Time-Random Multiple Access
TST	Time-Space-Time (Switching)
TTC	Telemetry, Tracking and Command (Subsystem of a Satellite)
TTR	Touchtone Receiver
TTS	Text-to-Speech (Conversion System)
TV	Television
TWTA	Travelling Wave Tube Amplifier
Tx	Transmitter

UC	Upconverter (in satellite communications)
UDP	User Datagram Protocol
UHF	Ultra High Frequency
UW	Unique Word
VC	Virtual Container
VCI	Virtual Channel Identifier
VDU	Video Display Unit
VGA	Video Graphic Adapter
VoD	Video on Demand
VPI	Virtual Path Identifier
VQ	Vector Quantisation
VQM	Voice Quality Manager
VSAT	Very Small Aperture Terminal
VSB	Vestigial Sideband (Modulation)
VTR	Video Tape Recorder
WAN	Wide Area Network
WWW	World Wide Web (of Internet)
ZOH	Zero-Order Hold

Appendix B

GUIDE TO SYMBOLS AND NOTATION

1. Symbols play a crucial role in the mathematical framework of digital telecommunications. Due to the paucity of symbols, the same symbol has to be used for denoting different physical quantities and its meaning in a particular application must be understood from the context.

2. Temporal symbols are denoted by lowercase letters. Capital letters are usd for transform operators.

3. Roman symbols are explained first, followed by Greek letters and then other symbols.

4. Brackets are used in the natural order [{( )}]. Curly brackets represent a sequence only if evident from the context of usage e.g. in {x}.

English Alphabet Symbols

A	Amplitude of a signal, a parameter associated with companding law, azimuth angle of an earth station antenna, antenna aperture area, $N \times N$ unitary matrix.
a	Traffic intensity in Erlang B formula, TV raster height
B	Bandwidth of a signal, Noise bandwidth of a satellite channel
BO	Output backoff of TWTA
b	Number of bits, TV raster width
C	Capacitance, Channel capacity, Complex plane, Contour of integration, Code block
$\vec{C} = \{c(k,n)\}$	$N \times N$ matrix of Discrete Cosine Transform
c	Velocity of light
c_k	Amplitudes of impulses, Previously encoded bit
D	Signal duration, Slant range (for a satellite)
d_d	Downlink slant range of a satellite
d_u	Uplink slant range of a satellite
E	Entropy of an information source, Elevation of the earth station antenna
E_b	Signal energy per bit
E_i	Received energy per coded bit

260

E_s	Energy per symbol
E_T	Total mean-squared error
$E(t)$	Error voltage
$E(x)$	Expectation of x
e	$\sum_{n=0}^{\infty} \dfrac{1}{n!}$
$e(n)$	Error signal, Residual, Secondary Excitation Signal
$e(nT_s)$	Prediction error
$e_q(nT_s)$	Quantised form of $e(nT_s)$
$e_q(t)$	Quantisation error
f	Linear continuous-time frequency
$f(.)$	Characteristics of image detector mechanisms
f_c	Carrier frequency
f_d	Downlink carrier frequency
f_m	Maximum frequency component of a signal
f_N	Nyquist frequency
f_0	Constant frequency shift of a signal
$f_0(y)$	Probability density function of correlator output for transmission of symbol 0.
f_s	Sampling frequency/rate
$f(t)$	Continuous-time signal
f_u	Uplink carrier frequency
$f(x, y, z, t)$	Motion-picture signal
G	A matrix, Arbitrary constant, Gain
G_p	Prediction gain
G_T	Transmit antenna gain
G/T	Antenna gain to noise temperature
G_u/T_u	Satellite gain to noise temperature
I_0	Peak current
$I_0(\beta)$	Modified Bessel function of the first kind
i	Integer, $\sqrt{-1}$
$i(t)$	Time-varying current
J	Current density
j	$\sqrt{-1}$, General discrete index
K	A constant
$K(m)$	Complete elliptic integral of the first kind
k_a	Amplitude sensitivity of the modulator
L	Number of quantum levels in a quantiser, Laplace transform operator, Average codeword length, Inductance, Satellite uplink tracking loss
L'	Antenna downlink tracking loss
l, l_i	An integer, Number of binary symbols assigned to i'th message event

M	Number of segments or blocks in M-ary modulation
m	Number of bits in each block of M-ary modulation
$m(t)$	Continuous-time message or information signal, Modulating wave
N	Size of a vector $\vec{x}$, Total number of raster scan lines per frame of TV
N_0	Noise density
$N_0(x, y)$	Number of photons of all energies registered at the detector
$N_i(E)$	Number of incident photons of energy E emitted by the source of X-rays
$N(t)$	White noise process
N_{vr}	Number of lines per field lost during vertical retrace
N_w	Number of pixels in window W
n	Integral variable termed sample number, Number of bits per sample
n_0	Number of samples by which a signal is shifted in the time domain
$n(t)$	Channel noise signal
P	Average power of a signal
P_0	First conditional probability of error if a symbol 0 is transmitted
P_b	Average probability of bit error
P_c	Probability of correct identification of a data sequence
P_e	Average power of prediction error sequence $e(nT_s)$
P_I	Probability of error for in-phase channel
P_m	Average power of message sequence $x(nT_s)$
P_Q	Probability of error for quadrature channel
$P_q(t)$	Average power of quantising error-sequence (noise)
P_s	Average probability of symbol error
P_T	Input power at antenna feed
$P(\theta)$	Linear combination of cosine functions
p_i	Probability of occurrence of i'th event
$Q(y)$	Gaussian integral function
$q_e(nT_s)$	Quantisation error
R	Resistor, Bit transmission rate, Code rate, Radius of a circle, Peak-to-peak excursion or dynamic range of quantiser input, Replica of message spectrum
R_s	Symbol transmission rate
r	Radius, ratio, integer
rect (t)	Rectangular function
res	Residue of a complex function
S	Set, Entropy
S_c	Cross Entropy
S_{nr}	Signal-to-noise power ratio
sinc (t)	Sinc function
sgn (t)	Signum function
T	Period, Absolute temperature

T_b	Bit interval, Delay
T_s	Sampling period/interval, Signalling interval, Delay
$\hat{u}$	Mean value of z
$u(\phi, m)$	Elliptic integral of the first kind
$u(m, n)$	Average value of the object $u(x, y)$ over a pixel area in the sampling grid
$\hat{u}(m,n)$	Best estimate of $x(m, n)$
V_0	Peak voltage of a signal
$V_{in}(t)/V_i(t),$ $V_{out}(t)/V_0(t)$	Input and output time-varying voltages
V_{in}, V_i	Input voltage
V_{out}, V_o	Output voltage
V_R	Reference voltage
$v(n)$	Innovation of $x(n)$
W	Highest frequency in a given signal in Hz (signal bandwidth)
W, W_N	N'th root of unity $= \exp\left(\dfrac{-j2\pi}{N}\right); W^N = 1$
$x_I(t)$	In-phase symbol in QPSK
$\tilde{x}(n)$	Approximate value of $x(n)$
$x(nT_s)$	Sampled form of signal $x(n)$
$\hat{x}(nT_s)$	Predicted value of signal $x(t)$
$x_p(t)$	Periodic signal
$x_Q(t)$	Quadrature symbol in QPSK
$x_q(t)$	Quantised value of signal $x(t)$
$x(t), y(t)$	Analog signals
$x(t_{inv})$	Time-inverted signal

Greek Symbols

γ_x	Variance of the probability distribution of a random variable
$\gamma_x(n)$	Variance of a discrete-time signal $x(n)$
Δ	Quantum step size (of a quantiser), Increment or decrement
Δ^2	Mean-square error
Δf	Change in carrier frequency
Δh	Horizontal resolution of a TV picture
Δv	Vertical resolution of a TV picture
$\delta(n-k)$ or δ_{nk}	Kronecker Delta
η	Efficiency, Antenna aperture efficiency
θ	Angle, Discrete-time angular frequency
$\{\theta_n\}$	Set of extremal frequencies

λ Integer, Constant scaling factor, Threshold, Number of intervals of shifting a signal $x(n)$ in the time domain, Call arriving rate in Erlang B formula, Additive noise consisting of an image dependent random part λ_1 and an image independent random part λ_2

μ Parameter associated with companding law (μ-law), Conditional mean, Linear attenuation coefficient or attenuation factor

μ_x Mean value of a random variable x

$\mu(x, y, z, E)$ Attenuation coefficient at a point (x, y, z) for energy E

ξ_w Spatial average of w (Intensity of incident light)

ρ Optical density of photographic film material

σ^2 Variance

σ_n Step-size controller in adaptive modulation

σ_x Standard deviation of a random variable x

$\sigma(x,y)$ Intensity of spectral noise

τ Pulse duration or width, Pitch period, Delay, Lag variable of a function $K_x(\tau)$

τ_g Group delay of a digital filter

ϕ_o Initial phase

$\phi_{i,j}$ A set of basis functions

$\vec{\phi}_k$ k'th column of ϕ

ϕ_m Modulation phase

ϕ_r Phase of the received carrier

ν Number of digits in a codeword, Discrete-time linear frequency corresponding to discrete-time angular frequency

Ω_{sat} Saturation power flux density at satellite transponder

ω Continuous-time angular frequency ($= 2\pi f$ or $2\pi \nu$)

Other Symbols

$R(x)$ Real part of complex number x

$I(x)$ Imaginary part of complex number x

$|x|$ Modulus or Absolute value of x

$\angle x$ Angle of the complex number x

$\overset{\Delta}{=}$ Equality by definition

$\cup$ Union of sets

$\cap$ Intersection of sets

$\forall k$ For all values of k

Index

NOTES

NOTES